BIOLOGICAL SCIENCE

interaction of experiments and ideas

BIOLOGICAL

SCIENCE

interaction of experiments and ideas

Biological Sciences Curriculum Study

PRENTICE-HALL, INC., ENGLEWOOD CLIFFS, N. J.

Biological Science: Interaction of Experiments and Ideas

07675-E

BIOLOGICAL SCIENCE: INTERACTION OF EXPERIMENTS AND IDEAS

THE WRITERS:

NORMAN ABRAHAM, Supervisor
BSCS,
Boulder, Colorado

PATRICK BALCH
Yuba City Union High School
Yuba City, California

DON E. BORRON
St. Stephens Episcopal School
Austin, Texas

FRANK C. ERK
State University of New York
Stony Brook, Long Island, N. Y.

WILLIAM KASTRINOS
Educational Testing Service
Princeton, New Jersey

JERRY P. LIGHTNER
Great Falls High School
Great Falls, Montana

ROBERT MILLER
Alhambra High School
Phoenix, Arizona

GLEN PETERSON
University of Houston
Houston, Texas

LAWRENCE M. ROHRBAUGH
University of Oklahoma
Norman, Oklahoma

GERALD SCHERBA
California State College
San Bernardino, California

PHILIP SNIDER
University of Houston
Houston, Texas

WILLIAM UTLEY
Yuba City Union High School
Yuba City, California

BETTY WISLINSKY
San Francisco College for Women
San Francisco, California

THE BSCS:

Chairman
BENTLEY GLASS

Director
ARNOLD B. GROBMAN

Associate Director
NORMAN ABRAHAM

Assistant Director
GEORGE CLARK

Project Director, Austin, Texas
ADDISON E. LEE

Consultants
TED ANDREWS
CLARENCE FLATEN
HULDA GROBMAN
URL LANHAM
JOHN SCHAEFER
CHARLES WINTER

Illustrations Supervisor
JANE LARSON

Business Manager
MARGARET STERLING

THE EDITOR

ERNEST SCHAFER
Prentice-Hall, Inc.

BIOLOGICAL SCIENCES CURRICULUM STUDY PUBLICATIONS

BIOLOGICAL SCIENCE: INTERACTION OF EXPERIMENTS AND IDEAS
    A BSCS Second Course—Prentice-Hall, Inc., Englewood Cliffs, New Jersey

BIOLOGICAL SCIENCE: MOLECULES TO MAN (BSCS Blue Version)
    A BSCS First Course—Houghton Mifflin Company, Boston

BIOLOGICAL SCIENCE: AN INQUIRY INTO LIFE (BSCS Yellow Version)
    A BSCS First Course—Harcourt, Brace and World, Inc. New York

HIGH SCHOOL BIOLOGY: BSCS GREEN VERSION
    A BSCS First Course—Rand McNally & Company, Chicago

BSCS LABORATORY BLOCKS—D. C. Heath & Company, Boston
    Microbes: Their Growth, Nutrition, and Interaction
    Animal Growth and Development
    Plant Growth and Development
    The Complimentarity of Structure and Function
    Regulation in Plants by Hormones
    Field Ecology

EQUIPMENT AND TECHNIQUES FOR THE BIOLOGY TEACHING LABORATORY
    D. C. Heath & Company, Boston

BIOLOGY TEACHERS HANDBOOK,
    John Wiley & Sons, Inc., New York

BIOLOGICAL INVESTIGATIONS FOR SECONDARY SCHOOL STUDENTS
    Doubleday & Company, Inc., New York

BSCS PAMPHLET SERIES—D. C. Heath & Company, Boston

BSCS BULLETINS—BSCS, Boulder, Colorado
    No. 1: Biological Education in American Secondary Schools
    No. 2: Guide to Working with Gifted Students
    No. 3: BSCS Biology, Implementation in the Schools

BSCS SPECIAL PUBLICATIONS, BSCS, Boulder, Colorado

BSCS NEWSLETTER, BSCS, Boulder, Colorado

FOREWORD

In 1959, the American Institute of Biological Sciences established the Biological Sciences Curriculum Study for the improvement of biological education at all levels. Since that time a number of working groups have been organized by the BSCS on various campuses both in the United States and abroad. Hundreds of American biologists and high school teachers, along with biologists from other nations, have been involved in the programs of the BSCS. Primary support for the work of the BSCS has been provided by the National Science Foundation. Among other activities, the BSCS has produced three versions of a first course in biology, each of which is currently in wide use in American high schools.

Since the advent of the BSCS Versions there has been an increasing demand for a second course in biology that would build upon the major BSCS themes. Such a course, while designed with high school seniors in mind, should also be useful in a variety of collegiate programs.

In planning to satisfy this demand, it was decided that the major emphasis in such a second course should be upon laboratory investigation, in depth, of selected areas of biology. The assumption is made that students who have had a general background in a first biology course, and who are interested in continuing their study of biology, would profit intellectually from an opportunity to experience laboratory work that partakes of actual research.

The present book, *Biological Science: Interaction of Experiments and Ideas,* is the culmination of a three-year program of testing experimental editions in classrooms throughout the United States. The second course materials were developed by a team of biologists under the supervision of Mr. Norman Abraham, Associate Director of the BSCS.

Teachers, students, and others who use this volume are invited to send their recommendations for improvement to the Director, Biological Sciences Curriculum Study, Post Office Box 930, Boulder Colorado, 80301. The BSCS would be happy to respond to requests for information about its other programs, including the Versions, Laboratory Blocks, Pamphlets, Films, Research Problems, Teacher's Handbook, Newsletters, and other items.

We hope that *Interaction of Experiments and Ideas* will serve to guide a substantial number of students and teachers into valuable and interesting pathways in science.

BENTLEY GLASS
Chairman, BSCS

ARNOLD B. GROBMAN
Director, BSCS

ACKNOWLEDGMENTS

In preparing this book, the writers have greatly benefited from the advice and assistance of many individuals. A considerable amount of experimental material has been adapted from the four BSCS Laboratory Blocks; *Plant Growth and Development*, Addison E. Lee, University of Texas; *Regulation in Plants by Hormones—A Study of Experimental Design*, William P. Jacobs and Clifford E. LaMotte, Princeton; *Animal Growth and Development*, Florence Moog, Washington University; and *Microbes: Their Growth, Nutrition, and Interaction*, Alfred Sussman, University of Michigan.

In designing the investigations on animal behavior, the authors have had the valuable advice and technical assistance of Vincent G. Dethier, University of Pennsylvania.

Joseph J. Schwab, University of Chicago, through his contributions to the BSCS, has provided much of the inspiration for presenting science as inquiry that pervades this and other BSCS publications.

Leonard Reynolds, Chairman, Mathematics Department, Yuba City Union High School, gave valuable assistance in editing the sections involving mathematics.

Individuals who have helped to guide the philosophy and practical implementation of the BSCS Second Course through active membership on a policy committee for the program include: Manert Kennedy, Fraser High School, Fraser, Michigan; Clarence Lange, Clayton High School, Clayton, Missouri; Addison E. Lee, Science Education Center, University of Texas, Austin; and Lester Heward, Capuchino High School, San Bruno, California.

Marjorie Behringer and Don Davis, Laboratory Block Project Associates at the University of Texas, assisted by conducting research into various aspects of yeast metabolism.

We are indebted to the Literary Executor of the late Sir Ronald A. Fisher, F. R. S., Cambridge, to Frank Yates, F. R. S., Rothamsted, and to Messrs. Oliver & Boyd Ltd., Edinburgh, for permission to reprint Tables II and IV from their book *Statistical Tables for Biological, Agricultural, and Medical Research*.

An acknowledgment would not be complete without mention of the hundreds of BSCS writers, committee members, test teachers, students, and reviewers who have individually and collectively influenced the preparation of this book through their contribution to the total BSCS program. Although it is impossible for us to acknowledge these contributors individually, we are grateful for their help.

NORMAN ABRAHAM, SUPERVISOR
The BSCS Second Course
Boulder, Colorado

PREFACE

The authors do not believe that a single text can provide the entire substance for a good course in biology. *The Interaction of Experiments and Ideas* should, therefore, be regarded as a *guide to learning* rather than as a complete instructional manual. It is assumed that much of the knowledge you gain will be as a result of outside reading in a variety of journals and reference texts. While the laboratory is the workshop of the biologist, it cannot be a productive laboratory without parallel readings in the literature. You will be expected to reflect upon laboratory investigations, seek a better understanding of experimental results, study related subject matter information, and use your own intellectual ability to purposefully expand your knowledge of biology. To this extent, you are your own teacher.

Most of the laboratory investigations are designed for team operation. Many problems in biology today are studied by teams of scientists rather than by a single worker. There is a good reason for this. Seldom can one person provide as much insight, imagination, creativity, and productive labor as a team whose members work toward a common goal. Good teamwork demands that each member of the team work to excel as an individual. Often members of a team, by combining their best *individual* efforts into an *organized* assault upon the problem, can generate new knowledge more efficiently than if each worked alone. An understanding of the value and problems of group effort should guide each team activity throughout the course.

Keeping accurate records of laboratory results is also *essential.* No effort should be spared to record accurate daily observations, to plan experiments carefully, and to discuss the significance of experimental results with others on the team. To further enrich your understanding, the experimental results and interpretations of different teams should be compared and discussed.

A primary goal of the course is to provide experiences that simulate biological research, so that you will gain an understanding of science from direct experience rather than from a superficial dissertation on the "scientific method." Yeast metabolism, population dynamics, microbial genetics, plant and animal growth, regulation, and development, and animal behavior provide the major subject areas for laboratory study.

There are thirty-eight scheduled laboratory investigations and numerous peripheral "Investigations for Further Study." Interspersed with the investigations are supplemental materials including excerpts from the literature of biology, both contemporary and historical, instruction in the application of elementary statistics to an evaluation of data, subject matter explanations that parallel the investigations, and other pertinent materials. The role of constructive controversy as an important mechanism of science is introduced as the culminating activity of the course.

This book was prepared by a *team* of biologists and biology teachers for those who find a challenge in learning more about life. The authors assume that you possess a good general knowledge about biology and are ready to explore, in depth, many questions about life that invite the intellectually curious.

NORMAN ABRAHAM
Supervisor

CONTENTS

PART ONE   THE NATURE OF BIOLOGICAL SCIENCE

PHASE ONE   ORIENTATION, 2

Section One   The Meaning of Science, 3

Section Two   The Increase of Biological Knowledge, 7

Section Three   The Role of Inquiry in Biology, 9

PHASE TWO   PROCESSES OF BIOLOGICAL INVESTIGATION, 11

Section Four   Hypotheses and the Design of Experiments, 12
INVESTIGATION 1: The Problem, 13
INVESTIGATION 2: A New Hypothesis, 18
Parallel Reading: Fermentation and Energy, 20

PRINCIPLES OF EXPERIMENTAL DESIGN, 23
INVESTIGATION 3: A Study of Variables, 24
Pattern of Inquiry 1: Interaction of Variables, 26
INVESTIGATION 4: A New Problem, 26
Pattern of Inquiry 2: Refining Hypotheses, 27

Section Five   **Problems in the Control of Variables, 28**

UNCERTAINTY IN SCIENCE, 28

INVESTIGATION 5: Temperature as a Variable, 30

Parallel Reading: Enzymes and Fermentation, 32

INVESTIGATION 6: Enzyme Concentration as a Variable, 35

Section Six   **Problems in Measurement, 38**

Pattern of Inquiry 3: Evaluation of Data, 39

Parallel Reading: Fermentation and Respiration, 40

INVESTIGATION 7: Measuring Rates of Respiration, 42

Pattern of Inquiry 4: The Respiratory Ratio, 47

Section Seven   **Statistical Evaluation of Data, 48**

Discrete Variables, 50

Continuous Variables, 50

Populations and Samples, 50

Statistical Computations, 52

Mean, 53

Normal Distribution, 54

Variance, 55

Standard Deviation, 57

Standard Error of the Mean($s_{\bar{x}}$), 60

PROBABILITY AND TESTS OF SIGNIFICANT DIFFERENCES, 61

Null Hypothesis, 63

The t Test, 63

Chi-Square, 71

Chi-Square with More Than Two Attributes, 75

Comparison of t and Chi-Square Tests, 76

Section Eight   **The Literature of Biology, 77**

Scientific Journals, 78

Scientific Papers, 80

Review Articles, 89

SEARCHING THE LITERATURE, 89

Biological Abstracts, 90

Personal Records, 95

SUMMARY, 97

PROBLEMS, 98

DESIGN OF EXPERIMENTS, 99

PART TWO   **EXPERIMENTS AND IDEAS IN BIOLOGICAL INVESTIGATIONS**

PHASE THREE   **GROWTH AND INTERACTIONS OF POPULATIONS, 102**

Section Nine   **Population Dynamics, 103**

STUDY OF POPULATIONS BY THE USE OF MICROBES, 103

Exponential or Logarithmic Growth, 104

Logarithms and the Calculation of Growth, 106

Plotting the Microbial Growth Curve, 111

Characteristics of the Microbial Growth Curve, 112

MICROBIAL METHODS AND TECHNIQUES, 114

Culturing Microorganisms, 114

Laboratory Rules, 118

Transfer of Agar Cultures, 118

Volumetric Transfer of Broth Cultures, 120

The Hemocytometer, 121

Counting the Cells in a Yeast Suspension, 124

INVESTIGATION 8: Growth of a Yeast Population, 126

Pattern of Inquiry 5: Factors Affecting Population Development, 130

MUTATION FREQUENCY, 131

INVESTIGATION 9: Determining Mutation Frequency in Bacteria, 133

Section Ten   **Interaction Without Cell Contact, 136**

INVESTIGATION 10: The Interaction of Two Mutants of a Bacterium, 137

Parallel Reading: Pigmentation in *Serratia marcescens*, 138

INVESTIGATION 11: A Verification of Results, 140

INVESTIGATION 12: A Study of Interactions Between Unknown Mutants, 141

INVESTIGATION 13: Preparation of a Scientific Paper, 142

Section Eleven   **Interaction Following Cell Contact, 144**

HETEROKARYOSIS IN *ASPERGILLUS*, 144

REPRODUCTION IN *ASPERGILLUS*, 145

INVESTIGATION 14: Confirmation of Strains and Genotypes, 148

INVESTIGATION 15: Heterokaryosis and Complementation, 152

INVESTIGATION 16: Genetic Recombination at Meiosis, 156

INVESTIGATION 17: Selection and Isolation of Diploids, 160

INVESTIGATION 18: Genetic Recombination at Mitosis, 161

PHASE FOUR   **GROWTH, DEVELOPMENT, AND BEHAVIOR OF INDIVIDUALS, 165**

Section Twelve   **Growth and Development in Plants, 166**

MEIOSIS, 166

LIFE HISTORY OF A FLOWERING PLANT, 166

Pattern of Inquiry 6: Developing Seedlings, 172

INVESTIGATION 19: Enzyme Activity in Germinating Seeds, 172

INVESTIGATION 20: Isolation of an Enzyme, 174

INVESTIGATION 21: Testing for Seed Viability, 175

Pattern of Inquiry 7: Factors Affecting Seed Germination, 177

Parallel Reading: Some Concepts of Light Energy, 178

INVESTIGATION 22: Effects of Light on Germination of Seeds, 181

INVESTIGATION 23: The Effects of Different Wavelengths of Light on Germination of Seeds, 182

INVESTIGATION 24: Mineral Requirements of Sorghum Plants, 184

Section Thirteen **Growth and Development in Animals, 188**

Gametogenesis, 189

The Beginning of an Individual: Fusion of Gametes, 190

Preparatory Technique 1: Obtaining Frog Pituitaries, 191

Preparatory Technique 2: Injecting Pituitaries, 193

Preparatory Technique 3: Fertilization *in Vitro,* 193

Preparatory Technique 4: Establishing and Maintaining Frog Embryo Cultures, 195

INVESTIGATION 25: Development of the Frog Embryo, 197

Summary of Development of the Frog Embryo, 200

Parallel Reading: The Genetic Control of Differentiation, 203

REGENERATION, 205

Regeneration of the Tadpole's Tail, 206

INVESTIGATION 26: Observation of Regenerating Tissues, 206

Parallel Reading: Regeneration in Other Multicellular Organisms, 208

Section Fourteen **Hormonal Regulation, 209**

Hormonal Regulation in Animals, 209

Hormones in Frogs, 210

Hormonal Control in the Frog Embryo, 211

INVESTIGATION 27: Hormonal Control of the Development of Frog Embryos, 212

INVESTIGATION 28: Control of Development in Chicks, 215

INVESTIGATION 29: The Gonads of Hormone-Treated Chicks, 219

Parallel Reading: Regulation in Plants, 221

INVESTIGATION 30: The Effect of Light on the Growth of Seedlings, 221

Parallel Reading: A Brief History of Our Knowledge of Auxins, 222

INVESTIGATION 31: A Biological Assay, 227

INVESTIGATION 32: Effect of Gibberellic Acid, 232

INVESTIGATION 33: Effects of Growth Regulating Substances on Plants, 236

Parallel Reading: Hormonal Influence on Plants—A Series of Papers, 240

Section Fifteen   **Animal Behavior, 264**

KINDS OF BEHAVIOR, 270

ORIENTATION IN ANIMALS, 278

COMMUNICATION AMONG ANIMALS, 282

Section Sixteen   **Analysis of Behavior, 289**

Preparatory Technique 1: Culturing Blowflies, 291

Preparatory Technique 2: Anesthetizing Flies, 292

Preparatory Technique 3: Handling Flies, 293

INVESTIGATION 34: The Effect of Food Contact on Locomotion, 294

INVESTIGATION 35: Detection of Food, 296

INVESTIGATION 36: Sensitivity to Sucrose, 297

INVESTIGATION 37: The Relation of Food Selection to Nutrition, 300

INVESTIGATION 38: Selection of Protein and Sugar, 302

GENES AND BEHAVIOR, 302

SUMMARY, 306

PART THREE   **CONCLUSIONS AND BEGINNINGS**

PHASE FIVE   **SCIENCE AND SOCIETY, 308**

Section Seventeen   **Responsibilities of the Scientist, 309**

"The Inquiring Mind" by L. A. DuBridge, 309

Section Eighteen   **The Role of Controversy in Science, 317**

THE USE OF INSECTICIDES, 318

    **"Insecticides in the 20th Century Environment"
by George C. Decker, 319**

    **Letter Replying to George C. Decker by Dr. Samuel A.
Graham, 328**

TOO MANY PEOPLE?, 332

    "Forecasting the Future" by Sir Charles Darwin, 333

    "Forecasting the Future?" by Fred Hoyle, 345

THE COURSE IN RETROSPECT, 348

APPENDICES

APPENDIX A   **General Laboratory Requirements, 353**

APPENDIX B   **Laboratory Requirements for Each Investigation, 362**

APPENDIX C   **Preparation of Chemical Solutions, 378**

APPENDIX D   **Preparation of Culture Media, 386**

APPENDIX E   **Maintenance of Living Organisms, 391**

APPENDIX F   **Math Tables, 394**

APPENDIX G   **Bibliography, 398**

INDEX **page 417**

BIOLOGICAL SCIENCE

interaction of experiments and ideas

IN BROKEN IMAGES

by *ROBERT GRAVES*

He is quick, thinking in clear images;
I am slow, thinking in broken images.

He becomes dull, trusting to his clear images;
I become sharp, mistrusting my broken images.

Trusting his images, he assumes their relevance;
Mistrusting my images, I question their relevance.

Assuming their relevance, he assumes the fact;
Questioning their relevance, I question the fact.

When the fact fails him, he questions his senses;
When the fact fails me, I approve my senses.

He continues quick and dull in his clear images;
I continue slow and sharp in my broken images.

He in a new confusion of his understanding;
I in a new understanding of my confusion.*

* Acknowledgment is given to International Authors N. V. for permission to reprint "In Broken Images" by Robert Graves from COLLECTED POEMS, Doubleday & Co. Inc., © 1955 International Authors N. V.

PART ONE THE NATURE

OF BIOLOGICAL SCIENCE

ORIENTATION

SECTION ONE

THE MEANING OF SCIENCE

One measure of civilization is man's understanding of the natural world and of his place in nature. In his search for this understanding, man has called upon magic, demons, spirits, gods, and essences to help him explain some of the perplexing and fearful events of nature. The bolt of lightning in a severe thunderstorm, the plague that leaves death and despair strewn across an entire continent, the death of plants and animals as a result of drought or as victims of relentless insects, the blotting out of the sun by the moon, the sudden occurrences of violent earthquakes—all these and more struck fear in the heart of man and left him with a sense of helplessness. But man continued to struggle and to learn, and eventually began to understand more about the mysteries of nature.

The growth of scientific knowledge has been uneven. Early civilized man, especially the Greeks and Romans, made great strides in beginning to understand the relationships of similar kinds of living beings and the structure and function of the human body. Some of this knowledge, although imperfect, was applied to the practical problems of living. However, there was no steady progress of scientific advance until the 17th and 18th Centuries brought new insights and hope for dispelling the shadows of ignorance.

It was during this period that biology began to emerge as a science. Careful observation, classification, and experimentation as the primary methods of studying life, gradually replaced superstition, speculation, and a reliance upon "authority." The subsequent rapid growth of biology as a science has led many scientists to predict that we are now entering the age of a biological revolution at least as comparable in its effect upon the future of mankind as was the Industrial Revolution.

To understand the nature of biology it is necessary to understand the meaning of science. This is not a simple task. Science is frequently defined as an organized body of knowledge or as a method of solving problems. Both of these definitions are unsatisfactory for our purposes. An encyclopedia can be described by the first definition, and even a two-year-old child has methods of solving problems. Most dictionary definitions of science are inadequate to describe this complex human endeavor that has revolutionized our way of life.

Understanding what science means is a goal that you should achieve through participation in the laboratory investigations and supplemental activities associated with this course. The opinions of three scientists on the meaning of science are given to help set the stage for what the authors hope will be a continuous effort on your part to read widely on the meaning of science in a variety of books and journals.

Dr. James B. Conant, (pp. 24–26)[1]:

. . . limiting one's attention merely to the experimental sciences by no means provides a satisfactory answer to the question "What is science?" For, immediately, diversity of opinion appears as to the objectives and methods of even this restricted area of human activity. The diversity stems in part from real differences in judgment as to the nature of scientific work but more often from the desire of the writer or author to emphasize one or another aspect of the development of the physical and biological sciences. There is the static view of science and the dynamic. The static places in the center of the stage the present interconnected set of principles, laws, and theories, together with the vast array of systematized information: in other words, science is a way of explaining the universe in which we live. The proponent of this view exclaims "How marvelous it is that our knowledge is so great!" If we consider science solely as a fabric of knowledge, the world would still have all the cultural and practical benefits of modern science, even if all the laboratories were closed tomorrow. This fabric would be incomplete, of course, but for those who are impressed with the significance of science as "explanations" it would be remarkably satisfactory. How long it would remain so, however, is the question. . . .

The dynamic view in contrast to the static regards science as an activity; thus, the present state of knowledge is of importance chiefly as a basis for further operations. From this point of view science would disappear completely if all of the laboratories were closed; the theories, principles, and laws embalmed in the texts would be dogmas; for if all the laboratories were closed, all further investigation stopped, there could be no re-examination of any proposition. I have purposely overdrawn the picture. No one except in a highly argumentative mood would defend either the extreme static or the extreme dynamic interpretation of the natural sciences.

. . . . My definition of science is, therefore, somewhat as follows: Science is an interconnected series of concepts and conceptual schemes that have developed as a result of experimentation and observation and are fruitful of further experimentation and observations. In this definition the emphasis is on the word "fruitful." Science is a speculative enterprise. The validity of a new idea and the significance of a new experimental finding are to be measured by the consequences—consequences in terms of other ideas and other experiments. Thus conceived, science is not a quest for certainty; it is rather a quest which is successful only to the degree that it is continuous.

Gerald Holton and Duane H. D. Roller, (pp. 231–232)[2]:

. . . Since the methods and relationships of one field frequently suggest analogous procedures in another, the working scientist is ever alert for the slightest

[1] Conant, James B. 1951. *Science and Common Sense.* Yale University Press, New Haven. 344 p.

[2] Holton, Gerald and Duane H. D. Roller. 1958. *Foundations of Modern Physical Science.* Addison-Wesley Publishing Co. Inc., Reading, Mass. and London, England. 782 p.

hints of new difficulties and of their resolutions. He proceeds through his problem like an explorer through a jungle, sensitive to every sign with every faculty of his being. Indeed, some of the most creative of theoretical scientists have stated that during the early stages of their work they do not even *think* in terms of conventional communicable symbols and words.

Only when this "private" stage is over and the individual contribution is formalized and prepared for absorption into "public" science does it begin to be really important that each step and every concept be made meaningful and clear. These two stages of science, which we shall have occasion to call science-in-the-making and science-as-an-institution, must be clearly differentiated. Once an adequate distinction has been made between these levels of meaning in the term "science," one of the central sources of confusion concerning the nature and growth of science has been removed.

The American nuclear physicist H. D. Smyth has thus characterized the distinction: "We have a paradox in the method of science. The research man may often think and work like an artist, but he has to talk like a bookkeeper, in terms of facts, figures, and logical sequence of thought." For this reason we must not take at their face value either the chronology or the methods set forth in scientific papers and treatises, including those of Galileo and Newton. It is part of the game of science, simply because it promotes economy of thought and communication, to make the results in retrospect appear neatly derived from clear fundamentals, until, in John Milton's phrase,

> . . . so easy it seemed
> Once found, which yet unfound most
>   would have thought
> Impossible!

A research worker may hide months of tortuous and often wasteful effort behind a few elegant paragraphs, just as a sculptor puts away his tools, preliminary studies, and clumsy scaffolds before unveiling his work.

A famous example shows how dangerous it is to refuse to accept provisional concepts into scientific work simply because they are not yet amenable to rigorous tests. Despite the large amount of indirect evidence for the hypothesis that matter is atomic in structure, a few prominent scientists, around the turn of this century, still rejected the atomic view stubbornly and vehemently as lacking "direct" confirmation. They eventually had to yield when all around them the atomic hypothesis led to an avalanche of testable conclusions and even to a revolution in classical science itself. Although perhaps an initial attitude of fundamental skepticism was justified, these men deprived themselves unduly long of a useful conceptual scheme (and the rest of science of their possible additional contributions) by waiting until the atomic picture had been fully fortified operationally. Today most scientists tacitly agree that their private creative activity must be unfettered by such preconceptions. "To set limits to speculation is treason to the future."

. . . It begins to appear that there are no simple rules to lead us to the discovery of new phenomena or to the invention of new concepts, and none by which to foretell whether our contributions will turn out to be useful and durable. But science does exist and is a vigorous and successful enterprise. The lesson to be drawn from history is that *science as a structure grows by a struggle for survival among ideas*—that there are marvelous processes at work which in time purify the meanings even of initially confused concepts. These processes eventually permit the absorption into science-as-an-institution (public science) of anything important that may have been developed, no matter by what means or methods, in science-in-the-making (private science).

Although each branch of science may have its own distinctive flavor, the philosophy presented in these quotations applies to all of science.

We will define the science of biology as *that human activity which is directed toward seeking new knowledge about living matter.* Learning *how* new knowledge is acquired will assume greater importance in this course than memorizing the details of what others have learned.

A serious study of biology requires a detailed study in books, reading articles in journals, identifying problems, asking questions, performing experiments, and making decisions. It requires asking questions about living things, questions they cannot answer directly, yet questions that must be asked if the riddles of life are to be investigated. The work is often dirty, sometimes tedious, and occasionally frustrating. However, with the frustration and the work *can* come some of the most rewarding experiences of life—those of discovery, of seeing for the first time a relationship between observations, or of sudden insights into previously obscure problems. This is the role of a biologist, a role that must be experienced to be appreciated.

PROBLEMS

1. Ask several students who are not enrolled in this course to give you their definition of science. Compare these opinions with those expressed in Section One.

2. In your own words, write a definition of science that takes into consideration all of the aspects of science mentioned in Section One.

QUESTIONS FOR DISCUSSION

1. Compare and discuss "Dynamic Science" and "Static Science."

2. Compare and discuss "Private Science" and "Public Science."

3. Describe the relationship between the terms used in questions 1 and 2. That is, relate dynamic to either private or public as these terms are used in the text.

4. A recent newspaper editorial ridiculed the U.S. Congress for approving funds to be used in various biological research programs. The projects criticized included an investigation of bee sounds, a study of the porpoise, and the maintenance of a colony of apes for behavioral studies. The editorial pointed out that this was a "foolish waste of tax money since studies of this kind are of no practical value."

    Comment on the rationale of this editorial in view of the meaning of science expressed in Section One.

SECTION TWO

THE INCREASE OF BIOLOGICAL KNOWLEDGE

One inescapable aspect of science is the rapid accumulation of knowledge about our environment. It has been (humorously) estimated that mankind need not concern itself with the problem of over-populating the world since, at the present rate of scientific publication, paper alone will completely bury the globe in 100 years!

The use of microfilm may solve the paper problem, but we should consider what this accumulation of knowledge means in terms of studying science. A knowledge of facts alone would be meaningless without some kind of organization of these facts into principles; however, principles cannot exist devoid of factual knowledge.

To visualize the staggering growth of *biological* knowledge alone is difficult. Professor Bentley Glass[1] of The Johns Hopkins University commented on this problem:

> The textbook of 1900 would have nothing about genetics, for Mendelian heredity was unrecognized, and the science of genetics did not really start until 1900. Biochemistry had begun in its modern sense only three years before. Edward Buchner's classic studies on the nature of the enzymes had just begun. Immunology did not exist. . . . Animal viruses had not been discovered at all.

[1] Glass, Bentley. "Revolution in Biology" (an address to participants at the BSCS 1960 Briefing Session for teachers in the BSCS 1960–61 Testing Program) 1961. *BSCS Newsletter No. 9,* September, pp. 2–5.

No one knew anything about specific vitamins in 1900. The science of experimental embryology was in its cradle. Pavlov was still to do his classic studies in experimental psychology showing conditioned reflex behavior. . . .

What will biology be in the year 2000? The biologists of 1930 would not have dreamed of what we know today, and I do not think I can dream of what biologists will know 30 years from now. But I can foresee, perhaps, a few directions in which our control over the forces of nature and the nature of life will extend.

We will probably learn not only how to increase the human life span, but how to maintain the vigor of mature life into advanced years. So far, we have not increased the human life span at all. The *average* length of life has gone up, but the *maximum* does not seem to have changed at all. I would suspect that by 1990 biologists will have learned how to create some simple forms of living organisms, something at about the order of complexity of a virus, and that geneticists will have learned how to replace defective genes with sound ones. This will depend, of course, on advances made by embryologists, who will— I suspect before very long—show us how to maintain in artificial culture outside the body the reproductive organs of animals to the extent that spermatozoa and ova can be produced *in vitro,* that is, in a glass dish.

I certainly expect that before the next 30 years are finished man will have learned how to conduct artificial photosynthesis and so will have finally assured himself of an inexhaustible—and I hope palatable—food supply. Man will certainly have learned to accelerate his own evolution in a desired direction, though I wonder what direction he will desire. And he will probably have eliminated infectious disease completely.

These conjectures may be wrong, but this would seem to be the general direction in which history is moving: a logarithmic increase of human power in the biological as well as physical realm.

PROBLEMS

Prepare a list of the *areas* of biology in which outstanding progress has been made since 1900. Do not confine your list to those areas mentioned by Professor Glass but search for others in various reference sources.

QUESTIONS FOR DISCUSSION

1. What is meant by "a logarithmic increase of human power in the biological as well as physical realm"?

2. Discuss the statement "Man will certainly have learned to accelerate his own evolution in a desired direction, though I wonder what direction he will desire."

SECTION THREE

THE ROLE OF INQUIRY IN BIOLOGY

It must be obvious that "coverage" of a body of knowledge is impossible and that the possession of a body of facts is not enough to qualify one as a person who understands science.

Rather than treat science as a series of absolute certainties, we should study science as a *process of inquiry*. We should see how an attitude of inquiry provides the mechanism for probing into the complexities of nature and how it enables the scientist to challenge his own conclusions. In this way the "conditional truth" of knowledge will be revealed and the full meaning of science understood.

Inquiry is broadly defined as a search for truth, information, or knowledge. It pertains to research and investigation and to seeking information by asking questions. Science is concerned with asking the *right kind of questions* so that the answers can be properly evaluated.

Patterns of Inquiry

A number of carefully planned teacher-student discussions entitled "Patterns of Inquiry" are provided throughout this book as an aid to understanding the nature of inquiry. Such understanding is necessary if proper use is to be made of the biology laboratory. The Patterns provide discussions that involve both teacher and student. These discussions will simulate, as closely as possible, the kind of thinking a scientist does in conducting research.

The Patterns of Inquiry involve the identification of problems, the formation of fruitful hypotheses, the design of experiments to test these hypotheses, and finally the analysis and interpretation of data resulting from the experimental work. The Patterns of Inquiry and the laboratory investigations which you will carry out throughout the course should complement each other.

Each pattern is a small sample of the operation of inquiry. It poses a problem and provides you with information which you are asked to use in the same way as if you were conducting the investigation. Additional problems may be introduced by the instructor. If you actively participate in these discussions, you will come to understand more fully that science involves much more than the learning of things which others already know. You will better understand Conant's characterization of science as an activity and a speculative enterprise. Also, you will better understand why Holton and Roller suggest that "the working scientist is ever alert" and "proceeds through his problem like an explorer through a jungle, sensitive to every sign with every faculty of his being."

As an illustration, the model Pattern will ask you to draw conclusions from very simple data. Later Patterns will involve other and more difficult aspects of the process of science.

PATTERN OF INQUIRY (MODEL)

Germination of Seeds

A student wished to learn what conditions were most favorable for the germination of seeds. He placed several bean seeds on moist filter paper in each of two glass dishes. One dish was placed in the light, and the other was placed in a dark box; both were kept at normal room temperature. He examined the seeds after a few days and found that all the seeds in each dish had germinated.

What inferences could you draw from the results of this experiment? Base your inferences solely on the data presented in this experiment and do not use facts which you may have obtained from other sources.

PROCESSES OF
BIOLOGICAL INVESTIGATION

Introduction

A study of biology involves a series of processes, which most biologists have found useful in order to conduct their research in the most productive manner.

If it were possible to define the term "process," as it is used here, in a few sentences, the teaching of science would be greatly simplified. Unfortunately, this is not possible because process in science involves all that scientists do in asking the right questions and in recognizing the direction research must take to provide answers to these questions. Process therefore includes observation, the recognition of ideas, the formulation of hypotheses, the design of experiments, the analysis of data, and much more. Similarly, knowledge in science has manifold significance. Knowledge resulting from the interpretation of data is always conditional; it is always subject to new interpretation or change as new data are acquired, recorded, and studied. Knowledge modifies process, which in turn modifies knowledge, and so on through an endless series of interactions.

As these processes are discussed, a series of laboratory investigations will introduce the role of process in research. No one investigation will necessarily present all aspects of scientific process, nor is a single investigation so confined as to illustrate only one process. Part of your task will be to identify the various processes of biological investigation as they unfold during the laboratory studies.

SECTION FOUR

HYPOTHESES AND THE DESIGN OF EXPERIMENTS

When we attempt to interpret an observation or to understand the meaning of a series of events, we are likely to formulate some form of working hypothesis or explanation. This working hypothesis may be followed by an experiment designed to yield data that will either support or refute the hypothesis.

A hypothesis has been described as a logical linkage between *if* and *then.* Consider the hypothesis that nerves are necessary for the action of some organ. In this case we are proposing that, *if* nerves are necessary for the action, *then* cutting the nerves leading to the organ should result in failure of action. This assumption leads us to design an experiment in which we sever the nerves, and the results produced will be our data. If these data indicate that cutting the nerves resulted in a loss of action in the organ, we may say that our hypothesis has been supported, and as far as our information goes, it is a good one. However, if the organ continues to act normally after the nerves have been cut, then the data place our hypothesis in doubt, and we will probably reject it as being invalid on the basis of our new information.

When an experiment is performed to test a hypothesis, new information usually will be gained. The new information may or may not be useful in evaluating the hypothesis. If the investigator is alert, however, it can lead to new questions, new problems, and new experiments. In this way science progresses.

As you work with the Investigations in this book, practice stating the hypotheses in the "if . . . then" form. This will guide you in the design of experiments and in the evaluation of the data which they may yield.

Common baker's yeast has been selected as an organism with which to begin our laboratory studies because it is readily available, because it is relatively easy to work with, and because a study of the growth and metabolism of yeast will offer an opportunity to experience many aspects of biological research.

The yeast you are to investigate derives its name from an early observation that it is a sugar-consuming fungus, hence the name *Saccharomyces* (*saccharum* = sugar, and *myces* = fungus).

Studies of brewer's or baker's yeast, both of which are varieties of the species *Saccharomyces cerevisiae,* have provided much of our present knowledge of carbohydrate metabolism.

As early as 1838, Charles Cagniard-Latour, and later in 1860, Louis Pasteur, attempted to explain how yeasts were able to convert sugar to ethyl alcohol (ethanol) and carbon dioxide. When maintained under anaerobic conditions (without oxygen), *S. cerevisiae* forms ethanol and carbon dioxide from sugar. This process is an ethanolic (alcoholic) fermentation. The following equation summarizes what happens in this kind of fermentation:

$$H_2O + C_{12}H_{22}O_{11} \xrightarrow{\text{yeast}} 4\ CH_3CH_2OH + 4\ CO_2 + \text{energy}$$
$$\text{(sucrose)} \qquad\qquad\qquad \text{(ethanol)}$$

INVESTIGATION 1   The Problem

After a problem is recognized, the investigator should (1) gather information from the literature that pertains to the problem, (2) construct a hypothesis that provides a possible explanation, and (3) plan and conduct experiments that tend to support or refute the hypothesis.

Note: A well-organized and safe laboratory operation is possible only when certain rules of procedure are carefully followed by the investigator.

1. *Keep all glassware and other laboratory equipment clean and in the proper place. The use of chemicals and microorganisms introduces potential hazards; cleanliness should always be stressed.*
2. *Carefully handle all laboratory equipment such as microscopes and balances according to instructions.*
3. *Prepare for each investigation in a professional way. Label all necessary containers and arrange your equipment in an orderly manner.*
4. *Discard living materials and other wastes in the place specified by your instructor.*

The yeast *S. cerevisiae* converts sucrose to carbon dioxide and ethyl alcohol as illustrated by the chemical equation for fermentation. Because molasses is known to contain a high percentage of sucrose, we can assume that yeasts will ferment molasses and produce both carbon dioxide and alcohol.

The first problem to be considered is: What is the relationship of food concentration to CO_2 production by yeast? Certain background information about yeasts has been provided so that you need not search the literature for this investigation.

Materials (per team)

1. One package of dry yeast
2. One graduate cylinder, 100 ml
3. Ten test tubes, 22 mm × 175 mm
4. Ten test tubes, 13 mm × 100 mm
5. Two Erlenmeyer flasks, 125 or 250 ml
6. Test tube rack
7. Cotton for stoppers

Materials (per class)

1. One pint of commercial molasses
2. A supply of distilled water
3. One Erlenmeyer flask, 1000 ml

Procedure Day I

1. Read through the complete procedure and then hypothesize what you think will be the outcome of this Investigation. Select the graph that

you think will most likely indicate the relationship of CO_2 production to the concentration of molasses when the same quantity of yeast is used to inoculate each tube of molasses.

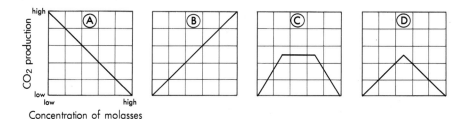

Figure 1   Concentration of molasses and CO_2 production.

2. Empty one package of dry yeast into one liter of distilled water. Shake well to insure a uniform suspension.

3. Prepare a yeast suspension approximately equivalent to one package of yeast per three liters by adding 33 ml of the first yeast suspension to 67 ml of distilled water in a 125 ml flask. Stopper for future use.

4. Prepare by serial dilution, in the ten large test tubes, a series of molasses concentration ranging from 100% to 0.19% molasses in water. This is easily done as follows:

Tube 1 = 100% molasses
Using the 100 ml graduate cylinder, measure 25 ml of pure molasses and add to tube 1.

Tube 2 = 50% molasses
Measure 25 ml of pure molasses in the graduate cylinder and add 25 ml of distilled water. Insure a uniform solution by pouring the molasses-water mixture back and forth between the graduate cylinder and a clean 125 ml (or larger) Erlenmeyer flask. Carefully pour one half (25 ml) of this solution into tube 2. Save the remaining half for tube 3.

Tube 3 = 25% molasses
Add 25 ml of distilled water to the 25 ml of molasses solution left over from the previous dilution. Again pour this molasses-water mixture back and forth between the graduate cylinder and the flask. Add one half (25 ml) of this dilution to tube 3.

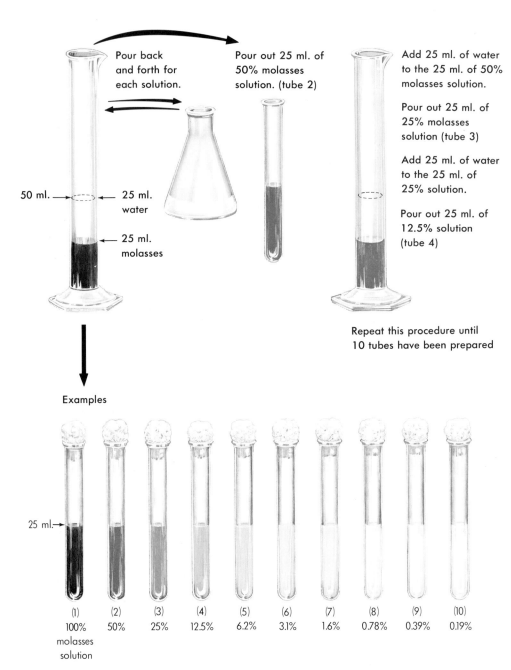

Pour back
and forth for
each solution.

Pour out 25 ml. of
50% molasses
solution. (tube 2)

Add 25 ml. of water
to the 25 ml. of 50%
molasses solution.

Pour out 25 ml. of
25% molasses
solution (tube 3)

Add 25 ml. of water
to the 25 ml. of
25% solution.

Pour out 25 ml. of
12.5% solution
(tube 4)

50 ml. ⟶   ⟵ 25 ml.
                    water

                   ⟵ 25 ml.
                      molasses

Repeat this procedure until
10 tubes have been prepared

Examples

25 ml. ⟶

(1)	(2)	(3)	(4)	(5)	(6)	(7)	(8)	(9)	(10)
100%	50%	25%	12.5%	6.2%	3.1%	1.6%	0.78%	0.39%	0.19%
molasses									
solution									

Figure 2   Dilution technique.

Repeat this operation until a final dilution of 0.19% (approximately)
molasses in water is obtained. Discard 25 ml of the 0.19% dilution; each
of the ten tubes should contain 25 ml of solution.

Tube 4 = 12.5% molasses
Tube 5 = 6.2% molasses
Tube 6 = 3.1% molasses
Tube 7 = 1.6% molasses
Tube 8 = 0.78% molasses
Tube 9 = 0.39% molasses
Tube 10 = 0.19% molasses

Note: The details of serial dilution will be omitted in future experiments. It should be seen that we have serially cut the concentration of each solution in half until the final desired concentration is reached. Each successive solution is $\frac{1}{2}$ the concentration of the preceding solution. Future experiments will require the same basic technique, although the dilution factor may vary.

5. Thoroughly shake the flask containing the 100 ml of yeast suspension and add 5 ml of yeast suspension to each tube. *Shake each tube of the yeast-molasses mixture thoroughly to insure a uniform mixture.*

6. Invert one small test tube into each of the 10 larger tubes containing the yeast-molasses mixture. Stopper the large tubes with tight fitting cotton plugs. Allow each of the small tubes to fill with the suspension by holding the larger tube on its side. When completed, each test-tube preparation should resemble the last tube in Figure 3. The amount of solution placed in each large tube will vary according to the relative sizes of small and large tubes. The suggested 25 ml works well when the tubes are 22 × 175 mm and 13 × 100 mm, respectively.

Note: A little care in technique is required. It is common for an air bubble to be trapped within the small tube. By *careful* and *gentle* rocking of the large tube it is possible to completely fill the smaller tube so that it is free of air bubbles. See the illustration in Figure 3.

Figure 3   Preparing the fermentation tubes.

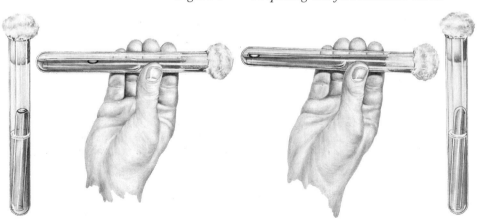

7. Label the tubes and place them in a convenient area where they will not be disturbed for 24 hours.

Procedure Day II

Each team should spend about 5 minutes looking over the test tubes. Observe what has taken place in the 24 hours since the Investigation was started. Record your observations and those of the other members of your team in preparation for a class discussion on the Investigation.

OBSERVATIONS

1. Measure the comparative quantities of gas collected in the top (actually the bottom) of each small test tube by measuring the height of the gas column with a millimeter ruler.
2. The different concentrations of molasses should be plotted on the horizontal axis of linear graph paper, and the quantity of CO_2 produced in 24 hours should be plotted on the vertical axis.
3. Plot the average readings reported by each team. Does this curve approximate the one for your team?

INTERPRETATIONS

1. Compare the graph prepared from your experimental results with the graph selected prior to the experiment. Be prepared to explain any differences or to substantiate any similarities.
2. Based only on the results observed in this Investigation, describe the relationship that seems to exist between the concentration of available food and the production of CO_2 by yeast cells.

INVESTIGATION 2   **A New Hypothesis**

We can assume that the results obtained from Investigation 1 were inadequate to completely answer the original problem. It would be unusual if a biological problem *could* be solved as the result of one investigation. Your data should reveal some general relationships between molasses concentration and CO_2 production. The data should also suggest additional investigations that could yield more information relevant to the problem.

Molasses is a complex material that contains up to 60% sucrose plus smaller amounts of glucose and fructose. Molasses also contains various amino acids and other organic compounds. There may be traces of sulfur dioxide, vitamins and other substances and it is conceivable that molasses contains something that could either inhibit or accelerate the rate of fermentation. Since sucrose is the major component of molasses and a relatively pure substance, a study of sucrose fermentation might provide a further insight into the problem.

Before beginning the experiment, state a hypothesis that you think will explain the fermentation rate of pure sucrose as compared with that of molasses. Consider the following questions as a possible basis for the formation of your hypothesis:

Do you think the rate of fermentation of sucrose will be faster or slower than that of molasses?

Will a graph plotted from the sucrose fermentation data be similar to, or different from, the graph constructed from molasses fermentation data?

Which concentration of sucrose is likely to result in the greatest CO_2 production?

Do not feel compelled to restrict your hypothesis to answering one of these questions. You may have an idea about the outcome of this investigation that is not taken into consideration by any of these questions.

Materials (per team)

1. Ten test tubes, 22 mm × 175 mm
2. Ten test tubes, 13 mm × 100 mm
3. One graduate cylinder, 100 ml
4. A millimeter ruler
5. Test tube rack
6. Two Erlenmeyer flasks, 125 or 250 ml

Materials (per class)

1. One Erlenmeyer flask, 1000 ml
2. One package of dry yeast
3. Sucrose

Procedure

1. Empty a package of dry yeast into 1 liter of distilled water. Shake well in order to insure a uniform suspension.

2. Add 33 milliliters of this suspension to 67 milliliters of distilled water. This will yield the equivalent of one package of yeast in three liters of water as was done in the last investigation.

3. Make a serial dilution of sucrose in the same way that you diluted the molasses in Investigation 1. Prepare a 60% sucrose solution by dissolving 90 grams of sucrose in a flask containing 60 ml of distilled water. *Assume* that the 60% sucrose solution is equivalent to pure molasses. The ten tubes will, therefore, give you a range of concentrations from 100% (actually 60% sucrose) to 0.19%.

4. Add 5 ml of the yeast suspension to each tube. Shake well.

5. Invert one of the small test tubes into each of the large tubes and fill the small tube with medium as before.

6. Stopper each tube with a cotton plug.

7. Label the tubes and place them in a suitable place for 24 hours.

OBSERVATIONS

At the end of 24 hours carefully observe each preparation, measure the amount of gas in each tube, and plot the data on graph paper.

INTERPRETATIONS

1. Were the results similar to those obtained with molasses in Investigation 1?
2. Was your hypothesis verified or refuted by the data?
3. What do the results indicate might be the next logical step in answering questions about food concentration and CO_2 production by yeasts?

Parallel Reading: Fermentation and Energy

Although some of the intermediate products may be of use in the synthesis of cell materials, the greatest value of fermentation to the yeast cell is probably the release of energy. All living things need the energy which is made available by exergonic (energy-yielding) reactions if they are to perform work. The work of the cell is done by endergonic (energy-using) reactions such as the various synthetic processes of cells. If the energy of exergonic reactions is evolved as heat, as when an organic substance undergoes combustion (burning of gasoline, etc.), it is generally of little use to the cell. Instead of heat energy, living cells require chemical energy for most of their activities.

How do cells transfer the energy from exergonic to endergonic reactions? There may be several ways, but the most efficient is the use of a compound which will be active in both kinds of reactions. Such a compound may, by a change of its structure, pick up a major part of the energy released in an exergonic reaction. Then, by changing back to its original structure, it can give up the energy needed to drive an endergonic reaction.

The most common compound of this sort found in cells is adenosine triphosphate, commonly called ATP. It is produced from a similar compound, adenosine diphosphate (ADP). ATP is produced when the energy from some exergonic reaction is used to cause the reaction of ADP with H_3PO_4 (phosphoric acid). We can write this as follows:

$$ADP \quad + \quad H_3PO_4 \quad + \quad energy \quad \longrightarrow \quad ATP$$

| (adenosine diphosphate) | (phosphoric acid) | (from an exergonic reaction) | (adenosine triphosphate) |

Conversely, an example of the utilization of ATP can be shown:

$$glucose + ATP \longrightarrow glucose\text{-}phosphate + ADP$$

The glucose-phosphate is much more reactive than was the glucose, partly because it contains most of the energy which was released when ATP gave up one phosphate group and became ADP. Again, look at the equation for alcoholic fermentation:

$$C_6H_{12}O_6 \xrightarrow{\text{yeast}} 2\ C_2H_5OH + 2\ CO_2 + energy$$

| (glucose) | (ethanol) | (carbon dioxide) |

One might think from this equation that the conversion of glucose to ethanol and carbon dioxide is a single step fermentation reaction. This is not so. The process involves a series of chemical reactions, each of which is controlled by a specific enzyme. Only two reactions, however, actually produce ATP, and only one step in fermentation actually uses ATP. Figure 4, shown on page 22, shows some of these steps.

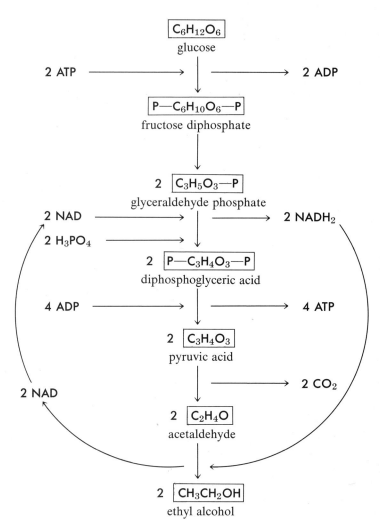

Figure 4   A summary of the steps in alcoholic fermentation.

Note that pyruvic acid is produced in the second to the last step; we will have more to say about the role of pyruvic acid in a later discussion of metabolism. The process by which glucose is converted to pyruvic acid is often called *glycolysis,* and the series of steps involved has been named (for three of the many men who worked out the reactions) the Embden-Meyerhof-Parnas (EMP) system.

We can summarize the steps shown on the chart:

$$C_6H_{12}O_6 + 2\ ADP + 2\ H_3PO_4 \longrightarrow 2\ CH_3CH_2OH + 2\ CO_2 + 2\ ATP + heat$$

The heat loss indicated in the equation is the energy which was in glucose but is not used in the formation of ATP or ethanol. Most of this heat will be of little use to the yeast cells and will be lost to the environment.

Principles of Experimental Design

An investigation begins with an awareness of a problem and a survey of related literature. It proceeds to the expression of a hypothetical answer, and the formulation of experimental procedure. It concludes with data collection, analysis, and interpretation. The design of an experiment is a step in problem-solving consisting of a detailed plan to be followed in obtaining the needed data. Such a plan specifies what organisms, materials, and equipment will be used and details the step-by-step procedures for carrying out the experiment.

Ideally, the design of the experiment is one that will give the greatest amount of reliable information with the least expense and effort. Often such a design is difficult to achieve. The complexity of living systems and the variability inherent in populations of living organisms contribute to the difficulty of research in the biological sciences. Furthermore, there is no common blueprint that will serve as a guide to the design of experimental procedure. Each problem attacked by the investigator may require its own design.

Five important principles may be kept in mind concerning experimental design in biology. First, the investigator must choose a *suitable organism* for the experiment. He wants to use organisms which are readily handled in the experimental procedure and which will give the needed data as rapidly as possible at the lowest cost commensurate with reliability. The choice of organisms to be used is often determined by their availability. If satisfactory experimental organisms can be found locally, it is more economical to use them than to choose others which may have to be shipped long distances.

Second, the investigator must try to assure *representative selection* of experimental organisms from the whole population.

Third, he must be aware of *experimental variables.* An investigator hopes that he can limit the experimental treatment given to the living plant or animal specifically to the introduced variable. This is not easily done. Merely moving a plant or an animal from its native habitat to a laboratory may so affect the organism that the accuracy of the investigation can be questioned.

Regardless of the care exercised, experimental variables may unobtrusively enter the design and ultimately affect the data obtained. For example, suppose you are investigating the germination rate of specific seeds. You have attempted to maintain perfectly uniform conditions for all of the germination trays, but can you put all the trays in your laboratory in identically the same place? This, of course, is a physical impossibility. Therefore, do all the trays receive the same light intensity? Are they all exposed to the same temperature and humidity? Do identical convection currents flow past all of them? Each of these numerous variables must be recognized and taken into consideration.

Fourth, the investigator should strive for *simplicity*. The casual observer often judges the importance of experimental work by the amount of elaborate instrumentation involved: an array of tubes, wires, pumps, stirrers, and dials appears to indicate that a significant experiment is under way. Expensive equipment may sometimes be essential to obtain required data, but it does not measure the true importance of the question being asked. In contrast, significant advances in biology have frequently resulted from apparently "simple" questions answered with a minimum amount of apparatus.

Finally, a *reasonable attitude* toward experimental organisms is essential in biological research. In all investigations, laboratory organisms must be conscientiously cared for. Animals must be fed and watered regularly, and kept clean. These practices, besides being dictated by humane considerations, are a practical necessity. Good experimental results cannot be expected from animals that have been subjected to the stress of hunger or to bad housing conditions. Plants must also be kept in good condition. A plant that becomes wilted or diseased through *neglect* is useless for experimentation.

The design of an experiment is dictated by the question it is to answer. The investigator has the responsibility for choosing organisms and procedures that will yield the maximum of reliable data.

QUESTIONS FOR DISCUSSION

1. Suppose that in Investigation 1 or 2 you took your yeast inoculum from the top of the flask while another student took his from the bottom. How might this have affected your results?

2. Compare the care needed for the experimental organisms when you use yeast to the care needed if you were experimenting with dogs or bean plants.

INVESTIGATION 3	A Study of Variables

The results of Investigation 1 revealed some relationships between the concentration of molasses in the culture medium and the rate of CO_2 production by yeast. Although the results of Investigation 2 differed from those of Investigation 1 they also indicated that a relationship exists between the concentration of sucrose and the rate of CO_2 production.

Molasses contains at least three kinds of sugar: sucrose, glucose, and fructose. Perhaps some of these are more readily used by yeast plants than others. Perhaps combinations of two or more of the sugars are more useful than any one by itself.

To save time, each team might investigate a different part of the problem.

Materials (per team)

1. One test tube rack
2. Ten test tubes, 22 mm × 175 mm
3. Ten test tubes, 13 mm × 100 mm
4. Two Erlenmeyer flasks, 125 or 250 ml
5. Sucrose, glucose, fructose
6. Molasses

Materials (per class)

1. One Erlenmeyer flask, 1000 ml
2. One package of dry yeast

Procedure

1. One team should prepare the diluted yeast suspension for the class as was suggested for Investigations 1 and 2.
2. Prepare serial dilutions of molasses, a single sugar, or a combination of sugars in the same manner as with Investigations 1 and 2. Use glucose, fructose, sucrose, and a mixture of all three. A solution of all three of the sugars can be prepared by adding 30 grams of sucrose, 15 grams of fructose, and 15 grams of glucose to 40 ml of distilled water. When completely dissolved, mix well and make serial dilutions as before.
3. Label each tube.
4. Add 5 ml of the yeast suspension to each tube. Shake well.
5. Insert the small test tubes and fill each with medium.
6. Stopper the large tubes with cotton plugs.
7. Label all tubes and place in a suitable place for 24 hours.

OBSERVATIONS

1. Measure the amount of gas produced in each tube. Plot your data on a graph and compare your results with those of other teams.
2. Plot the data of all teams on a single graph.

INTERPRETATIONS

1. How do the rates of CO_2 production from the different sugars compare with each other and with those from the mixture of sugars? How do each of these compare with molasses?
2. Consider the parts done by each team as parts of a single experiment. How can you explain the results of this experiment?
3. Can you think of other variables which may be affecting the fermentation process?

PATTERN OF INQUIRY 1

Interaction of Variables

A few decades ago, the average yield of corn grown in the South was much below that grown in the Corn Belt states of Illinois and Iowa. Why do you suppose this was true?

INVESTIGATION 4   A New Problem

To determine if a relationship exists between the quantity of food available to yeast and the amount of carbon dioxide produced during fermentation is the problem that initiated our study of yeast metabolism. As is typical of many (if not most) biological investigations, we have uncovered more questions than answers, and the solution to our original problem remains obscure.

Although we have learned something about the nature of fermentation, the data gathered from the first three investigations have revealed a new problem that must be solved before the factors influencing CO_2 production can be identified. The new problem is to determine *why* the quantity of CO_2 produced is significantly different when molasses is the substrate rather than when pure sugars or a combination of pure sugars, as normally found in molasses, is provided as the substrate.

Procedure

You were given detailed directions for carrying out each of the previous investigations. In contrast, no procedural detail will be given for Investigation 4. The problem has been outlined, the rest is up to you. Consider the problem carefully, re-examine the data gathered from previous experiments, consult the literature if necessary, and formulate a hypothesis that could lead to a solution to the problem. After formulating a hypothesis, make an "if . . . then" statement which can be tested experimentally. Design the experiment in such a way that the results obtained might either verify or negate your hypothesis.

It is quite likely that several directions for experimentation will emerge. This is also typical of research in science. Perhaps each team will perform a different experiment and perhaps the results of each different experiment, when examined together, will provide the necessary evidence for a final solution to the problem.

PATTERN OF INQUIRY 2

Refining Hypotheses

It is difficult to say when science began. Certain aspects of science appear to be about as old as history. Modern science, however, is quite recent, and its rate of development has been rapid. The formulation of hypotheses and their gradual revision, because of more and better evidence, have been typical of attempts to understand biological processes.

The microscope was probably invented independently by Jansen in Holland and by Galileo in Italy in about 1609. Even though inferior to present-day equipment, the microscope opened the door to observations of microorganisms. The first description of bacteria was probably rendered by Antony van Leeuwenhoek in 1676. This Dutch microscopist described a number of microorganisms in letters which were published in the *Philosophical Transactions of the Royal Society of London* during the period 1677–1684.

The process of alcoholic fermentation was known to the ancients, but the understanding of the nature of the process was not developed until the latter two-thirds of the 19th century.

In 1837, Theodore Schwann (The German zoologist who is given much of the credit for the development of the cell theory), published the results of a series of experiments on fermentation. He summarized these as follows[1]:

(1) A boiled organic substance or a boiled fermentable liquid does not putrefy or ferment, respectively, even when air is admitted, so long as the air has been heated.

[1] From the translation given by Brock, Thomas H. 1961. *Milestones in Microbiology.* Prentice-Hall, Inc., Englewood Cliffs, N. J. 275 p.

(2) For putrefaction or fermentation or other processes in which new animals or plants appear, either unboiled organic substance or unheated air must be present.

(3) In grape juice the development of gas is a sign of fermentation, and shortly thereafter appears a characteristic filamentous fungus, which can be called a sugar fungus. Throughout the duration of the fermentation, these plants grow and increase in number.

(4) If ferments which already contain plants are placed in a sugar solution, the fermentation begins very quickly, much quicker than when these plants must first develop.

(5) Poisons which only affect infusoria and do not affect lower plants . . . [an alcoholic extract of *Nux vomica*] prevent the manifestations of putrefaction which are characteristic of infusoria, but do not affect alcoholic fermentation or putrefaction with molds. Poisons which affect both animals and plants (arsenic) prevent putrefaction as well as alcoholic fermentation.

The connection between the alcoholic fermentation and the development of the sugar fungus should not be misunderstood. It is highly probable that the development of the fungus causes the fermentation. Because a nitrogen-containing substance is also necessary for the fermentation, it appears that nitrogen is necessary for the life of this plant, as it is probable that every fungus contains nitrogen. The alcoholic fermentation must be considered to be that decomposition which occurs when the sugar fungus utilizes sugar and nitrogen-containing substances for its growth, in the process of which the elements of these substances which do not go into the plant are preferentially converted into alcohol. Most of the observations on alcoholic fermentation fit quite nicely with this explanation.

What hypotheses did Schwann develop?

SECTION FIVE

PROBLEMS IN THE CONTROL OF VARIABLES

Uncertainty in Science

The problem of obtaining data needed for the evaluation of some hypotheses may lead to uncertainties concerning the validity of these data. In our studies with yeast, we have seen some of the difficulties which may arise when we try to control several variables individually. Perhaps a more common difficulty arises from attempts to study individuals or populations through time. What is the effect of our collection of data on the subsequent behavior of our experimental material? An animal which has been used in one experiment is no longer the same as it was before the experiment. A similar situation exists when we try to study changes in a small population. If our sampling removes individuals from the population, or disturbs their breeding behavior in any way, we may never know what the population might have been like if it had not been disturbed. We can do little in the study of individuals or populations without some danger of disturbing the organisms we are studying.

Data (selected facts) have been called the raw materials of science, but data are seldom complete. We can define an experiment as a situation planned to provide the data needed for evaluating a hypothesis. The logical inferences which can be drawn from data are important. Data almost always involve variability which the scientist must interpret before he can properly draw inferences. Perhaps the major difficulty in carrying out an experiment is providing adequate controls for all important variables.

In Investigations 1, 2, 3, and 4, you saw that there were several variables. The differences in the concentration of molasses resulted in several of these—different concentrations of sugars, other organic compounds, and minerals. Attempts to repeat these experiments with different brands of molasses might be complicated by differences in the composition of the molasses. Also, you might have a problem of duplicating the amount of inoculum added, since different packages of yeast may contain different numbers of living cells. Length of time and other conditions of storage may influence the activity as well as the survival of yeast cells. You might find that changes in the weather will cause changes in the temperature of your laboratory, and this, in turn, may affect the experiment you are conducting.

If we can vary only one factor in an experiment while keeping all others constant, we can say that the experiment is controlled. In the earlier Investigations, we attempted to keep all factors constant except for the kind of carbohydrate supplied to the yeast. In Investigation 4, you experimented with several other variables in an attempt to solve a problem. In all these investigations, temperature has been treated as a controlled variable; that is, all tubes in a particular experiment were supposedly incubated at the same temperature.

Knowing that most chemical reactions are dependent on temperature, it would be reasonable to suppose that the biochemical conversion of glucose to CO_2 and ethanol is affected by temperature changes. We assumed in the earlier Investigations that there would be no differences in temperature among the several tubes; however, because the temperature was not measured, we cannot avoid the possibility that some differences in temperature may have affected the experimental results.

Before you proceed with your work on the next investigation, write a statement expressing what you think will be the effects of various different temperatures on CO_2 production by yeast.

Materials (per team)

1. Ten test tubes, 22 mm × 175 mm
2. Ten test tubes, 13 mm × 100 mm
3. A 4% solution (by weight) of glucose in distilled water
4. One package of dry yeast
5. Two temperature gradient tube holders, one equipped with a $7\frac{1}{2}$ watt bulb for use in the refrigerator and the second equipped with a 15 watt bulb for use at room temperature
6. Thermometers calibrated from 0°C to 100°C
7. Millimeter rule

Materials (per class)

1. One Erlenmeyer flask, 1000 ml
2. Refrigerator
3. An incubator with a fairly constant temperature of approximately 20°C to 25°C

Procedure

1. Calibrate the temperature gradient tube-holders by placing five 22 mm × 175 mm tubes containing 30 ml of distilled water each into the holes in each of the temperature gradient tube-holders. Place one temperature gradient tube-holder in the refrigerator in an inclined position as shown in the illustration. Keep the other at room temperature. Measure and record the temperature of the water in each of the tubes. Repeat the measurements until a constant temperature (±2°C) has been established in each tube. Calculate an average of five successive "constant-temperature" measurements as a temperature value for water in each position. The temperature range of the temperature gradient tubes in the refrigerator should be from about 5°C to 25°C; those at room temperature, from about 25°C to 55°C.
2. Place 25 ml of the 4% glucose solution and 5.0 ml of yeast suspension (prepared as in previous investigations) into each of the 10 large test tubes. Mix thoroughly.
3. Add the small tubes and cotton plugs, as was done in previous Investigations.
4. Incubate the test tubes at the ten different positions in the calibrated temperature gradient tube-holders.

5. Measure CO_2 production every 24 hours for 5 days. (If possible, read CO_2 production every few hours during the first day of incubation.)
6. When the inverted tubes fill with CO_2, you may continue to measure CO_2 production by tipping the tube and displacing the gas with more medium.
7. For each temperature, plot the amount of CO_2 produced on the y-axis of graph paper against the time of incubation (x-axis). Place all curves on the same graph.
8. Also, for each time period at which the amount of CO_2 was measured, plot the amount of CO_2 (y-axis) against temperature (x-axis). Place all curves on the same graph.

Figure 5   Test tube warming apparatus.

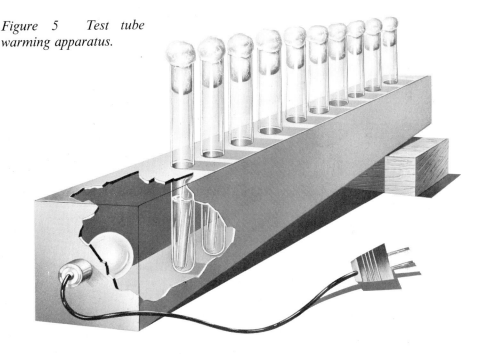

INTERPRETATIONS

1. If constantly increasing amounts of CO_2 appear on the curves described in step 8 of the procedure, calculate the rates of CO_2 production during these periods for each temperature. Usually portions of the curves will have at least 3 points on a nearly straight line.
2. Was CO_2 produced at different rates, at different temperatures? If so, did these differences correspond to those predicted in your hypothesis?

3. If the data show deviations from your original hypothesis, how might you account for the deviations?
4. Do you think the optimum temperature for CO_2 production might be similar for each of the utilizable carbohydrates? Explain.
5. Do you think changes in temperature might cause *S. cerevisiae* to use certain of the carbohydrates it failed to use in Investigation 2?
6. What is the effect of increasing temperature on the solubility of gases in liquid?
7. What factors in the design of these fermentation tubes could affect the reliability of the relative measurements of the CO_2 being produced by these yeast cultures?
8. Did light appear to affect the rate of fermentation? Consider the position of the lightbulb in relation to each of the tubes.

INVESTIGATIONS FOR FURTHER STUDY

1. Spoilage of certain materials containing high concentrations of sugar occurs most readily in hot weather. In ordinary laboratory media, however, yeasts will often grow best at the more moderate temperatures. Perhaps the optimum temperature for CO_2 production from sucrose solutions can also be changed with changes in sugar concentration. Design and perform an experiment to test this hypothesis. If significant support is found for this hypothesis, how might you expect varied concentrations of a single sugar such as glucose to compare with sucrose in changing the optimum temperature of fermentation?

2. Suggest an experiment for obtaining strains of yeast that will grow at a lower or at a higher temperature than does the parent strain.

Parallel Reading: Enzymes and Fermentation

All chemical reactions are affected by the concentrations of the reactants. In our first investigations, the reactants considered were chiefly the carbohydrates. Another group of substances play an important part in fermentation; these are the enzymes from the yeast. We might investigate the effects of varying yeast (enzyme) concentrations on the rate of fermentation.

The rates of chemical reactions are affected by catalysts. *Catalysts* are substances which change the rates of chemical reactions, but can themselves be recovered from the reaction in an unchanged form. The catalysts of biochemical reactions are called enzymes.

An *enzyme* is commonly defined as a protein which acts as a catalyst. Enzymes are specific in their action; that is, ordinarily a given enzyme will act on only one kind of substrate and catalyze only one kind of a reaction. Enzymes are said to be heat-labile, meaning they are destroyed by heat. Most proteins are coagulated by heat. (Recall what happens when the protein of an egg is heated.)

Some enzymes are made up only of amino acids. Others contain various chemical groups in addition to the protein. It is usually the nonprotein part of the enzyme which reacts with the substrate. The presence of the protein greatly increases the rate of the reaction and often narrows the specificity to a single reaction. If the nonprotein part of the enzyme is easily separated from the protein, it is called a *coenzyme.*

Some coenzymes are inorganic ions such as Mg^{++}; others are organic compounds. Many of the B-vitamins serve as parts of coenzymes. In some cases, inorganic ions serve as activators; that is, they enhance the activity of the enzyme but do not become a part of it. In these cases, the ions probably do not enter into the primary reaction in the same way coenzymes enter.

The catabolism of glucose is a process which yields energy to the cell. In alcoholic fermentation, this energy comes from a series of reactions in which some chemical bonds are broken and others are formed. These reactions, although energy-releasing, do not occur in cells in an uncontrolled manner. All matter would exist as simple substances of minimum energy levels if complex molecules broke down spontaneously; no complex molecules would exist for long. Many molecules, however, such as those of glucose, are stable even though they possess large amounts of energy. Such stable molecules can react rapidly if they acquire sufficient energy. The energy necessary to cause the molecules to react is called the *energy of activation.*

At any temperature above absolute zero the molecules of a substance will be in motion and will have kinetic energy, but not all of the molecules in a given system have the same kinetic energy. Some are moving very rapidly; others are moving slowly. As the result of this motion and the corresponding collisions, some molecules will acquire enough energy to react; those which have little energy will not react. We find that the rates of chemical reactions will increase with increasing temperatures because the average kinetic energy of the molecules increases with increasing temperature. The increased average kinetic energy will cause an increasing number of the molecules to acquire the necessary energy of activation. The energy of activation may also be supplied by electricity or light. Photosynthesis uses light energy, but most other biochemical reactions depend on heat as the source of their energy of activation. How then, can an enzyme speed up a reaction when no additional heat is supplied?

Consider a simple reaction which is catalyzed by an enzyme. First the substrate may combine with the enzyme to yield a substrate-enzyme

complex. This complex then breaks down to release the enzyme and form
a product. We can write this as follows:

$$S \; + \; E \; \rightleftharpoons \; ES \; \longrightarrow \; E \; + \; P$$

(substrate)   (enzyme)   (enzyme-   (enzyme)   (product)
                               substrate
                               complex)

The substrate molecule must acquire a certain amount of activation
energy in order to be changed into some other kind of molecule, such as P,
even if P has less energy than S. It may have to form a complex with some
other compound, or it may have its structure changed somewhat and
become less stable. This relationship is shown in Figure 6, where e is the
energy of activation.

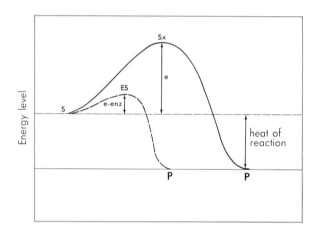

*Figure 6   Energy of activation
of a reaction with and without an
enzyme.*

In this figure are shown the relative energy levels of the substrate S, the
substrate complex without an enzyme S_x, the enzyme substrate complex
E-S, and the product P. The energy of activation when no enzyme is
present is represented by e. When the enzyme is present, the energy of
activation is represented by e_{enz}. The net amount of energy produced is the
heat of the reaction and is equal to the difference in the energy levels of
S and P.

When an enzyme is present, a much lower energy of activation is
required. This is explained by the assumption that less energy is required
to form the substrate-enzyme complex E-S than to form a substrate complex S_x. Thus e is much greater then e_{enz}.

The heat of the reaction is the same regardless of whether or not the
enzyme is present. In the cell, the temperature of the environment is
sufficient to activate a reasonable percentage of the substrate molecules to

react with the enzyme, but not sufficient to provide the energy of activation needed if no enzyme is present. The heat of the reaction will then provide enough energy to activate other molecules. This is probably the way most enzymes act in biological systems. The hydrolysis of sucrose to form glucose and fructose provides an example.

In the hydrolysis of sucrose by HCl, the activation energy required is 26,000 calories, but the activation energy for the hydrolysis of sucrose by the enzyme invertase is only 13,000 calories. Thus the amount of energy which must be acquired for a sucrose molecule to be hydrolyzed by the enzyme is only half that required for hydrolysis by the acid. In some cases, the rate of a reaction in the absence of the enzyme at physiological temperatures is too slow to be measurable. In the presence of the enzyme, however, it may be quite rapid.

The names of most enzymes end in *ase,* and the prefix indicates something about the nature of the enzyme. For example, a dehydrogenase is an enzyme which catalyzes the transfer of hydrogen from a substrate to a hydrogen acceptor. In this case, the enzyme is named for the kind of reaction which it catalyzes. In other cases, enzymes are named on the basis of the substrate with which they react. *S. cerevisiae* produces an enzyme called maltase. Maltase splits the disaccharide, maltose, into two molecules of the monosaccharide, glucose. This reaction may be written to correspond with the generalized enzyme substrate reaction:

maltose $+ H_2O +$ maltose $\rightleftharpoons$
  (substrates)   (enzyme)

            complex of maltose, water, and maltose $\longrightarrow$
                  (enzyme-substrate complex)

                              glucose $+$ maltase
                        (final product)   (recovered enzyme)

INVESTIGATION 6   Enzyme Concentration as a Variable

We should expect that the concentration of enzymes would be one of the variables affecting the rate of fermentation. There are several ways in which we might study the effect of enzyme concentration on this process. One way is the extraction and purification of enzymes. We will not use this method, because it is difficult and time-consuming even though we might control more variables by using pure enzymes. Instead we will use the cells of *S. cerevisiae* as a source of enzymes for our experiment.

Materials (per team)

1. Seven test tubes, 22 mm × 175 mm
2. Seven test tubes, 13 mm × 100 mm
3. One package of dry yeast
4. One Erlenmeyer flask, 250 ml
5. A 4% solution (by weight) of glucose in distilled water
6. One graduated 10 ml pipette
7. One graduated 1 ml pipette

Procedure

1. Place 25 ml of glucose solution into each of the seven large test tubes.
2. Add 1 gram of dried yeast to 40 ml of distilled water. Serially dilute this solution five times so that each solution is $\frac{1}{2}$ the concentration of the previous solution. Add 5 ml of each dilution to six of the large test tubes; add 5 ml of plain water to the seventh tube.
3. Shake each tube well. Invert the small test tubes inside the large ones and fill them with medium as before. Plug the tubes with cotton and label each.
4. Incubate the tubes at the temperature found to be optimum for glucose fermentation during Investigation 5.
5. Measure carbon dioxide production as frequently as possible during the next 4 days. If possible, measure carbon dioxide production every few hours during the first day of incubation.
6. The small inverted tubes may fill with carbon dioxide before your next reading. If this happens, record the amount of CO_2 and then carefully tip the culture and replace the carbon dioxide with medium.
7. For each dilution of yeast, plot the quantity of carbon dioxide produced against time (the time since inoculation of the fermentation tubes).
8. Select one of the time intervals and plot the amount of CO_2 produced against the concentration of yeast cells.

INTERPRETATIONS

1. Was CO_2 formed with some dilutions of yeast only after extended lag periods? If so, what explanations can you offer for this phenomenon?

2. Examine the graph you made in Step 8 of the Procedure. Was the rate of CO_2 production proportional to the concentration of yeast cells? If not, can you explain?

3. Do you think the results of this study would be about the same if you used the other utilizable substrates employed in Investigation 3? Explain.

INVESTIGATIONS FOR FURTHER STUDY

1. Add different concentrations of known poisons to fermenting yeast cultures, and determine which are the most effective inhibitors of the fermentation process. Determine if all inhibitors have the same degree of effectiveness at similar concentrations. CAUTION: *Remember, these are also poisonous to humans.*

2. To determine if all yeast preparations have the same enzyme activity, obtain suspensions of other yeasts, and test each as was done in this experiment. You may use your own culture of yeast, other dried yeast, or compressed yeasts for this purpose. Be sure to determine the water content of non-dried yeast preparations and base all calculations on CO_2 produced per unit weight of dry cells.

3. Do you think it is necessary to have an intact yeast cell before its enzymes will operate? Explain. Suggest an experiment to test your hypothesis.

4. Average the carbon dioxide measurements for each reading from each team. Note the range (interval between the smallest and the largest number) of each set of readings. Plot the readings on a bar graph. Do most of the readings concentrate toward the center or the ends of the range?

QUESTIONS FOR DISCUSSION

1. Define or describe:
   a. coenzyme
   b. enzyme-substrate complex
   c. activation energy

2. If a large number of yeast cells autolyzed in a solution of sugar in water, what effect do you think this might have on the survivors? Explain.

SECTION SIX

PROBLEMS IN MEASUREMENT

The questions, "How many?" "How long?" and "How much?" are essential to the study of modern science.

Progress toward a theoretical explanation of hereditary events was very slow until Gregor Mendel counted the various kinds of offspring he obtained from crossing certain parent plants. Once Mendel knew how many of each kind of offspring resulted from a particular cross, he was able to explain his experimental results mathematically. Modern genetics owes much to Mendel's pioneer work in applying mathematics to the study of heredity.

The general theory that hormones regulate the bending of plants in response to light or to gravity was fairly well developed before a method was found to *measure* the amount of the hormone. Once such methods were developed, the theory was substantiated and practical application followed rapidly.

The accuracy with which a measurement is made depends on the measuring device used and the observer. For ease in converting one unit to another, most laboratories use the metric system. It is clearly much easier to convert 1788 centimeters into 17.88 meters than to convert 1788 inches into 149 feet.

The following rules help to make measurements easy and accurate:

1. Choose units of measurement that are convenient and meaningful. One would not express the length of a table in miles, nor the weight of a man in milligrams. The most common units of measurements used in the biology laboratory are centimeters or millimeters (for length), grams or milligrams (for weight), and liters or milliliters (for volume).

2. Choose a scale that offers the number of subdivisions necessary to permit the accuracy you need. A 1 ml pipette may be subdivided into either tenths of milliliters or hundredths of milliliters.

3. Read the scale to the nearest subdivision. When an object is measured with a meter stick subdivided into centimeters, it is difficult to express the

length to the nearest millimeter. It is often possible to estimate points between the subdivisions of the scale, but estimates to more than one decimal place are likely to be of no significance.

4. When you add, subtract, multiply, or divide, remember that the answer is no more accurate than the least accurate measurement. For example, suppose you measured the heights of 100 bean plants with a meter stick, the smallest divisions of which were centimeters. As you made the readings, you estimated the heights to the nearest millimeter. You then summed the heights and found the total was 1953.4 centimeters. What is the average height of the bean plants? Of course, the arithmetical mean is 19.534 centimeters, but you probably would be stretching your limits of accuracy to say that you could tell the difference between 19.4 and 19.6 on your measuring scale. Therefore, it is misleading to imply that you have any faith in the last two figures. When you record the average as 19.5, there may be some doubt as to the accuracy of the .5, but very little about the 19. The figure in question should be rounded off to the nearest whole number. In rounding off numbers whose last digit is 5, it is customary to add the half when the number is odd and to drop the half when the number is even. Thus, 67.5 would be rounded off to 68, while 66.5 would be rounded off to 66.

QUESTIONS FOR DISCUSSION

1. Students with different meter sticks report the length of the same table as 179.73 cm, 180.00 cm, 180 cm, and 180.003 cm. What is the average of these measurements?

2. What is the difference between a measurement of 180 cm and 180.00 cm?

PATTERN OF INQUIRY 3

Evaluation of Data

Each day for five days, four students were asked to conduct laboratory tests in order to determine the normality of an acid solution which was supplied to them. Although all samples were taken from the same bottle, the students were led to believe that each might be different. They determined the normality of the acid by titrating it with a solution of a base whose concentration they had found to be 0.200 N.

In neutralizing an acid with a base (or vice versa), the volume of the acid times its normality is equal to the volume of the base times its normality. That is,

$$\text{ml} \times \text{Normality} = \text{ml} \times \text{Normality}$$
$$(\text{acid}) \quad (\text{acid}) \quad\quad (\text{base}) \quad (\text{base})$$

The record of their measurements of the amount of base (in milliliters) required to neutralize the acid is as follows:

TABLE 1.   **Titration Results**

Day of measurement	Student 1	Student 2	Student 3	Student 4
1	24.8	25.0	24.90	25.18
2	24.8	25.0	24.95	25.24
3	24.9	25.0	25.05	25.28
4	25.0	25.0	25.15	25.34
5	25.1	25.0	25.20	25.42

Suppose that you needed to use the acid in a subsequent experiment, and a reasonable estimate of its concentration (normality) was required. If this experiment were to involve many titrations, and thus many calculations, what estimate of the normality would you find most convenient and perhaps accurate enough?

If the experiment required the greatest accuracy of which you were capable, what value would you choose as the most accurate estimate of the concentration of the acid?

Parallel Reading: Fermentation and Respiration

Like many other terms, fermentation and respiration are defined differently by different people. It would not be possible to repeat all these definitions here, nor would it be very useful. Most biologists probably think of fermentation as a process whereby food materials are only partially oxidized by microorganisms; that is, *some* of the products still contain energy which can be released by further oxidation.

To many, respiration means the process of breathing. (The word respiration is derived from the Latin word *respirare,* meaning to blow back or to breathe.) Ordinarily when a physician speaks of a patient's rate of respiration, he means how many time the patient inhales (or exhales) in a minute. Many biologists define respiration as a process in which food material is broken down and most of its energy released in the cell. Those who use this definition regard alcoholic fermentation as an example of *anaerobic respiration* because free oxygen is not utilized. If molecular oxygen *is* used, the process is called *aerobic respiration.*

Other biologists define respiration as a process in which energy is liberated from food materials and in which the final oxidizing agent is molecular oxygen. If we use this definition, respiration is always an aerobic process, and since alcoholic fermentation is anaerobic, it would not be called respiration. Acetic acid fermentation (the process in which bacteria of the genus *Acetobacter* convert ethanol to acetic acid and water) is an example of fermentation which involves respiration since molecular oxygen is used. Most researchers in the field of respiration consider incomplete oxidations, such as those in acetic acid fermentation, to be respiration if they involve the oxidation of hydrogen to water.

The conversion of sugar to carbon dioxide and water by complete oxidation provides more energy than the conversion of sugar to alcohol and carbon dioxide by fermentation. The summary equations for these two processes are,

1. alcoholic fermentation of glucose:

$$C_6H_{12}O_6 \longrightarrow 2\ CH_3CH_2OH + 2\ CO_2 + 54\ kg\ calories$$

2. respiration of glucose:

$$C_6H_{12}O_6 + 6\ O_2 \longrightarrow 6\ CO_2 + 6\ H_2O + 686\ kg\ calories$$

Those organisms which can ferment sugar may have an advantage over those which cannot when free oxygen *is not* available, but they are at a disadvantage if they cannot carry out respiration when oxygen *is* available.

If molecular oxygen is available, most cells, including yeast, can oxidize pyruvic acid to carbon dioxide and water. This is accomplished by a series of enzymatic reactions which have been called the Krebs cycle, the citric acid cycle, or the tricarboxylic acid cycle.

The net result of this complex series of simple chemical reactions is the production of 38 molecules of ATP from the respiration of one molecule of glucose. By comparison, recall that a net gain of only 2 molecules of ATP results from the alcoholic fermentation of glucose.

Another respiratory mechanism has been recognized in recent years called the pentose-phosphate pathway. This mechanism is not quite as efficient as a combination of glycolysis and the Krebs cycle since only 36 molecules of ATP may be formed from a molecule of glucose. The results of a number of experiments indicated that the pentose-phosphate cycle is a common oxidative pathway in many microbes and in most plant tissue. A discussion of the pentose-phospate cycle is beyond the scope of this book but can be found in several recent biochemistry texts.

It may be useful to examine some of the characteristics of respiratory processes. We can measure the rate of respiration by measuring the rate of consumption of either oxygen or food, or the rate of production of carbon dioxide, water, or heat.

While respiration occurs both in the light and in the dark, the release of oxygen during photosynthesis may mask the utilization of oxygen involved in green plant respiration. Here we see the importance of the proper choice of experimental organisms. It would be extremely difficult to measure respiration in a photosynthesizing green plant. For this reason, germinating seeds, which have not yet begun photosynthesis, are often used in studying respiration.

INVESTIGATION 7	Measuring Rates of Respiration

Precise measurements of the rate of respiration require elaborate equipment. We can, however, obtain reasonably accurate measurements using simpler methods. This is often done by placing the living materials in a closed system and measuring the amount of oxygen which goes into the system or the amount of carbon dioxide which comes out. By using suitable techniques, we can measure the amounts of one or both of these gases over a given period of time and determine the respiration rate. A simple volumeter can be set up as illustrated in Figure 7.

The volumeter should be arranged as follows. The material for which respiration measurements are desired is placed in one or more test tubes of uniform size. Each tube contains a stopper and pipette as shown in the illustration. One of the test tubes contains an inert material such as glass beads or washed gravel and is used to correct changes in temperature and pressure which cannot be completely controlled in the system. This tube is called a *thermobarometer.* Equal volumes of both test and inert materials must be placed in all the tubes. This precaution is necessary to assure that an equal volume of air is present in each tube. A very small drop of colored liquid is inserted into each pipette at its outer end. This closes the tube, so that if there is any change in the volume of gas left in the tube, the drop of

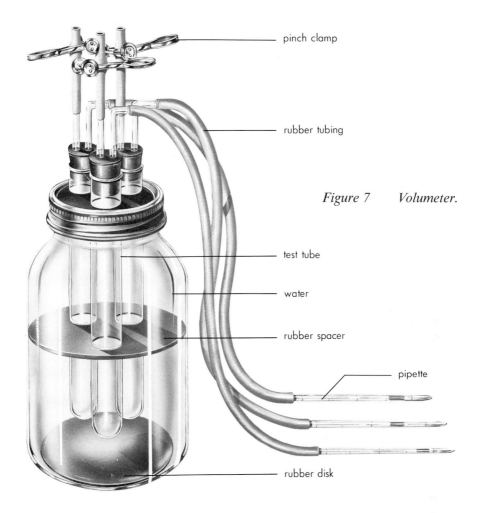

pinch clamp

rubber tubing

Figure 7   *Volumeter.*

test tube

water

rubber spacer

pipette

rubber disk

colored liquid will move. (The direction of movement depends on whether the volume of gas in the system increases or decreases.) The distance of movement over a given period of time can be read from a ruler placed on the side of the pipette. The *volume* of gas added or removed from the system can be read directly from the calibrated pipette.

In attempting to measure respiration with the equipment just described, we must take into consideration not only that oxygen goes into the living material (and thus out of our volumeter test tube), but also that carbon dioxide comes out of the living material (and thus enters into the volumeter test tube). If we are to measure the oxygen uptake in our respiring material we must first trap the carbon dioxide as it evolves. This can be done by adding any substance (ascarite is commonly used) which will absorb the carbon dioxide as fast as it is evolved. Efficient removal prevents the carbon dioxide from being added to the volume of gas in the tube.

Each team should set up one volumeter and compare the respiration of dry seeds with those which have been soaked for 24 hours. The work involved in setting up the volumeter and in obtaining measurements is difficult to complete in one laboratory period. It is very important that certain preparations be made in advance, and that each member of the team understands clearly what is to be done.

Materials (per team)

1. One volumeter (complete)
2. One thermometer
3. One hundred Alaska pea seeds
4. Germination tray
5. 100 ml graduate cylinder
6. Glass beads
7. Three beakers, 150 ml
8. Solution of dye
9. Cotton
10. Ascarite
11. Eye-dropper

Procedure Day I

Each team should place 40 pea seeds in a germination tray between layers of wet paper towels and allow them to soak for 24 hours. (Label the trays as to team, class, experiment, and date.)

Procedure Day II

1. Determine the volume of the 40 soaked seeds. This volume will be used as a standard for preparing materials for the other two test tubes in the volumeter. (Volumes of solid objects, including seeds, can be determined readily by adding them to a measured volume of water in a graduated cylinder and reading the volume of displaced water.)
2. Determine how many glass beads must be put in the tube with the dry seeds so that the volume of air in the tubes with soaked and with dry seeds will be the same. To do this, place 25 ml of water in a 100 ml graduate cylinder. Add the dry seeds. Then add enough beads so that the *increase* of the water level in the cylinder containing both seeds and beads is equal to the volume of the seeds soaked for 24 hours. Dry the 40 seeds and the glass beads by blotting them with paper towelling or cleansing tissue. Place the dried seeds and beads together in a beaker. Label the beaker and store it in the laboratory until you are ready to use the volumeter the following day.
3. Obtain the same volume of glass beads as that determined for the soaked pea seeds. Place these in a beaker, label the beaker, and store it in the laboratory until you are ready to set up the volumeter on the third day.
4. Mix about 25 ml of a dilute solution of vegetable dye (food coloring) in water and add a drop of detergent.

5. Set up the volumeter as illustrated in Figure 7. Add water to the jar in which the test tubes are immersed, but do not add anything to the test tubes.

Procedure Day III

1. Remove the stoppers from each of the three test tubes. Add the 40 soaked pea seeds to one tube; add the dry pea seeds and glass beads which you measured out in Step 2 to the second tube; and add the glass beads measured out in Step 3 to the third tube. Loosely pack cotton over the material in each tube to a depth of $\frac{1}{2}$ inch. Add $\frac{1}{4}$ teaspoon of ascarite or sodium hydroxide to the top of the cotton in each tube. CAUTION: *Ascarite is caustic. Be very careful not to get it on your hands, your body, or on your clothes. If some is spilled, clean it up with a dry paper towel or paper cleansing tissue. Do not use damp cloth or paper as ascarite reacts strongly with water.* The tube should now be packed as illustrated in the diagram.

Figure 8   Volumeter tubes after preparation.

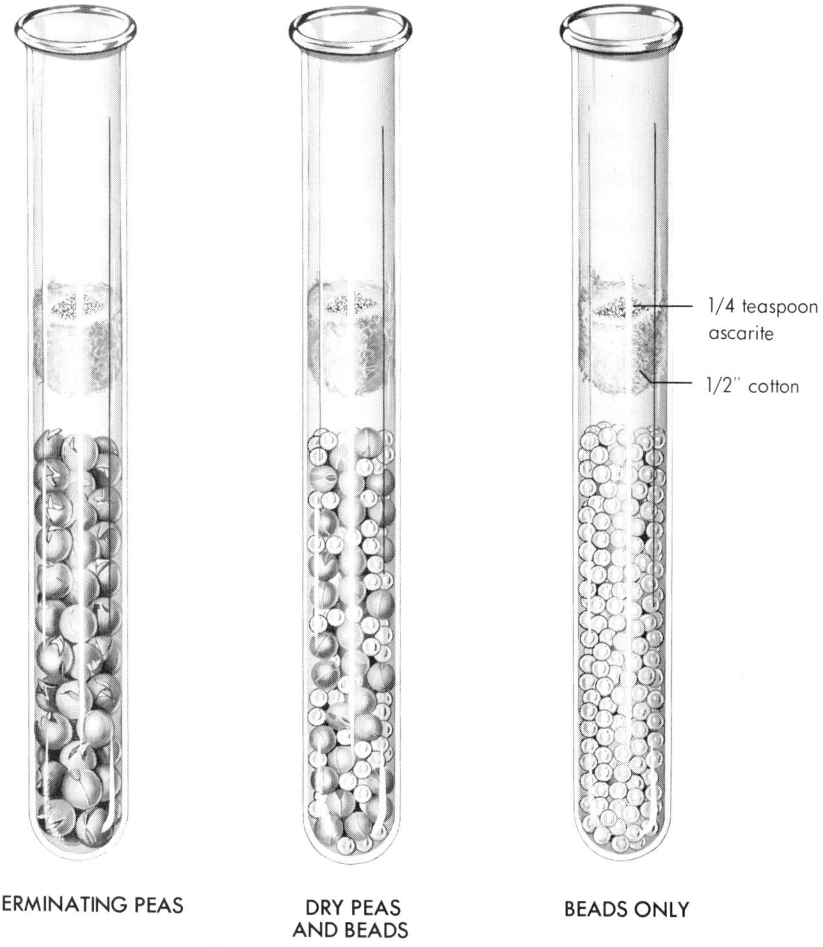

1/4 teaspoon ascarite

1/2" cotton

GERMINATING PEAS   DRY PEAS AND BEADS   BEADS ONLY

2. Replace the stoppers and arrange the pipettes so that they are level on the table.

3. With a dropper, add a small drop of colored water to each of the three pipettes. (See Step 4 of Procedure, Day II.)

   The diagram shows setup of stopper and pipettes attached to each tube in volumeter. After colored water indicator has been introduced at outer end of pipette, it can be adjusted by opening pinch clamp and drawing air from system or pushing it into system with eye dropper inserted into rubber tube at top of apparatus.

   Adjust the marker drops so that the drop in the thermobarometer is centered in the pipette and the other drops are placed near the outer ends of the pipettes.

4. Allow the apparatus to sit for about 5 minutes before making measurements.

5. For 20 minutes, at 2-minute intervals, record the distance the drop moves from its starting point. (If respiration is rapid, it may be necessary to readjust the drop with the medicine dropper as described in Step 3. If readjustment is necessary, add the new readings to the old readings so that the total change during the time of the experiment will be recorded.) Record your results in a table like the one illustrated.

Note: If the drop in the thermobarometer pipette moves toward the test tube, subtract the distance it moves from the distance the drop moves in each of the other pipettes. If the drop in the thermobarometer pipette moves away from the test tube, add the distance it moves to the distance the drop moves in each of the other pipettes.

TABLE 2. **Gas Volume Changes in a Closed System Containing Germinating Peas and Dry Peas**

Time	Thermo-barometer readings ml	Readings for germinating peas ml	Readings for dry peas ml

The readings in each case should be recorded as the change in volume from the original reading. If the observed volumes are corrected to volumes at standard temperature and pressure, the equivalent weights of glucose used may be calculated with greater accuracy.

QUESTIONS FOR DISCUSSION

1. What is the effect of moisture on the germination of pea seeds?

2. Would adding more water to the soaked seeds result in an increased rate of respiration?

3. What is the significance of the difference in the respiration rate of dry seeds compared with that of germinating seeds as far as the ability of the seed to survive in nature is concerned?

INVESTIGATIONS FOR FURTHER STUDY

1. Design a modification of this experiment which will allow you to measure the amount of *carbon dioxide* given off by seeds during respiration.

2. Measure the effects of temperature on the respiratory rates of two different insects.

3. Compare the rates of respiration of different kinds of plant tissues. You might use tissues such as carrot root, potato tuber, or leaves. If green tissues are used, keep them dark by use of black paper or cloth.

PATTERN OF INQUIRY 4

The Respiratory Ratio

After completing Investigation 7, a student wished to study other aspects of respiration in seeds. He decided to see if the *respiratory quotient* or *ratio* is different in different kinds of seeds. The respiratory quotient is defined as the ratio between the volume of CO_2 produced and the volume of O_2 used ($RQ = CO_2/O_2$). He experimented with seeds of wheat and castor bean, and obtained the results shown in Table 3 on page 48.

TABLE 3. **Production of Carbon Dioxide and Utilization of Oxygen by Germinating Seeds of Wheat and Castor Bean**

Milliliters of carbon dioxide produced		Milliliters of oxygen used	
Wheat	Castor bean	Wheat	Castor bean
11.5	7.0	11.3	9.0
13.7	4.5	13.9	7.0
5.5	20.0	5.2	28.5
20.0	14.5	19.4	19.5
17.6	3.1	17.9	4.2
6.2	8.0	6.4	10.5
7.8	10.0	8.0	15.0
15.7	12.5	15.8	18.3

Plot the data for each species on graph paper with milliliters of carbon dioxide produced as the ordinate and milliliters of oxygen used as the abscissa. Can you connect all of the points for either species with a straight line? Why?

SECTION SEVEN

STATISTICAL EVALUATION OF DATA

Assume that your class used the volumeters described in Investigation 7 to study the difference in respiration rates between germinating seeds of pea and corn plants. Further assume that a number of readings were made and recorded as shown in Table 4.

What is the difference between the rates of respiration of germinating seeds of pea and corn at 25° C? Is the difference between corn and pea seedlings a real difference? Could you expect similar differences between the two sets of pea seedlings and the two sets of corn seedlings if you were to repeat the experiments?

TABLE 4.   **Amount of O$_2$ Used by Germinating Seeds of Corn and Pea Plants**

Milliliters of O$_2$ Used Per Hour at 25°C		
Reading number	Corn	Pea
1	0.20	0.25
2	0.24	0.23
3	0.22	0.31
4	0.21	0.27
5	0.25	0.23
6	0.24	0.33
7	0.23	0.25
8	0.20	0.28
9	0.21	0.25
10	0.20	0.30
Total	2.20	2.70
Mean (Average)	0.22	0.27

In Pattern of Inquiry 3, you became familiar with two kinds of error: systematic error and random error. Can you detect evidence of systematic error in the data above? How might you check to determine if this source of systematic error is present?

If we assume that the differences are not the result of differences in the apparatus, what are the chances that you might get differences of this magnitude simply as a result of random error? Notice that in reading numbers 2 and 5, more oxygen was used by corn than by pea seedlings.

Fortunately, mathematicians have developed techniques which are useful in determining what the probability is that differences such as those suggested here may be due to chance. These techniques are included in the branch of mathematics called *statistics*. Many decisions you make in regard to experimental data may be stated in terms of probabilities, and some understanding of probability and statistics is fundamental to an understanding of research in science. Statistical applications are based on probability statements despite the fact that quite often you hear that anything can be proved with statistics. The reverse is true—nothing can be proved definitely with statistics. All you can do is report the probability that similar results would occur if you were to repeat the experiment. This probability is based upon the data that you have collected. It must be emphasized that unless proper care is taken in planning investigations, the use of statistical procedures may not lead to any valid conclusions.

Statistics deals with numbers, and in order to decide what type of statistic to use, a biologist must be familiar with the nature of the numbers obtained in collecting his data. These numbers may be referred to as *variables,* and we can classify them as either *discrete* variables or *continuous* variables.

Discrete Variables. Numbers of this type are often referred to as counting or categorical data. Numbers of boys or girls, number of students preferring biology to engineering, numbers of green and yellow corn plants, number of students ranked according to grades, number of seeds germinating —all of these are examples of discrete data. Families can only be made up of a discrete number of children. They are not made up of 1.2 children. In other words, this kind of variable can take on only a limited number of values.

Continuous Variables. Numbers of this type are associated with measuring and weighing. The data may take any value in a continuous interval of measurement. Hence, the weight of students, the height of pea plants, and the time it takes for plants to flower are all examples of continuous variables. Although 1.2 inches is a very acceptable measurement, you cannot have 1.2 children in a family. (Of course, you might find that a given group of families have an average of 1.2 children each.)

PROBLEMS

What kind of data are the following?
1. the numbers of people preferring Brand X in 5 different towns
2. the weights of high school seniors
3. the lengths of oak leaves
4. the number of seeds germinating
5. 35 tall and 12 dwarf pea plants

Populations and Samples. A population includes all members of any specified group. For example, all of the students in the United States constitute a population. Even though this is a rather large group of individuals, populations are not always large. The number of students in a given school can also constitute a population. Thus, no absolute number of individuals is required to make up a population; it is the researcher who sets up the limits that define the population with which he is concerned.

Nevertheless, the researcher often wishes to make inferences about large populations. If he defines his population as a single biology class, then conclusions from his data can only apply to this one class. However, if the researcher defines his population as all of the biology classes in the United States, he can make inferences about this population from data obtained on small groups, or samples within the population.

Populations do not always consist of intact organisms. An investigator may deal with populations of parts of either organisms or objects of various kinds. For example, one might be interested in the heights, weights, or metabolic rates of individuals, the numbers of red blood cells in individuals of a certain population, or in the types of textbooks used in various schools.

Samples are parts of populations, and statistics are the values used to describe samples. You are a member of a population consisting of all the biology students in the United States. Assume that we are interested in the average reading level of students in these biology classes. Gathering these data could go on for a long time if we attempted to compute the average reading level of students from the total of *all* the reading level scores of *every* student in *all* biology classes in this country. However, we can readily give a reading test to selected students and compute an average reading level score for this group. This group of selected students would constitute a *sample*. Statistics describing samples are used as estimators of the corresponding population.

Naturally, there will be a great deal of variation in the type of students represented by the sample. When samples are used to make inferences about a population, it is important that the individuals selected be a fair representation of the population. An experimenter attempts to insure representative samples by taking *random samples*. These are samples drawn with as little bias as possible from a population. In other words, extreme care is taken to make sure that all individuals or elements within the population have an equal chance of being selected.

For example, assume that there are 100,000 students in the United States who are studying advanced biology. We want to estimate the reading level of these 100,000 students by using data from a sample of only 100 students. How may we obtain this random sample? We could assign a different number to each of the students and the numbers could be written on separate slips of paper and placed in a container. A number could be drawn, recorded, and returned to the container. After thorough mixing of the numbers this procedure could be repeated until 100 numbers were drawn. These 100 numbers representing 100 students would be our random sample representing the population of 100,000 students.

In theory, each number drawn should be returned to the container. However, in actual practice this is not always possible nor is it always necessary with large samples.

Suppose that instead of being selected at random, the 100 students represented groups with above-average reading abilities. The sample average would be too high to use as an estimate of the reading ability of the 100,000 students. The estimate is *biased* upward. Random sampling is intended to produce unbiased estimates of the population.

PROBLEM

If you had 1,000 rats in a cage and you wanted to select a sample of 20, what might be the bias if you selected the first 20 that you could catch?

There are many examples which would illustrate the danger in forming judgments based on biased samples. The field of politics has provided many such examples. One which has become classic was the public opinion poll conducted by a national magazine during the 1936 presidential campaign. Several million postcard ballots were circulated to obtain a large sample of the voting population. On the basis of the returns of these ballots, the magazine predicted that the winning candidate would be Alfred Landon and the loser would be Franklin D. Roosevelt. The magazine selected its sample from listings in telephone directories and automobile registration records. Apparently the nontelephone subscribers and the noncarowners, both of whom were more numerous in 1936 than they are now, voted in a manner that completely reversed the prediction. The magazine made the error of making inferences about this presidential election from samples which were not random and which gave a biased estimate of the proportion of votes for Landon. Many advertising claims seen in the newspapers and on TV are based on biased samples.

As an exercise, you should attempt to give other examples of inferences based on biased samples.

As pointed out earlier, populations are usually so large that they cannot be dealt with in their entirety. Also, a study of entire populations is too expensive and requires too much time. In fact, many are considered to be infinite in number. Consequently, the scientist usually works with samples that represent a population, and on the basis of the data from his samples, he makes inferences about this population. Of course, the accuracy of the inferences depends upon the degree to which the sample was representative.

Statistical Computations. In the handling of data concerning populations and samples of populations, certain statistical tools are of particular value. These tools represent simple devices for using familiar number relationships in order to help describe data.

Mean. In some of your earlier work with the Investigations and the Patterns of Inquiry, you used the "average" or arithmetic mean to help describe your data. Of course there are mathematical means other than arithmetic means, but they do not apply to this course. Throughout this text we shall refer to the arithmetic mean simply as the mean. The mean is used in computing average grades in school, average weight of football players, average temperature for the month of June, and so on. The sample mean or average, symbolized by $\bar{x}$ (x-bar), is a basic computation in statistics. A mean is the summation (symbolized by the Greek letter sigma, Σ) of the individual observations (x_1, x_2, x_3, . . . etc.) divided by the number of observations (n). Thus we may write:

$$\bar{x} = \frac{(x_1 + x_2 + x_3 \ldots, \text{etc.})}{n}$$

or, in mathematical shorthand,

$$\bar{x} = \frac{\sum_{}^{n} x_i}{n} \qquad \text{(Formula 1)}$$

The symbol $\sum^{n} x_i$ represents the sum of the individual measurements; that is, $x_1 + x_2 + \ldots + x_n$ where i takes on all integral (whole number) values from 1, 2, . . . , n. For example, $\sum^{4} x_i$ would represent the sum of 4 measurements, $x_1 + x_2 + x_3 + x_4$.

For example, five groups of students conducted an experiment regarding the effect of temperature on the growth of peas. In one part of the experiment, each group grew a plant in the refrigerator at 10°C and measured the length of the shoot at the end of a given time. The results were as follows:

TABLE 5. **Sample Data for Calculation of the Mean**

Group	Length of shoots in inches
A	10
B	7
C	6
D	8
E	9

$$\sum_{}^{5} x_i = 40$$

$$\bar{x} = \frac{10 + 7 + 6 + 8 + 9}{5} = \frac{40}{5}$$

$$\bar{x} = 8$$

The values for the individual members of a "normal" population or of a sample tend to fall on either side of a particular value. The mean is an estimate of this value.

PROBLEMS

Find the means for the following sets of data:

1. 7, 7, 5, 3, 3
2. 10, 9, 8, 7, 6, 5, 4, 3, 2
3. 20, 16, 10, 6, 2

Normal Distribution. The relation of individual values to the mean is often important in statistics. Graphs which represent the frequency of occurrence of different values in a population are called frequency distributions, or simply, distributions. To graph a distribution, we can place the frequencies of our values either on the vertical or on the horizontal axis. As a matter of convenience, the frequencies are generally placed on the vertical axis, and the classes of the measured values for which the frequencies are determined are placed on the horizontal axis. A population with a bell-shaped distribution of values about its mean is said to have a

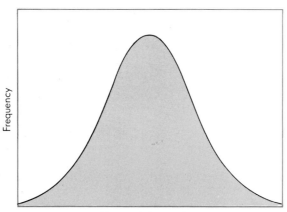

Measured characteristic

Figure 9   The normal curve. Notice that in a normal curve the measurements cluster around the mean with relatively few measurements in the tails.

"normal" distribution. We place the word "normal" in quotes because most populations appear to vary somewhat from the predictable normal curve.

Note the bell shape as shown in Figure 9. Most of the samples examined by biologists are assumed to come from "normally distributed" populations. Therefore, it is important to know some of the characteristics of such a distribution. Since a true "normal" distribution is an ideal theoretical distribution based upon an infinite number of measurements, it is unlikely that the curve plotted from most data will look exactly like the curve of normal distribution.

Variance (s^2). We can see from the data on the amount of O_2 used by the corn and pea seedlings (Table 4, page 49), that the results vary for the different readings. It is often convenient to have a way of expressing this variation; one such expression is called variance. Variance is a measure of the degree of variation of scores from the mean. A large variance indicates that the individual scores in the sample deviate considerably from the mean, whereas a small variance indicates that the scores deviate little from the mean.

The method of computing variance requires some explanation. Individual deviations from the mean can be described in terms of the number of units between a measurement and the mean. If the mean is 8, then a measurement of 10 is 10 minus 8, or positive 2 units from the mean. Similarly, a measurement of 6 is 6 minus 8, or negative 2 units from the mean. To compute the variance of a set of deviations, we are tempted to sum all the deviations and find an average. However, the sum of the positive and negative deviations would always be zero for all samples. This would be of no use to us. To avoid this useless average of zero, each deviation from the mean is squared, and these squares are then added. Squaring the deviations gives us a series of positive numbers, because when a negative number is squared the result is positive. The variance is then calculated by dividing the sum of the squared deviations by n — 1, the total number of measurements minus 1. We use n — 1 instead of n because it has been shown that when deviations are taken from a sample mean instead of from a population mean, division by n — 1 gives an unbiased estimate of the population variance; division by n does not.

The formula for variance is therefore:

$$s^2 = \frac{\sum_{}^{n} (x_i - \bar{x})^2}{n - 1} \qquad \text{(Formula 2)}$$

As we have mentioned earlier, the variance helps to characterize the data concerning a sample by indicating the degree to which individual members within that sample vary from the mean.

TABLE 6. **Heights in Centimeters of Five Randomly Selected Pea Plants Grown at 8–10°C**

Plant	Heights of pea plants (x_i)	Deviations from mean $(x_i - \bar{x})$	Squares of deviations from mean $(x_i - \bar{x})^2$
A	10	2	4
B	7	−1	1
C	6	−2	4
D	8	0	0
E	9	1	1
	$\sum_{}^{5} x_i = 40$	$\sum_{}^{5} (x_i - \bar{x}) = 0$	$\sum_{}^{5} (x_i - \bar{x})^2 = 10$

The data in Table 6 can be used to demonstrate both the calculation of the mean and the variance.

$$\bar{x} = \frac{\sum_{}^{5} x_i}{5} = \frac{40}{5} = 8$$

$$s^2 = \frac{\sum_{}^{5} (x_i - \bar{x})^2}{n - 1} = \frac{10}{5 - 1} = \frac{10}{4} = 2.5$$

PROBLEMS

1. Compute the mean and variance for an experiment similar to the above but in which the heights of pea plants were 9, 9, 8, 7, and 7 centimeters. Is the variance greater or less than in the previous example? Do your results bear out the conclusions that can be made by merely examining the data?
2. Compute the variance for the data on the amount of oxygen used by corn and pea plants as shown in Table 4, page 49.
3. Compute the variance for scores 10, 9, 8, 7, 6, 5, 4, 3, and 2.
4. Compute the variance for scores of 20, 15, 10, 5, and 2.

Standard Deviation. This is an important statistic that is used in many statistical operations and is associated with the interpretation of the normal curve. It is another measure of variation that is used to describe samples. We will use the symbol (s) as a designation for standard deviation. The standard deviation is calculated by taking the square root of the variance.

$$s = \sqrt{\frac{\sum_{i}^{n}(x_i - \bar{x})^2}{n - 1}} \qquad \text{(Formula 3)}$$

The standard deviation of the heights of our sample of pea plants (Table 6) is as follows:

$$s = \sqrt{\frac{10}{4}}$$
$$= \sqrt{2.5}$$
$$= 1.6$$

While the standard deviation is shown to be 1.6, it refers to a measurement ±1.6 centimeters.

Examine the relationship of the standard deviation of a sample to the "normal" distribution curve. Consider a curve in which each interval on the x-axis is a unit of standard deviation (s). The numbers of individuals are plotted on the y-axis. In our example, s = 1.6. The concept of a normal distribution may be used to predict the percentage of individuals in a sample which should fall within a particular range of standard deviations. This relationship is shown graphically in Figure 10.

Figure 10   Percentage of individuals in a normal distribution falling within a plus or minus 1, 2, or 3 standard deviations from the mean.

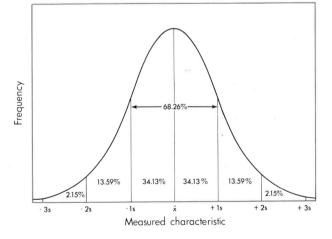

Figure 11 shows that about 68 per cent of the measurements in a normal population have values which are within plus or minus 1 standard deviation from the mean. About 95% will fall within plus or minus 2 standard deviations, and nearly all members (over 99%) will fall within plus or minus 3 standard deviations from the mean.

One standard deviation in the example of pea plants was shown to equal 1.6. Since one standard deviation from the mean can be either positive or negative, 1.6 *added* to a mean of 8 equals 9.6 while 1.6 *subtracted* from a

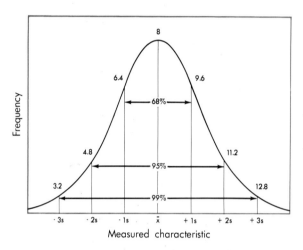

Figure 11   Percentage of classes in a normal distribution falling within a plus or minus 1, 2, or 3 standard deviations in a population with a mean of 8.

mean of 8 equals 6.4. Therefore, in a sample representative of a normally distributed population, approximately 68% of the same species of pea plants, grown under the same conditions, can be expected to range from a height of 6.4 centimeters to a height of 9.6 centimeters. If 2 × 1.6 (two standard deviations) is added to and subtracted from the mean of 8, it can be predicted that about 95% of the same population of pea plants will range in height from 4.8 cm to 11.2 cm. Three standard deviations (in this case 3 × 1.6) will yield a range of 3.2 to 12.8 which should account for 99% of the population. From this it can be predicted that the probability of finding a pea plant that is grown under the same condition and is over 12.8 cm in height is remote—less than 1 out of 100.

For another example, consider the litter sizes of a certain species of dog. Assume the population has a mean of 10 pups per litter and a standard deviation of 2. We can then predict that slightly over 68% of the litters of this species will contain from 8 to 12 pups (±1 standard deviation from the mean); 95+% will have from 6 to 14 (±2 standard deviations from the mean); and 99 + % of our sample will be in the range from 4 to 16 pups (±3 standard deviations from the mean). These relationships can be seen in Figure 12.

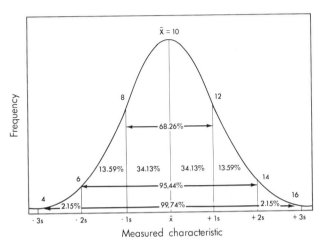

Figure 12   Samples (litters of pups) with a mean score of 10 pups and a standard deviation of 2.

To illustrate further the relationship between the standard deviation and the mean, consider the plot of dog-litter sizes in Figure 12. If we wrote the litter sizes of all individual litters on slips of paper and placed the slips into a hat, what would be the probability of drawing a score of 16? It would be rather unlikely; however, the chances of selecting a score of 11 might be rather good. The normal distribution curve provides the basis for making these probability statements.

Thus the standard deviation, s, can be a valuable tool in statistics because it reveals predicted limits within which one has a stated chance of being correct. It is also valuable in further statistical analysis.

PROBLEMS

1. Refer to the data for oxygen consumption by germinating corn and pea seeds given in Table 4, page 49. The standard deviation for corn was 0.02 and for peas was 0.035. If you made additional readings under similar conditions, between what values would you expect:
    a. 68% of the readings for corn to fall?
    b. 68% of the readings for peas to fall?
    c. 95% of the readings for corn to fall?
    d. 95% of the readings for peas to fall?

2. Compute the standard deviations for the data on oxygen consumption in germinating corn and peas (Table 4, page 49).
3. In any normal distribution, what percentages of the individuals will be found under that part of the curve which extends from the mean to plus 2 standard deviations from the mean?
4. With a specific disease, the white blood counts of randomly selected patients were (cells per mm^3) 11,200, 10,600, 10,600, 11,800, 11,000, 11,200, 10,400, 12,200, 10,800, and 11,600. We can expect 95% of all persons having this disease to fall in what white blood count range?

Standard Error of the Mean ($s_{\bar{x}}$). The mean, the variance, and the standard deviations are helpful in estimating characteristics of the population from a single sample. Statisticians have shown that if many random samples of a given size, n, are taken from the same population, the means ($\bar{x}$) of these samples would themselves form a normal distribution. This distribution of sample means would have a mean either equal or nearly equal to the population mean.

From this distribution a standard deviation of sample means can be estimated. The standard deviation of sample means is called the standard error of the mean ($s_{\bar{x}}$) or simply the standard error. Because there is less dispersion in the distribution of the sample means, the standard error is less than the standard deviation. We will use the idea of standard error later on in our work to test the reliability of our data. It is usually either impractical or impossible to take a large number of samples, compute the means of all the samples, and then determine the standard error of this distribution of means. It is important that we have a rather simple method for estimating the standard error. As was mentioned earlier, the dispersion in the distribution of means is very small, and, therefore, an estimation based on a single sample will be adequate. It can be shown that our best estimate of the standard error is given by the following formula:

$$s_{\bar{x}} = \frac{s}{\sqrt{n}} \qquad \text{(Formula 4)}$$

where

$$s_{\bar{x}} = \text{standard error}$$
$$s = \text{previously calculated standard}$$
$$\text{deviation of a sample of size (n)}$$

Assume that a sample of ten corn plants revealed a standard deviation of 0.02 inches.

$$s_{\bar{x}} = \frac{0.02}{\sqrt{10}}$$

$$= \frac{0.02}{3.16} = 0.006$$

Thus, 0.006 represents one standard deviation in the distribution of the means of samples of size 10.

Note that a larger sample size (n) lowers the standard error. In the above example, an n of 100 with a standard deviation of 0.02 reduces the standard error from 0.006 to:

$$s_{\bar{x}} = \frac{0.02}{\sqrt{100}} = \frac{0.02}{10} = 0.002$$

This is logical, since one would expect a larger sample to represent the population better.

In this section we have examined some of the basic ideas of the normal distribution curve. The mean, variance, and standard error of the mean will take on more significance as they are applied throughout this course.

PROBLEMS

1. What is the standard error of the mean for the data on oxygen consumption by pea plants (Table 4, page 49)?
2. What is the standard error of the mean for the data on the height of pea plants (Table 6, page 56)?
3. Five randomly selected boys received the following grades on a standardized examination: 76, 90, 85, 72, and 81. A second grouping of ten boys received the following scores on the same examination: 79, 84, 83, 86, 89, 76, 90, 85, 72, and 81. Calculate and compare the standard errors for these two groups.

In dealing with populations, the experimenter often compares two samples which have been treated differently. He wants to know if the two samples differ sufficiently to warrant a decision that they represent two different populations. This may be done by determining that the difference in the means of the two samples did not come about by "normal" sampling variations. To make such a decision, it is necessary to know how large the difference must be between the two samples (usually a treated sample and an untreated control sample) in order to state that the difference was caused by the treatment and not by "normal" sampling variation. To make such a decision requires a knowledge of the "laws" of probability.

Probability and Tests of Significant Differences

We often ask, "What is the probability of the occurrence of a particular event?" We are concerned with probability when we toss a coin, roll a die, draw a card, or select individuals from populations in some other way. The symbol p is commonly used to represent probability; its value may be expressed either as a common fraction or as a decimal fraction. Thus, the probability that a coin will come up heads may be expressed as either $p = 0.5$, $p = \frac{1}{2}$, $p = \frac{5}{10}$, and so on. Likewise, the chance that it will come up tails is $p = 0.5$. It is important to remember that the total probability for a coin turning up heads and for a coin turning up tails is always equal to 1 when all possible events are accounted for.

Statistics is largely a science of probabilities, and to understand their use one must be familiar with three basic principles of probability:

1. *The results of one trial of a chance event do not affect the results of later trials of the same event.* No matter how many times in a row a coin comes up heads (if it is an honest coin), the next tossing of the coin has the same probability value of being either heads or tails, namely, $p = 0.5$.

2. *The chance that two or more independent events will occur together is the product of their chances of occurring separately.* (Two or more events are said to be independent if the occurrence or non-occurrence of one in no way affects the occurrence or non-occurrence of any of the others.) If you roll a die, what is the chance that a 3 will come up? Since a die is six sided, and the 3 occupies only one of the sides, the probability of rolling a 3 is $\frac{1}{6}$. However, if there are two dice, the probability of rolling a 3 on both dice is the product of the individual probabilities, or $\frac{1}{6} \times \frac{1}{6} = \frac{1}{36}$. Remember that all the probabilities must add up to 1. Thus there are 35 chances out of 36 that you may roll some combination other than two threes. For this, $p = \frac{35}{36}$. Assuming the sex of an individual is a chance event, what is the probability that fraternal twins will be both boys? both girls?

3. *The probability that either of two or more mutually exclusive events will occur is the sum of their probabilities.* (Events are said to be mutually exclusive if when one of them happens on a particular occasion, the other cannot happen.) What is the chance of rolling a total of either two or twelve with a pair of dice? The probability of rolling a two (a one on each die) is $\frac{1}{6} \times \frac{1}{6}$ or $\frac{1}{36}$. Similarly, the probability of rolling a twelve (a six on each die) is $\frac{1}{36}$. Therefore, the p for rolling a two or a twelve is $\frac{1}{36} + \frac{1}{36} = \frac{2}{36}$ or $\frac{1}{18}$.

PROBLEMS

1. Assume that the probability that your car will have a tire blow-out next month is 0.06, and that the probability that a second blow-out will occur next month is 0.25. (This is predicted on the likelihood that a first blow-out may indicate that all of your tires are more worn than those found on the average car.) What is the probability that you will have two blow-outs next month?

2. The following is called a two-way frequency table. The population which it represents is a hypothetical class of 1000 biology students.

TABLE 7.   **Two-Way Frequency Table**

Sex	Hair Color			Totals
	Brunette	Blond	Redhead	
Male	300	150	25	475
Female	310	160	55	525
Totals	610	310	80	1000

   a. What is p for a particular student's being a male?
   b. What is p for a particular student's being a brunette?
   c. What is p for a particular student's being a male brunette?
   d. What is p for a particular student's being a female blond?
   e. What is p for a particular female's being a blond?
   f. What is p for a particular female's being either brunette or redhead?

Null Hypothesis. When we use probability as a guide in deciding whether two samples (such as one from a treated and one from a control group) are really different, we may make the assumption that any differences are due to chance and are not valid reflections of the populations. This assumption is called the *null hypothesis.* The null hypothesis assumes that there will be no difference as a result of the experimental treatment. If, after assuming that treatment A is no better then treatment B, we find evidence to the contrary, we reject the null hypothesis. That is, we say that the noted differences probably did not result from chance alone.

Statisticians use two common formulas to determine the probability that the null hypothesis is valid. These are known as the t test and the chi-square (χ^2) test. Each test has its own use.

The t Test. The t test is a valid technique for random samples of continuous variables (page 50) from normally distributed populations. When the conditions are met, the t test can determine the probability that the null hypothesis concerning the means of two small samples is correct; that is, the probability that the two samples are representative of a single population or of different populations. The t statistic was proposed in 1908 by a statistician, W. S. Gosset, who called himself "Student." It was developed as the relationship between series of sample means and the true mean of a population from which the samples were drawn. "Student" showed the areas under the distribution curve to be inconsistent with that of the normal curve when the sample size varies.

Usually we use the t test to determine the probability that two samples, A and B, came from the same or from different populations. We can then compute a standard error of the difference between the means based on the consideration that all the measurements in the two samples represent a single sample. If we divide this standard error of the difference in the means into the difference between the means of the two samples,

$$\frac{\bar{x}_1 - \bar{x}_2}{s_{\bar{x}_1 - \bar{x}_2}}$$

the result is the number of deviation units which separates the mean of Sample A from the mean of Sample B.

For example, if Sample A has a mean of 8, Sample B a mean of 12, and the standard error of the difference is 1, then if these two measurements are from the same population, they are separated by $\frac{12 - 8}{1}$ or 4 standard deviation units. To illustrate, assume that 8 is actually a true estimate of the mean of the population from which Sample A was taken. Suppose we plot a normal distribution about $\bar{x} = 8$ (see Figure 13), and visually estimate the probability that Sample B was derived from the same population as was Sample A. As can be seen, when the standard error of the difference is 1, the probability of drawing two samples with means of 8 and 12 from the same population is rather unlikely. A more probable conclusion would be the alternative possibility that Samples A and B represent samples from different populations.

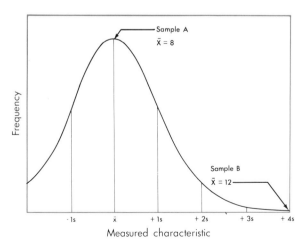

Sample A
$\bar{x} = 8$

Sample B
$\bar{x} = 12$

Frequency

- 1s $\bar{x}$ + 1s   + 2s   + 3s   + 4s

Measured characteristic

Figure 13   A comparison of two samples, assuming they are from the same population.

.There are a number of formulas by which t may be determined, the choice depending on several factors. For data collected in this course, the following formula may be used:

$$t = \frac{\bar{X}_1 - \bar{X}_2}{\sqrt{\frac{(n_1 - 1)s_1{}^2 + (n_2 - 1)s_2{}^2}{n_1 + n_2 - 2} \cdot \left(\frac{1}{n_1} + \frac{1}{n_2}\right)}} \qquad \text{(Formula 5)}$$

where

$$
\begin{aligned}
\bar{X}_1 &= \text{mean of Sample 1} \\
\bar{X}_2 &= \text{mean of Sample 2} \\
n_1 &= \text{the number in Sample 1} \\
n_2 &= \text{the number in Sample 2} \\
s_1{}^2 &= \text{the variance of Sample 1} \\
s_2{}^2 &= \text{the variance of Sample 2}
\end{aligned}
$$

If the samples are equal in size, then $n_1 = n_2 = n$ and, the above formula can be simplified as follows:

$$t = \frac{\bar{X}_1 - \bar{X}_2}{\sqrt{\frac{s_1{}^2 + s_2{}^2}{n}}} \qquad \text{(Formula 6)}$$

It should be noted that the value of t depends on both the numerator and denominator of this equation. The larger the numerator $(\bar{X}_1 - \bar{X}_2)$ is, the larger is the value of t, assuming a constant value for the denominator.

The denominator is the standard error of the difference between the means. In Formula 5, the assumption is made that the variance of Sample 1 is similar to the variance of Sample 2. You may recall that we assumed both samples were from the same population. If this assumption is not valid and the two variances are in fact so different that they cannot be pooled, we would need to use a different formula for t. This should not be necessary in this course. If you are interested in further refinement of the t test, the several references on statistics in the back of this book may be consulted.

We will use the t test to determine if the data on the rate of oxygen consumption in corn seedlings is significantly different from that of pea seedlings. (See Table 4, page 49.) First we must state the hypothesis we wish to test. In this case, perhaps the most useful hypothesis to test is as follows: The rates of O_2 consumption in the two kinds of seeds are not different. (We did observe a difference, however; and if our null hypothesis is not rejected, we must be able to assume that there is a reasonable probability that such a difference might be obtained by chance sampling of the same population.)

The two sample sizes are equal—that is, $n_1 = n_2$. Therefore, we may use Formula 6.

$$t = \frac{\bar{x}_1 - \bar{x}_2}{\sqrt{\dfrac{s_1^2 + s_2^2}{n}}}$$

We have already found:

$$\bar{x}_1 = 0.22$$
$$\bar{x}_2 = 0.27$$
$$s_1^2 = 0.0004$$
$$s_2^2 = 0.0012$$
$$n = 10$$

Substituting these values in the formula, we have:

$$t = \frac{0.22 - 0.27}{\sqrt{\dfrac{0.0004 + 0.0012}{10}}}$$
$$= \frac{-0.05}{\sqrt{0.00016}}$$
$$= \frac{-0.05}{0.0126}$$
$$= 3.97$$

This indicates that the means of Sample 1 and Sample 2 are almost 4 standard deviations apart. From our earlier discussion we would not expect to draw two such samples from the same population by chance, and we can immediately guess that we may reject our null hypothesis. However, we can make more critical use of our value of t by examination of a table of the distribution of t (Table 8).

TABLE 8.   Distribution of *t* Probability

		Probability			
		0.1	*0.05*	*0.01*	*0.001*
	1	6.314	12.706	63.657	636.619
	2	2.920	4.303	9.925	31.598
	3	2.353	3.182	5.841	12.941
	4	2.132	2.776	4.604	8.610
	5	2.015	2.571	4.032	6.859
D	6	1.943	2.447	3.707	5.959
e	7	1.895	2.365	3.499	5.405
g	8	1.860	2.306	3.355	5.041
r	9	1.833	2.262	3.250	4.781
e	10	1.812	2.228	3.169	4.587
e					
s	11	1.796	2.201	3.106	4.437
	12	1.782	2.179	3.055	4.318
o	13	1.771	2.160	3.012	4.221
f	14	1.761	2.145	2.977	4.140
	15	1.753	2.131	2.947	4.073
F					
r	16	1.746	2.120	2.921	4.015
e	17	1.740	2.110	2.898	3.965
e	18	1.734	2.101	2.878	3.922
d	19	1.729	2.093	2.861	3.883
o	20	1.725	2.086	2.845	3.850
m					
	21	1.721	2.080	2.831	3.819
	22	1.717	2.074	2.819	3.792
	23	1.714	2.069	2.807	3.767
	24	1.711	2.064	2.797	3.745
	25	1.708	2.060	2.787	3.725
	26	1.706	2.056	2.779	3.707
	27	1.703	2.052	2.771	3.690
	28	1.701	2.048	2.763	3.674
	29	1.699	2.045	2.756	3.659
	30	1.697	2.042	2.750	3.646
	40	1.684	2.025	2.704	3.551
	60	1.671	2.000	2.660	3.460
	120	1.658	1.980	2.617	3.373
	∞	1.645	1.960	2.576	3.291

Note: *The shading in this table emphasizes the areas of increasing probability that the null hypothesis should be rejected—that is, the areas of increased confidence that the two samples represent two different populations. In evaluating data from the Investigations in this course,* p *values of less than 0.05 will generally be considered as adequate for rejection.*

Source: Abridged from Table III of R. A. Fisher and F. Yates: *Statistical Tables for Biological, Agricultural, and Medical Research,* published by Oliver and Boyd Ltd., Edinburgh, by permission of the authors and publisher.

This table shows what value for t may be expected at the various levels of probability. It employs, along the top, a series of p values, and along the left side a listing of the degrees of freedom (d.f.). Degrees of freedom may be defined as the number of individuals or events, or sets of individuals or events, which are free to vary in a given sample. For example, if the total of five numbers is 20, the first four numbers can be a combination of quite a few numbers, but the fifth number will be determined by the first four numbers. If our total is 20 and our first four numbers are 1-3-5-7, the fifth number must be 4. Of n numbers, with a fixed mean, only $n - 1$ are free to vary. In our data, we had 10 readings in Sample 1 and 10 readings in Sample 2. Each sample has $n - 1$ degrees of freedom and the total is $(n_1 - 1) + (n_2 - 1) = 18$. Therefore, we enter the table with 18 degrees of freedom. With 18 d.f. our t must be 2.101, if the difference between the means is to be significant at the 5% level of probability. At the 1% level it must be 2.878, and at the 0.1% level it must be 3.922. Our value of 3.97 is greater than any of these.

Conclusion: We reject the null hypothesis that the rates of oxygen consumption are the same. We reject it at the $p = 0.001$ level of significance. In so doing, we are running the risk of being in error, but only 1 time in 1000.

If such data were reported in the literature, the authors would usually report the data with the means and point out that "the difference between the means is highly significant." In most biological research, if $p < 0.05$, we say the results are *significant* (we reject the null hypothesis); if $p < 0.01$, we say the results are *highly significant*.

Our table of t includes only p values of 0.1, 0.05, 0.01, and 0.001. Any one of these levels of probability might be used for rejection of the null hypothesis in a given research problem. The nature of the problem will determine what level we will use. Other tables may include p values of 0.2, 0.3, 0.4, or even 0.9. These values are sometimes useful even if we do not use them for rejection of a null hypothesis.

In order to gain more experience in the use of the t test, consider the data in Table 9. We are hopeful, of course, that other conditions such as light intensity, soil fertility, available moisture, and others were the same in both samples. If any differences do occur, we are hopeful that they are due to the difference in temperature. What, then, should our null hypothesis be?

Having stated the hypothesis, compute the value of t. Because the sample sizes are equal, we can use Formula 6. Note, however, that you will need to know the values of the following: $\bar{x}_1$, $\bar{x}_2$, s_1^2, s_2^2, n_1 and n_2. Determine each of these values and then substitute them into the formulas. Remember that $n_1 = n_2 = n$ in the formula.

TABLE 9. Heights of Pea Plants Grown Under Different Temperatures

Plant	Room Temperature (22° C) (Sample 1)			Temperature in Refrigerated Growth Chamber (10° C) (Sample 2)		
	Heights of plants in inches x_i	Deviations from mean $(x_i - \bar{x})$	Squares of deviations from mean $(x_i - \bar{x})^2$	Heights of plants in inches x_i	Deviations from mean $(x_i - \bar{x})$	Squares of deviations from mean $(x_i - \bar{x})^2$
A	12	1	1	10	2	4
B	12	1	1	7	−1	1
C	10	−1	1	6	−2	4
D	11	0	0	8	0	0
E	10	−1	1	9	1	1
Totals	$\sum_{}^{5} x_i = 55$	$\sum_{}^{5}(x_i - \bar{x}) = 0$	$\sum_{}^{5}(x_i - \bar{x})^2 = 4$	$\sum_{}^{5} x_i = 40$	$\sum_{}^{5}(x_i - \bar{x}) = 0$	$\sum_{}^{5}(x_i - \bar{x})^2 = 10$

Now enter the table for the distribution of t. How many degrees of free-dom are there? With your values for t and d.f., what is the probability that you might have obtained the observed differences in the means by chance alone? Can you reject the null hypothesis? If so, at what level of confi-dence? What conclusion might you draw from the data?

The following is a summary of the requirements for use of the t test in evaluation of a null hypothesis:

1. Samples must be randomly chosen.
2. Samples must have the characteristics of a "normal" distribution.
3. Measurements must be of continuous variables.

If these criteria can be met, proceed as follows:

1. State your null hypotheses.
2. Compute the means (Formula 1, page 53).
3. Compute the variances (Formula 2, page 55).
4. Determine which formula for t is applicable. If n_1 and n_2 are different, use Formula 5 (page 65); if $n_1 = n_2 = n$, use Formula 6 (page 65).
5. Substitute the proper values into the formula and calculate t.
6. Determine the number of degrees of freedom (page 68).
7. Refer to a table of t and determine the proper level of probability for your data.
8. State your conclusion.

PROBLEMS

On page 54, data were given for three samples with instructions to calculate the means ($\bar{x}$). These data are listed below as Samples A, B, and C. Compute the variances (s^2) for each of the samples.

$$\text{Sample A:} \quad 7, 7, 5, 3, 3$$

$$\text{Sample B:} \quad 10, 9, 8, 7, 6, 5, 4, 3, 2$$

$$\text{Sample C:} \quad 20, 16, 10, 6, 2$$

Assume that each set of data meet the three requirements listed for appli-cation of the t test.

1. a. Hypothesize that the means of Samples A and B are not different.
   b. Which t formula should you use to test this null hypothesis?
   c. Find t for Samples A and B.
   d. How many degrees of freedom are there?
   e. Interpret the t value.

2. a. Hypothesize that the means of Samples A and C are not different.
   b. Which *t* formula should you use to test this null hypothesis?
   c. Find *t* for Samples A and C.
   d. How many degrees of freedom are there?
   e. Interpret the *t* value.

3. a. Hypothesize that the means of Samples B and C are not different.
   b. Which formula should you use to test this null hypothesis?
   c. Find *t* for Samples B and C.
   d. How many degrees of freedom are there?
   e. Interpret the *t* value.

Chi-Square. You will recall that one of the requirements for application of the *t*-test was that the data be made up of continuous variables. When we have data that are made up of discrete variables, we often use a *chi-square* $(X)^2$ *test* to determine if our null hypothesis is tenable. (The chi-square method was devised in 1900 by Karl Pearson of England.) It is most often used to evaluate differences between experimental data and expected or hypothetical data, and can be used with two or more samples.

Suppose that we have collected a number of snails, and that after examining a few, we have the feeling that $\frac{3}{5}$ of all snails twist clockwise and $\frac{2}{5}$ of all snails twist counterclockwise. Suppose that we have caught and observed 1000 snails. Acording to our theory, 600 should twist clockwise and 400 counterclockwise. Now suppose that our actual study population of snails turns out to have 615 which turn clockwise and 385 which turn counterclockwise.

As we look at these numbers, it is very hard to know whether they are an accidental departure from our theorized 600 and 400, or a somewhat unusual departure from, say, 500 and 500. This is the question we want to test. For this kind of testing we first make a null hypothesis, and then test it by the chi-square method. To use chi-squares, it is necessary only to identify, count, or classify samples. Once a chi-square value has been determined, it can be used for estimating the probability of the null hypothesis in much the same way as we used the *t* value.

Often when chi-square is applied, a modified form of the null hypothesis is used. Rather than compare two experimental samples, researchers may predict that certain results will occur, and then note how closely their actual results approximate the predicted ones. When this technique of experimentation is used, the predicted results are analogous to what are often the control samples. In such cases the null hypothesis states, in effect, that "no difference exists between the hypothetical population (or predicted population) and the population from which the experimental sample was drawn." The chi-square value for the sets of data is then calculated. The probability that the hypothesis is tenable can then be determined by consulting a table of chi-square values. Small values of chi-square lend support to the null hypothesis, while large values indicate that it should be rejected.

Chi-square is easy to calculate; the following formula is used:

$$\chi^2 = \Sigma \frac{(\text{observed No.} - \text{expected No.})^2}{\text{expected No.}}$$

The formula states that chi-square is determined by squaring each difference between the number of a certain attribute expected (or hypothesized) and the number actually observed. The value squared is then divided by the expected number in each case. The quotients are then added together.

We will examine our problem concerning the direction in which snails twist. Our hypothesis is that $\frac{3}{5}$ of all snails twist clockwise and $\frac{2}{5}$ twist counterclockwise. Our null hypothesis states that there will be no difference between our predicted ratio of clockwise to counterclockwise twisting and the ratio actually found in the 1000 snails that make up our sample.

Of the 1000 snails, our hypothesis (not the null hypothesis) predicts that 600 will twist clockwise and 400 will twist counterclockwise. The null hypothesis states that there will be no difference between the hypothesized sample and the sample actually observed. In our actual sample we found 615 twisted clockwise and 385 counterclockwise. From the formula,

$$\chi^2 = \Sigma \frac{(\text{observed} - \text{hypothetical})^2}{\text{hypothetical}}$$

$$\chi^2 = \frac{(615 - 600)^2}{600} + \frac{(385 - 400)^2}{400}$$

$$\chi^2 = \frac{(15)^2}{600} + \frac{(15)^2}{400} = \frac{225}{600} + \frac{225}{400}$$

$$\chi^2 = 0.375 + 0.562 = 0.937$$

Table 10 is a modified table of chi-square values. In chi-square tests used in this text, the degrees of freedom (d.f.) are one less than the number of attributes being observed, or $n - 1$, where n equals the number of

TABLE 10.   **Critical Values of χ^2**

Values of χ^2 equal to or greater than those tabulated occur by chance less frequently than the indicated level of p.

d.f.	$p = 0.9$	$p = 0.5$	$p = 0.2$	$p = 0.05$	$p = 0.01$	$p = 0.001$
1	.0158	.455	1.642	3.841	6.635	10.827
2	.211	1.386	3.219	5.991	9.210	13.815
3	.584	2.366	4.642	7.815	11.345	16.268
4	1.064	3.367	5.989	9.488	13.277	18.465
5	1.610	4.351	7.289	11.070	15.086	20.517
6	2.204	5.348	8.558	12.592	16.812	22.457
7	2.833	6.346	9.803	14.067	18.475	24.322
8	3.490	7.344	11.303	15.507	20.090	26.125
9	4.168	8.343	12.242	16.919	21.666	24.877
10	4.865	9.342	13.442	18.307	23.209	29.588

attributes. The attributes in our snail problem are two: one twisting clockwise and one twisting counterclockwise. Hence, in this case we have two attributes but only one degree of freedom. We enter Table 10 with one degree of freedom and find that our obtained chi-square of 0.937 for the sample problem falls between $p = 0.5$ (0.455) and $p = 0.2$ (1.642).

In conclusion, we can say that if we had selected $p = 0.05$ as our level of rejection, we would not reject the null hypothesis. (The null hypothesis states that our hypothetical value and that of the actual sample were from the same population.) We would say that our observed data is consistent with our hypothesis that the ratio of clockwise to counterclockwise twisting is $\frac{3}{2}$.

For another example, suppose that in studying a genetic cross between two kinds of tomato plants, it is expected that half the offspring will have green leaves and half will have yellow leaves. (This supposition is based on the hypothesis that a single pair of genes is responsible for the difference between green leaves and yellow leaves.) In one actual experiment, it happened that of 1240 seedlings there were 671 with green leaves and 569 with yellow leaves. This is clearly different from the 620 of each kind which our hypothesis has predicted would occur. The null hypothesis is that there will be no difference in the hypothesized $1 - 1$ ratio and the actual results observed in the experiment. Is the observed difference large enough to cause a rejection of our null hypothesis? In other words, is it likely that the difference between the observed and expected values is due to sampling variation rather than to some real difference not accounted for by our hypothesis?

In this case, we would expect or predict that half of our seedlings would have green leaves and half would have yellow leaves. This expectation is based upon our knowledge of what is inherited by the offspring when a homozygous recessive parent is crossed with a heterozygous parent, and one of the characters is dominant over the other.

Our null hypothesis states that there will be no difference between the expected number (based on the ratios from Mendel's principles) and the observed value in the actual sample.

Expected were 620 yellow plants and 620 green plants; observed were 569 yellow plants and 671 green plants.

We now apply Pearson's chi-square formula to these data.

$$\chi^2 = \frac{(671 - 620)^2}{620} + \frac{(569 - 620)^2}{620}$$

$$\chi^2 = \frac{(+51)^2}{620} + \frac{(-51)^2}{620}$$

$$\chi^2 = 8.4$$

Our attributes are two in number—green and yellow leaves—and 2 minus 1 gives us 1 degree of freedom. From Table 10, we see that a chi-square of 8.4 with 1 degree of freedom indicates that there is less than one chance in one hundred ($p < 0.01$) that these or more extreme values would occur in a sample if the expected values were true of the population. If we decided that 0.01 would be our level of rejection, then the null hypothesis should be rejected at this level. In this case, since the two hypotheses are similar, rejection of the null hypothesis means rejection of the original hypothesis. The original hypothesis states that the crossing of those two strains of tomato should yield progeny which are $\frac{1}{2}$ green and $\frac{1}{2}$ yellow. This does not exclude the possibility that we may be rejecting the null hypothesis when actually the difference between the observed and predicted results are due to chance. A difference of this magnitude can be expected to occur, however, less than one time in 100 ($p < 0.01$).

At this point, the investigator has another important question to ask. How consistently will repetitions of the same experiment produce differences of nearly the same magnitude as that between actual and expected numbers? If repeated crosses produce about the same results, it is time to search for a suitable explanation for this departure of the obtained ratios of green to yellow from those which are expected. (In the case of the tomato plants, further crosses did show about the same results. The investigator found that the difference was caused by a loss of yellow-leaved plants. They were constitutionally less sturdy than the others, and fewer of them germinated and lived.)

PROBLEM

The same investigator looked into the inheritance of red flesh and yellow flesh in tomatoes. He hypothesized that the F_2 generation should have a 3:1 ratio of red to yellow. (Once again, the expectations were based on classical genetics and the assumptions that one pair of genes determines the difference between red-fruited and yellow-fruited tomatoes—and that one allele is dominant over the other.) The red-fleshed class turned out to have 3629 fruits, and the yellow-fleshed class had 1176. From the expected 3:1 ratio of the theory, we might expect to have 3604 red-fleshed and 1201 yellow-fleshed. Is the difference between the expected and observed numbers due to the action of something we had not taken into account in our theory, or is it only a chance departure from what our theory says should occur? What is the value? What is your conclusion?

Using the example, what would have happened if our hypothesis predicted that the ratio would be 4 to 1? 2 to 1?

PROBLEM

The following experiment with the vaccine against polio was performed by Dr. Salk and his colleagues. Equal numbers of students received the vaccine and the placebo (plain shot without the vaccine). In this group of students, 862 cases of polio occurred. Of these cases 112 received the vaccine and 750 received the placebo. To evaluate such data, we would use the chi-square statistic. Why? Interpret your results.

Chi-Square with More Than Two Attributes. When more than two attributes occur in the experimental design, it is necessary to use degrees of freedom other than 1 in determining the probability that chance alone could have been responsible. This new number of degrees of freedom is needed when we want to consider the significance of results for several classes in some series of ratios. For example, there are four attributes and three degrees of freedom $(n - 1)$ in a $9:3:3:1$ ratio for the F_2 generation of a hypothetical, dihybrid cross.

PROBLEM

When pink four-o'clocks are crossed, it is expected that the offspring will turn out to be red-, pink-, and white-flowered in a $1:2:1$ ratio. This is equivalent to saying that $\frac{1}{4}$ of the flowers will be red, $\frac{2}{4}$ or $\frac{1}{2}$ pink, and $\frac{1}{4}$ white. An experimenter made the cross and found that he had 66 red-flowered plants, 115 pink-flowered plants, and 55 white-flowered plants. The total number of plants was $66 + 115 + 55 = 236$.

Use the chi-square test to determine if the observed data are consistent with the hypothesis that such a cross should produce a $1:2:1$ ratio of phenotypes in the offspring.

1. State your null hypothesis.

2. What was the expected (or hypothetical) number of (a) red-flowered plants, (b) pink-flowered plants, and (c) white-flowered plants?

3. Substitute in the formula for x^2, and compute its value.

4. Determine the number of degrees of freedom.

5. Consult the table for x^2. What p value does this value of x^2 with your d.f. represent?

6. Will you reject the null hypothesis?

7. What is your conclusion?

Comparison of t and Chi-Square Tests. One might legitimately ask at this point, what is the consequence of making an error in the selection of a test of significance? The t is a very powerful statistic and will make maximum use of the data, but you must be able to meet the assumptions of random sampling and normal distribution, and your data should consist of continuous variables. If you use the chi-square test in its place, you run the risk of not using your data to its greatest advantage. On the other hand, to use chi-square you do not have to meet the assumption of normal distribution, and you can use discrete data. Chi-square does not have the power of t, but it serves a purpose in being usable for some types of data that cannot be tested by t. If you use t when you should use chi-square, you run the risk of overstating the confidence levels provided by your data.

Conclusion. In analyzing data with statistics, it should be emphasized that the end product of research experiments are considered "conditional truths." In research there is always the probability of error whether you reject or do not reject the null hypothesis. It is relatively easy to see the potential importance of research where the null hypothesis is rejected, but quite often the value of negative results are underestimated. Negative results are valuable because they can eliminate some hypotheses that, at first thought, might seem to be possible solutions to a problem. Also, negative results may serve as an impetus to refine a given bit of research. They may be the first clues, and they may reveal insights that eventually lead to possible answers.

For example, in comparing the use of a new method of skin transplanting with an old method, you might get a t value which indicates a probability level of 0.2 that the two methods are equally effective. This p value, while not small enough to reject the null hypothesis, might indicate that further experimentation with this method is justified. Perhaps a slight change in the technique or use of an additional drug might be all that is needed to make this method acceptable and beneficial.

Statistics are valuable, whether the results are significant or not, because they provide tools with which we can quantitatively analyze data.

SECTION EIGHT

THE LITERATURE OF BIOLOGY

All knowledge about the natural world results from ideas and observations. Many of the observations are data recorded in experiments designed to test hypotheses or to better describe certain phenomena. From your own experimental observations, you have learned much about the metabolism of yeast cells. Scientific work, carried out in a similar manner, may lead to understandings of many other aspects of the natural world. The more careful the work, the more accurate is our knowledge of nature.

Any experiment, observation, or idea is interesting to the person who does the work, but it is not really a contribution to scientific knowledge until it is published for others to read and ponder. The work then becomes a part of the *scientific literature* to which other persons who are interested in the same or related problems can refer.

The great bulk of new scientific information and understanding results from the work of professional scientists. Today, as in the past, amateur naturalists and experimenters also make important contributions to science. In North America, for example, hundreds of members of the National Audubon Society make a careful count of birds they observe around Christmas time. These data, when assembled, provide a "bird census" which is important information about the abundance of bird species, and which would be impossible to obtain without the help of thousands of amateur observers. Without their aid, we would know much less about our natural populations of birds.

Scientific Journals. The hundreds of thousands of scientists in the world work in many different fields of science. Scientists work on a problem until they think they have something of interest and importance to report to other scientists. Then they write an article, or "paper," which summarizes their work and thoughts. The paper is submitted to the editors of one of the thousands of scientific journals published throughout the world. It is reviewed by other scientists who are acquainted with the subject with which it deals, and who are able to judge whether the article makes a contribution to science. If it does, the editor arranges to have it published in a forthcoming issue of the journal.

As a rule, each scientific journal publishes papers that deal primarily with a single field of science; the name of the journal usually gives a clue to the subject matter involved. In the field of biology, for example, it is not difficult to tell what kinds of articles are probably found in *The American Journal of Anatomy, The American Journal of Botany, The British Journal of Nutrition, The Canadian Journal of Zoology, The Japanese Journal of Genetics,* or *The Journal of Cell Biology.* Sometimes, just the name of the subject matter makes up the name of the journal, such as the publications entitled *Developmental Biology, Ecology, Evolution, Genetics, Growth, Heredity,* and *Human Biology.* Other journals carry the names of the societies that publish them, such as The *Journal of the American Medical Association,* The *Proceedings of the Indian Academy of Sciences,* and The *Transactions of the American Microscopical Society.*

In addition to the journals which publish articles primarily on biology, chemistry, physics, or geology, there are some which publish articles of interest to scientists in all fields. The weekly journal *Science* is published in the United States and covers all areas of science; its British counterpart is called *Nature.* These two journals contain not only reports of original research, but also general articles, announcements, and advertisements of interest to scientists. Other periodicals of general scientific interest are *Scientific American* and *American Scientist.*

Scientific journals are published in many countries. The articles may be written in the language of the country, but this is not always the case; many foreign journals publish articles in English. Some journals (such as *Experientia* and *Die Naturwissenschaften*) accept articles in more than

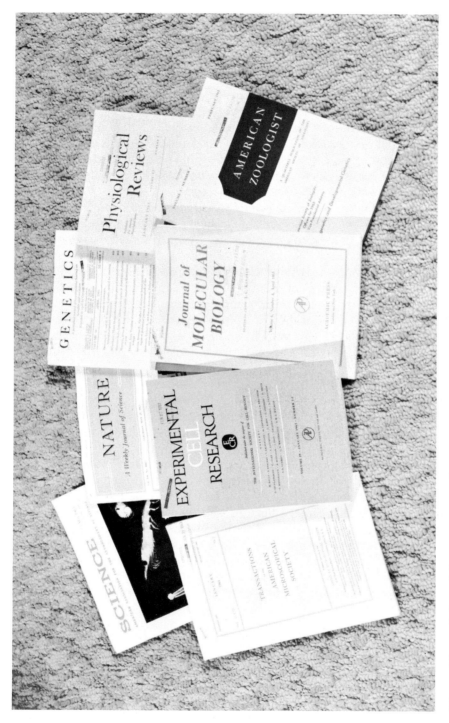

Figure 14   A few of the many scientific journals that are received by a university library.

one language, such as English, French, German, or Italian. Other journals publish papers in one language, but provide summaries of each selection in one or two other languages. Journals that contain articles written in languages with distinctive alphabets or symbol systems, such as Chinese, Japanese, and Russian, may have summaries or aids in English or in other languages. A number of Russian science journals are now regularly translated into English. Scientific names of organisms are given in Latin and thus appear the same around the world to people of all languages.

Hence, the search for knowledge about natural events recognizes no national boundaries. Libraries subscribe to the journals of the world. One measure of the value of a library to scientists is the number of scientific journals to which it subscribes.

Scientific Papers. There is no single way in which a scientific paper must be written, but most papers are similar in structure. The title of the paper should tell, in a few words, as much as possible about the content of the paper. Some titles are very general, such as "Studies in the genus *Caliciopsis.*" Other titles may give experimental conclusions, such as "The mutagenic equivalence of continuous and intermittent ultraviolet in *Drosophila melanogaster.*" Some papers present primarily data: "Further data on the over-dominance of induced mutations." Papers presenting a theoretical point of view may have titles such as "Selective forces in the evolution of man" or "The bearing of philosophy on the history of science."

Consider a scientific paper on a topic that may be of interest to you to see how it is organized. The paper on "The oxidation and fermentation of sugars by yeast protoplasts" appeared in the February, 1963, issue of *Experimental Cell Research,* and is reproduced on pages 81 through 88. The name and address of the author, Dr. J. W. Millbank, are listed below the title of the paper. Scientists who want to learn more about the material presented in a paper may then correspond with the author.

Most papers begin with a short introduction to the problem, including references to earlier papers that relate to the problem. The experimenter then describes the materials and methods used in his work. In this section, Millbank lists the organisms used (the exact strains of yeast), the media, the method used to prepare the protoplasts, and the various biochemical techniques employed. This detailed information is necessary if the reader is to evaluate the results or to repeat the experiments.

In the next section of the paper, the author reports his results in some detail; data are listed in tabular form in this paper. Sometimes graphs or other means of presenting the data are also used. After the results are presented, Millbank discusses the significance of the work (see "Discussion" on page 87). The paper closes with a brief summary of his conclusions and a list of references for the reader.

422   *Experimental Cell Research* **29**, *422–429 (1963)*

THE OXIDATION AND FERMENTATION OF SUGARS
BY YEAST PROTOPLASTS

J. W. MILLBANK

Brewing Industry Research Foundation, Nutfield, Surrey, England

Received May 21, 1962

Eddy and Williamson [3, 4] described the preparation of protoplasts of yeast cells using snail crop juice. These studies were supplemented by Friis and Ottolenghi [6] with comparative data on the distribution of invertase between the cell wall and the protoplast. They found that at least 74 per cent of the total invertase was associated with the cell wall and was released into solution by the action of the snail crop juice. However, as pointed out by Burger, Bacon and Bacon [1] it is not possible from these results to form an accurate estimate of the invertase activity of their yeast on either a fresh or dry-weight basis. Moreover, Burger *et al.* in a parallel set of studies found that snail crop juice liberated over 95 per cent of the invertase from their yeast under conditions where the protoplasts remained intact. The distribution of invertase may well vary from one yeast to another.

Further studies by Holter and Ottolenghi [8] have shown that over a limited period, protoplasts behave similarly to normal cells with respect to their oxygen consumption when metabolising glucose. The measurements of the respiratory activity of protoplasts and intact cells were not however strictly comparable since a satisfactory basis of comparison was not established.

There is thus a lack of quantitative data on the metabolism of yeast protoplasts and this paper reports the results of studies of the respiration and fermentation of four selected sugars by protoplasts obtained from three strains of brewing yeasts and compared with the corresponding intact cells. During the course of the investigation it emerged that sucrose was rapidly metabolised by protoplasts of all the strains examined. It was evident that appreciable amounts of invertase were present in the protoplasts and so the opportunity was taken to estimate the distribution of the enzyme in one of the strains on a quantitative basis.

MATERIAL AND METHODS

Organisms.—The following yeasts from the National Collection of Yeast Cultures (NCYC) were used: *Saccharomyces cerevisiae*, Strain NCYC 366 and *Saccharomyces carlsbergensis*, Strains NCYC 74, 519.

Oxidation and fermentation of sugars   423

These strains were selected for their susceptibility to the action of snail crop juice.

Media.—The yeasts were maintained as stock cultures in a liquid medium (MYGP) due to Wickerham [14] and containing malt extract, yeast extract, glucose and peptone. Young cells, in a suitable state for conversion to protoplasts, were obtained by transferring a small inoculum (0.1–0.2 ml) of a mature culture to fresh medium (400 ml) in a Roux flask and incubating at 25°C with gentle shaking for 16–18 hr.

Preparation of protoplasts.—The method described by Eddy and Williamson [4] was used. With the growth conditions described above, suspensions of young, actively growing cells at a concentration of $5–8 \times 10^6$/ml were obtained after 18 hr. Cells in this condition are essential for consistent and satisfactory conversion to protoplasts. These cells were freed from the growth medium by centrifuging and washed in distilled water. Using populations of the above mentioned strains at a concentration of 10^8 cells/ml, complete conversion was achieved in 90–120 min at 30°C, using 10 mg/ml freeze-dried snail enzyme, 12.5 per cent (w/v) mannitol as the osmotic stabiliser and 0.005 M citrate + phosphate buffer, pH 5.8.

Estimation of protein.—This was carried out using the Folin-phenol method of Lowry *et al.* [9] as modified by Williamson and Scopes [15].

Estimation of trichloroacetic acid–insoluble nitrogen.—Approximately 5 mg dry weight of cell material was suspended in 5 ml of 5 per cent (w/v) trichloroacetic acid (TCA) and heated to 100°C for 15 min in a boiling water bath. After centrifuging, the precipitate was washed once with 10 ml of 5 per cent TCA and finally re-suspended in 10 ml water. An aliquot part was carried through a micro-kjeldahl procedure, followed by colorimetric estimation using Nessler's reagent, as described by Umbreit, Burris and Stauffer [13]. The estimates of nitrogen when multiplied by the factor 6.25 gave figures for protein content which agreed closely with those obtained by the method of Lowry *et al.*

Quantitative isolation of cell wall material.—The method used was that described by Northcote and Horne [11] using a Mickle disintegrator [10].

Preparation of homogenates.—These were prepared from protoplast suspensions by exposure to ultrasonic vibration at a frequency of 540 kc/sec. A power of 100 W was used, with oil as the transducing medium. Normally 10 ml of protoplast suspension contained in a 50 ml glass beaker was exposed by lowering the beaker into the oil to half its depth. Complete disruption of the protoplasts was effected in 60 sec.

Dialysis of homogenates.—This was carried out using "visking" tubing which had been treated with ethylene diamine tetraacetic acid to remove possible heavy metal contamination. Dialysis was against approx. 5 l of distilled water at 4°C, over 24 hr. The water was changed three times. After this period the contents of the tube were washed out and made up to 25 ml with distilled water. Aliquot parts were then assayed for invertase activity.

Invertase assay.—Convenient amounts of the solution or suspension to be tested were added to 10 ml of a system comprising sucrose (1 per cent w/v) in 0.03 M sodium acetate buffer pH 5.3. Incubation was at 25°C and samples were taken at 0, 10, 20 and 30 min. Estimates of reducing sugar were made using alkaline ferricyanide under conditions similar to those of Hagedorn and Jensen [7], using a standard curve prepared from equimolar solutions of glucose and fructose.

The activity is expressed in units, one unit being the amount of enzyme liberating 1 mg invert sugar/hr.

424   *J. W. Millbank*

Measurement of carbon dioxide evolution and oxygen consumption. These were carried out in a conventional Warburg apparatus at 25°C. Cell material corresponding to 3 mg dry weight was normally used in each vessel. Substrates were prepared in $M/15$ citrate + phosphate buffer, pH 5.0, together with isotonic mannitol where appropriate.

RESULTS

Because of the osmotic sensitivity of yeast protoplasts isotonic solutions must be employed and therefore the estimation of dry weight is impracticable. In order to compare the metabolic activity of protoplasts and whole cells an alternative basis for expressing results was required. Protein content was chosen and estimates were made using cells, cell walls, and protoplasts. As young active cultures were used under standard conditions of growth, variation caused by different physiological ages of the yeast was minimal.

Protein content of young cells, cell walls, and protoplasts of Saccharomyces carlsbergensis 74, 519; and Saccharomyces cerevisiae 366.—Cells grown on MYGP for 18 hr were harvested by centrifuging, washed and suspended in distilled water. Three aliquot portions were dried to constant weight at 105°C. Three other portions were centrifuged and the cells resuspended in the snail crop juice system for conversion to protoplasts. Three further portions were incubated without snail crop juice and finally one portion was treated in the Mickle disintegrator and the cell wall fraction prepared. Its dry weight and protein content was then estimated.

After 120 min incubation at 30°C the cells treated with snail crop juice had undergone complete conversion to protoplasts. These were separated from the medium by centrifuging, washed in 12.5 per cent (w/v) mannitol, made up to volume and the TCA insoluble nitrogen estimated. The control incubations were also washed, made up to volume, and similarly assayed.

The results of these trials are summarised in Table I.

It can be seen that the protein contents of the component fractions do not account for all that found in the corresponding whole cells. This is most likely due to lysis of a small proportion of the protoplasts during preparation and washing.

When protein content was related to protoplast numbers it was consistently found that 2×10^8 protoplasts contained 3.0 mg protein, the quantity associated with the protoplast fraction of 10.0 mg whole cells. A convenient conversion, therefore, is that 2×10^7 freshly prepared protoplasts are equivalent to 1 mg dry weight young cells.

Oxidation and fermentation of sugars by cells and protoplasts of Saccharo-

84 BIOLOGICAL INVESTIGATION

Oxidation and fermentation of sugars 425

myces carlsbergensis 74, 519; and Saccharomyces cerevisiae 366.—Cells were grown in MYGP broth for 18 hr and after harvesting and washing, one portion was converted to protoplasts. A second portion was incubated under similar conditions in the absence of snail crop juice. The protoplasts and cells were then washed twice with 12.5 per cent (w/v) mannitol buffered to pH 5, and

TABLE I. *Protein content of yeast cells, cell walls, and protoplasts.*

Yeast	Whole cells mg protein/10 mg dry wt.	Cell Walls[a] mg protein	Protoplasts[a] mg protein
Saccharomyces carlsbergensis NCYC 74	3.57	0.55	2.93
Saccharomyces carlsbergensis NCYC 519	3.40	0.40	2.90
Saccharomyces cerevisiae NCYC 366	3.55	0.55	2.93

[a] Derived from 10 mg dry wt. cells.

transferred to Warburg vessels. Glucose, fructose, sucrose and maltose were added after temperature equilibration at an initial substrate concentration of 0.5 per cent (w/v). Endogenous gas exchange was estimated in control vessels throughout the experimental period. The parameters Q_{O_2} and Q_{CO_2} were measured over the period 15–60 min after addition of substrate, and have been expressed on a dry weight basis in the case of cells, and a dry weight equivalent basis for protoplasts using the conversion factor of 2×10^7 protoplasts/mg dry weight.

The results for all the yeasts and sugars are summarised in Table II in which the figures given are in every case the mean values obtained from several estimates.

There was some variation between the batches of cell material; an explanation for this is perhaps to be found in the results of Ephrussi *et al.* [5] who demonstrated that large changes in Q_{CO_2} and Q_{O_2} occurred at the beginning and towards the end of the exponential growth phase of a yeast. Thus the precise point at which cells are taken for investigation may have considerable bearing on the figures obtained.

It is evident from Table II that with glucose and fructose, the respiratory and fermentative activities of cells and protoplasts were generally similar. With sucrose and maltose, several features were noticed. Sucrose was at

426   *J. W. Millbank*

once oxidised by protoplasts of all strains at the same rate as intact cells, although fermentation in two strains was slower. This contrasts with the findings of Burger *et al.* [1] that virtually complete liberation of invertase is brought about by the action of snail crop juice.

TABLE II. *Oxidation and fermentation of sugars by yeast cells and protoplasts.*

| | | Saccharomyces carlsbergensis | | | | Saccharomyces cerevisiae NCYC 366 | |
| | | NCYC 74 | | NCYC 519 | | | |
		Q_{O_2}	$Q_{CO_2}^{ferm}$	Q_{O_2}	$Q_{CO_2}^{ferm}$	Q_{O_2}	$Q_{CO_2}^{ferm}$
Glucose	cells	20	175	22	180	32	68
	protoplasts	36	70	22	188	35	71
Fructose	cells	20	160	22	140	32	68
	protoplasts	36	70	22	188	35	35
Sucrose	cells	19	140	21	141	31	45
	protoplasts	21	66	22	187	31	30
Maltose	cells	0	0	19	100	35	110
	protoplasts	0	0	22	122	40	90

TABLE III. *Oxidation and fermentation of maltose by cells and protoplasts of Saccharomyces carlsbergensis NCYC 74.*

Maltose present throughout growth of the cells and preparation of the protoplasts.

	Q_{O_2}	$Q_{CO_2}^{ferm}$
Intact cells	34	35
Protoplasts	27	27

With regard to maltose, comparable rates of oxidation and fermentation by protoplasts and cells were observed with the exception of *Saccharomyces carlsbergensis* 74. No measurable increase in gas exchange was noted with either cells or protoplasts of this strain when maltose was added after pretreatment in the normal manner. Exposure of cells to snail crop juice in the presence of 1 per cent w/v maltose, however, facilitated the preparation of protoplasts having the ability to oxidise and ferment maltose (Table III). It would seem that incubation of cells of this strain in the absence of maltose brings about a rapid loss of activity of maltase, maltose permease, or both enzymes.

Oxidation and fermentation of sugars　　　427

The invertase content of cells, cell walls, and protoplasts of Saccharomyces carlsbergensis 74.—Since appreciable amounts of invertase were evidently present in protoplasts of all the strains examined, estimates of the amounts present in the cell wall and the protoplast fraction were made using strain No. 74 which was found to be most satisfactory when treated with snail crop juice.

TABLE IV. *Invertase activity of two preparations of Saccharomyces carlsbergensis NCYC 74.*

	Invertase activity, units		% total activity	
	(a)	(b)	(a)	(b)
Total homogenate	12.9	13.7	100	100
Cell wall fraction	9.4	8.5	73	62
Protoplasts	3.6	4.6	28	34

Dry weight of yeast in total homogenate: (a) 3.0 mg, (b) 3.7 mg.

A suspension of protoplasts was prepared from cells of known dry weight and protein content. An aliquot part of this suspension in snail crop juice was exposed to ultrasonic vibration and the homogenate taken as representing total cell material. The remaining suspension of protoplasts in snail enzyme was centrifuged and an aliquot part of the clear supernatant liquid taken. This was assumed to contain the invertase originally present in the cell walls. The sedimented protoplasts were washed twice, resuspended, and one portion taken for protein estimation. From the two estimates of protein content, the extent of lysis of the protoplasts could be estimated. The remaining portion was disintegrated. The three extracts (total homogenate, cell wall, and protoplast homogenate) were then dialysed to remove hexokinase cofactors, made up to a standard volume, and invertase assayed as described earlier. Allowance was made for the invertase activity of the snail enzyme preparation; the results of two separate trials are given in Table IV.

It is evident that the distribution of invertase between the protoplast and cell wall follows the pattern reported by Friis and Ottolenghi [6], and the proportion of invertase within the protoplast is accessible to sucrose in the strains used in this investigation. This is in contrast with the results of Sutton and Lampen [12].

428   *J. W. Millbank*

DISCUSSION

Protoplasts are not as yet widely used in studies of yeast metabolism, despite their advantage of being readily disrupted which greatly facilitates the preparation of cell-free systems and cytoplasmic particles. The apparent difficulty of relating the activities of protoplast suspensions and derived systems to those of intact cells can be surmounted since a ready basis of comparison exists in their protein content. Given cells and protoplasts of comparable physiological age this criterion can also be used to estimate the "dry weight" of the protoplasts.

From the results presented here, it seems that protoplasts oxidise and ferment carbohydrates in a similar manner to intact cells. So far, the only important difference concerns invertase, which, being largely associated with the cell wall, is to some extent lost when the wall is hydrolysed. Thus, in studies concerned with the metabolic pathways of oxidation and fermentation at least, conclusions from the use of protoplasts should be directly applicable to whole cells.

In connection with the location of invertase, all reports that have so far appeared agree that a large proportion is associated with the cell wall. Some authors [1, 12] report that the whole of the activity appears to be so located. On the other hand Friis and Ottolenghi [6] found that up to 26 per cent remained associated with the protoplasts; a similar proportion is reported in this paper. The latter authors concluded that the enzyme is secreted and "trapped" by the cell wall, the process of secretion being stimulated by the presence of sucrose in the growth medium. Further, yeasts grown in such media are capable of splitting sucrose both intra and extra-cellularly but the invertase present in the cell wall region is normally sufficient. With two of the yeasts used in this investigation this concept can be extended further in that the "cytoplasmic" invertase is also sufficient for their metabolic requirements. It is clear from these reports and that of Dworschack and Wickerham [2] on invertase secretion that considerable strain variation exists and that the conception of a "typical" distribution of enzyme in a "typical" yeast must be treated with reserve.

SUMMARY

The rates of oxidation and fermentation of glucose, fructose, sucrose and maltose by protoplasts of three strains of brewing yeasts have been studied and compared with those of intact cells. Direct comparisons have been ac-

Oxidation and fermentation of sugars   429

complished by the use of protein nitrogen as a basis for determining the parameters Q_{O_2} and $Q_{CO_2}^{ferm}$.

All four sugars were oxidised by protoplasts at rates equal to or greater than those of the corresponding intact cells. The fermentation rates were also similar in two of the strains used; protoplasts of the third strain fermented more slowly than the corresponding cells.

Cells and protoplasts of one strain normally able to metabolise maltose, lost this ability after incubation for two hours in media lacking this sugar.

The distribution of invertase was studied in one strain where 76 per cent was found to be associated with the cell wall. The remainder, associated with the protoplasts, was active and generally adequate for the metabolic requirements of the yeasts.

The author is grateful to the director of this foundation, Dr. A. H. Cook, F.R.S., for his encouragement of this work.

REFERENCES

1. BURGER, M., BACON, E. E. and BACON, J. S. D., *Biochem. J.* **78**, 504 (1961).
2. DWORSCHACK, R. G. and WICKERHAM, L. J., *Appl. Microbiol.* **9**, 291 (1961).
3. EDDY, A. A. and WILLIAMSON, D. H., *Nature* **179**, 1252 (1957).
4. —— *Nature* **183**, 1101 (1959).
5. EPHRUSSI, B., SLONIMSKI, P. P., YOTSUYANAGI, Y. and TAVLITSKI, J., *Compt. Rend Trav. Lab. Carlsberg* **26**, 87 (1956).
6. FRIIS, J. and OTTOLENGHI, P., *Compt. Rend. Trav. Lab. Carlsberg* **31**, 259 (1959).
7. HAGEDORN, H. C. and JENSEN, B. N., *Biochem. Z.* **135**, 46 (1923).
8. HOLTER, H. and OTTOLENGHI, P., *Compt. Rend. Trav. Lab. Carlsberg* **31**, 409 (1960).
9. LOWRY, H. O., ROSENBROUGH, N. J., FARR, A. L. and RANDALL, R. J., *J. Biol. Chem.* **193**, 265 (1951).
10. MICKLE, H., *J. Roy. Microscop. Soc.* **68**, 10 (1948).
11. NORTHCOTE, D. H. and HORNE, R. W., *Biochem. J.* **51**, 232 (1952).
12. SUTTON, D. D. and LAMPEN, J. O., *Biochim. Biophys. Acta* **56**, 303 (1962).
13. UMBRIET, W. W., BURRIS, R. H. and STAUFFER, J. F. Manometric methods and related techniques used in the study of tissue metabolism. Burgess Pub. Co. Minneapolis, third ed., 1957.
14. WICKERHAM, L. J., Technical Bulletin No. 1029, *U.S.A. Dept. Agric.* (1951).
15. WILLIAMSON, D. H. and SCOPES, A. W., *J. Inst. Brew.* **67**, 39 (1961).

A list of references enables the reader to refer to any paper or book mentioned in the article. Names of journals are usually abbreviated, and standard abbreviations for most journals can be found in the *Style Manual for Biological Journals* (Second Edition, 1964, American Institute of Biological Sciences, 2000 P Street NW, Washington, D. C. 20036, $3.00).

The titles of papers may or may not be given in a list of references; in this paper they are omitted. In most cases a paper is referred to by author and date—e.g., Jones, 1964—rather than by title. Reference 1 at the end of Millbank's paper says that in 1961 three scientists, M. Burger, E. E. Bacon, and J. S. D. Bacon, published a paper which began on page 504 in volume 78 of *Biochemical Journal.* The dash in Reference 4 means that the authors of that paper are the same as those for Reference 3 directly above. See if you can "translate" the other references at the end of this paper.

Review Articles. Not all papers are reports of original experimental work. Since the amount of scientific knowledge grows so rapidly, it is difficult for an individual scientist to keep up with all that is done in his own field, to say nothing of related fields. The problem is partially solved by special "review" articles, which attempt to summarize in brief form the state of knowledge in limited fields. Some review articles list and classify significant papers in a specific field which have appeared during the past year or other recent periods of time.

Some journals are devoted solely to review papers and usually appear quarterly (every three months), while books of review articles may appear annually or even less frequently. Some examples of review journals are *Bacteriological Reviews, Physiological Reviews,* and the *Quarterly Review of Biology* (which also contains reviews of recent books in the biological sciences). Examples of review volumes are *Annual Review of Physiology, Advances in Genetics,* and *Advances in Enzymology.*

Searching the Literature   How does a scientist find out what work has been done on a particular problem? This necessary task is becoming more difficult every year. It has been estimated that there are more than 15,000 publications in the world that carry articles important to some phase of biology. How is it possible for a scientist to keep himself informed of all these articles?

The major job of organizing information about articles that appear in particular fields is done by special agencies that abstract and index these articles. These agencies regularly publish summaries of current literature and employ a system in which they assign scientists to read articles appearing in certain journals. The scientists, in turn, write short summaries, or abstracts, of the important points made in the article. In many cases, the author himself has been known to provide the abstract. The abstracts are then sent to a central agency, where they are sorted according to area

Figure 15   Biological Abstracts *and the accompanying* subject index, B.A.S.I.C., *are published twice a month.*

of knowledge and are given a number. The numbered abstracts are then published in an issue of the abstracting journal.

Biological Abstracts. This journal (see Figure 15), published in the United States, contains abstracts of articles appearing in over 5000 journals from some 88 countries. In a single calendar year more than 100,000 abstracts are published.

To illustrate how a particular article is handled by *Biological Abstracts,* return to Millbank's article on yeast protoplasts. This article was summarized by the author, and his abstract was assigned No. 20556. It was published on page 1614 of Volume 43 of *Biological Abstracts.* The page containing this abstract is shown on page 91.

Once abstracts are numbered and published, the journal helps the scientist find recent articles on a particular topic; the most important aid in this respect is the subject index. The title of each paper that has been abstracted is placed on a special card which can be "read" by a computer-printer. The computer then identifies all the "key words" in the title and arranges them in alphabetical order. The subject index is an alphabetical list, produced by the computer-printer, of all the key words in all the titles of those articles the abstracts of which were published either during a certain period of time or in a particular issue.

Figure 16 Page from Biological Abstracts *with the abstract of Millbank's paper.*

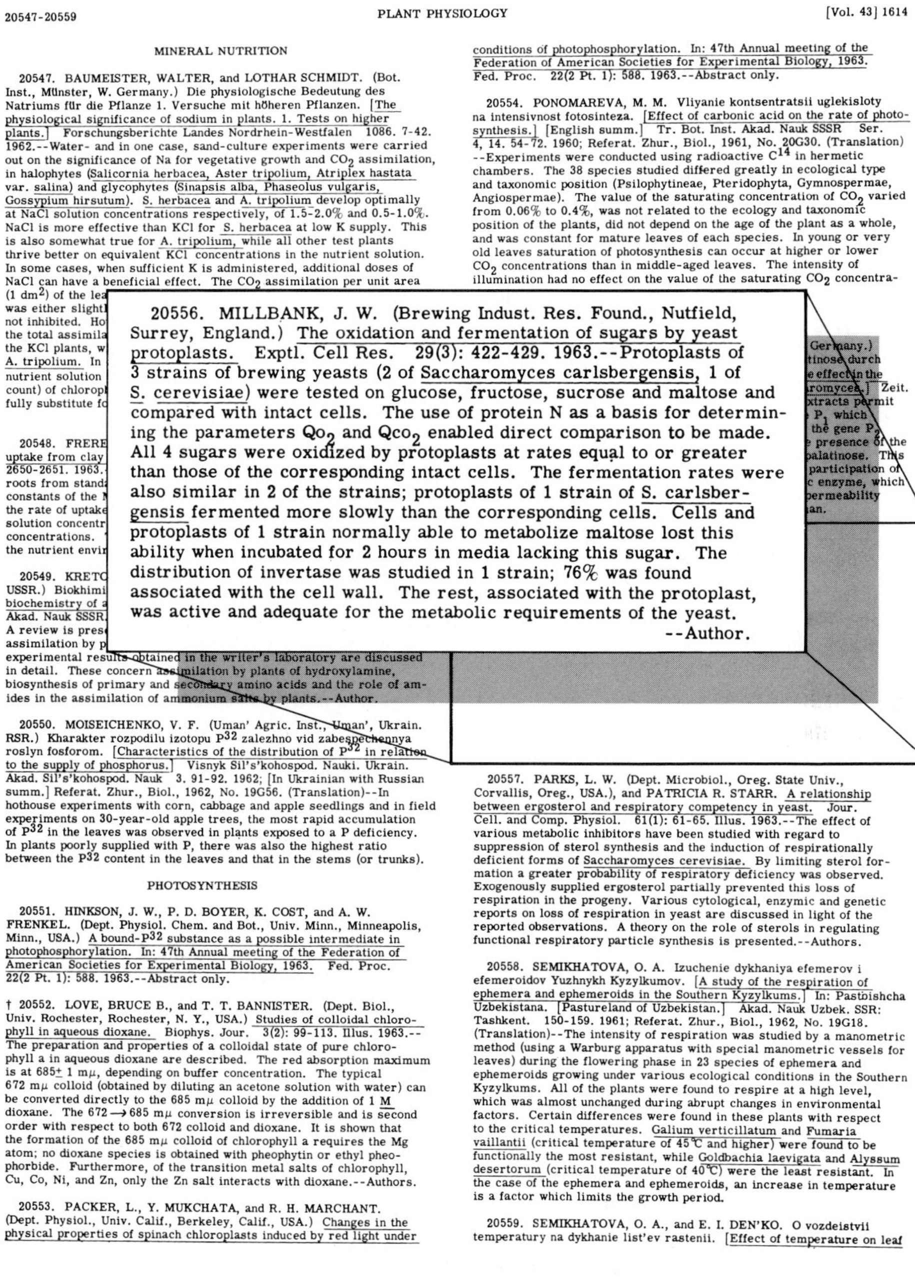

20547-20559   PLANT PHYSIOLOGY   [Vol. 43] 1614

MINERAL NUTRITION

20547. BAUMEISTER, WALTER, and LOTHAR SCHMIDT. (Bot. Inst., Münster, W. Germany.) Die physiologische Bedeutung des Natriums für die Pflanze 1. Versuche mit höheren Pflanzen. [The physiological significance of sodium in plants. 1. Tests on higher plants.] Forschungsberichte Landes Nordrhein-Westfalen 1086. 7-42. 1962.--Water- and in one case, sand-culture experiments were carried out on the significance of Na for vegetative growth and CO_2 assimilation, in halophytes (Salicornia herbacea, Aster tripolium, Atriplex hastata var. salina) and glycophytes (Sinapis alba, Phaseolus vulgaris, Gossypium hirsutum). S. herbacea and A. tripolium develop optimally at NaCl solution concentrations respectively, of 1.5-2.0% and 0.5-1.0%. NaCl is more effective than KCl for S. herbacea at low K supply. This is also somewhat true for A. tripolium, while all other test plants thrive better on equivalent KCl concentrations in the nutrient solution. In some cases, when sufficient K is administered, additional doses of NaCl can have a beneficial effect. The CO_2 assimilation per unit area (1 dm^2) of the lea... was either slight... not inhibited. Ho... the total assimila... the KCl plants, w... A. tripolium. In... nutrient solution... count) of chlorop... fully substitute fo...

20548. FRERE... uptake from clay... 2650-2651. 1963... roots from stand... constants of the... the rate of uptak... solution concentr... concentrations.... the nutrient envir...

20549. KRETO... USSR.) Biokhimi... biochemistry of a... Akad. Nauk SSSR... A review is pres... assimilation by p... experimental results obtained in the writer's laboratory are discussed in detail. These concern assimilation by plants of hydroxylamine, biosynthesis of primary and secondary amino acids and the role of am- ides in the assimilation of ammonium salts by plants.--Author.

20550. MOISEICHENKO, V. F. (Uman' Agric. Inst., Uman', Ukrain. RSR.) Kharakter rozpodilu izotopu P^{32} zalezhno vid zabespechennya roslyn fosforom. [Characteristics of the distribution of P^{32} in relation to the supply of phosphorus.] Visnyk Sil'skohospod. Nauki. Ukrain. Akad. Sil'skohospod. Nauk 3. 91-92. 1962; [In Ukrainian with Russian summ.] Referat. Zhur., Biol., 1962, No. 19G56. (Translation)--In hothouse experiments with corn, cabbage and apple seedlings and in field experiments on 30-year-old apple trees, the most rapid accumulation of P^{32} in the leaves was observed in plants exposed to a P deficiency. In plants poorly supplied with P, there was also the highest ratio between the P^{32} content in the leaves and that in the stems (or trunks).

PHOTOSYNTHESIS

20551. HINKSON, J. W., P. D. BOYER, K. COST, and A. W. FRENKEL. (Dept. Physiol. Chem. and Bot., Univ. Minn., Minneapolis, Minn., USA.) A bound-P^{32} substance as a possible intermediate in photophosphorylation. In: 47th Annual meeting of the Federation of American Societies for Experimental Biology, 1963. Fed. Proc. 22(2 Pt. 1): 588. 1963.--Abstract only.

† 20552. LOVE, BRUCE B., and T. T. BANNISTER. (Dept. Biol., Univ. Rochester, Rochester, N. Y., USA.) Studies of colloidal chloro- phyll in aqueous dioxane. Biophys. Jour. 3(2): 99-113. Illus. 1963.-- The preparation and properties of a colloidal state of pure chloro- phyll a in aqueous dioxane are described. The red absorption maximum is at 685± 1 mμ, depending on buffer concentration. The typical 672 mμ colloid (obtained by diluting an acetone solution with water) can be converted directly to the 685 mμ colloid by the addition of 1 M dioxane. The 672 → 685 mμ conversion is irreversible and is second order with respect to both 672 colloid and dioxane. It is shown that the formation of the 685 mμ colloid of chlorophyll requires the Mg atom; no dioxane species is obtained with pheophytin or ethyl pheo- phorbide. Furthermore, of the transition metal salts of chlorophyll, Cu, Co, Ni, and Zn, only the Zn salt interacts with dioxane.--Authors.

20553. PACKER, L., Y. MUKCHATA, and R. H. MARCHANT. (Dept. Physiol., Univ. Calif., Berkeley, Calif., USA.) Changes in the physical properties of spinach chloroplasts induced by red light under

conditions of photophosphorylation. In: 47th Annual meeting of the Federation of American Societies for Experimental Biology, 1963. Fed. Proc. 22(2 Pt. 1): 588. 1963.--Abstract only.

20554. PONOMAREVA, M. M. Vliyanie kontsentratsii uglekisloty na intensivnost fotosinteza. [Effect of carbonic acid on the rate of photo- synthesis.] [English summ.] Tr. Bot. Inst. Akad. Nauk SSSR Ser. 4, 14. 54-72. 1960; Referat. Zhur., Biol., 1961, No. 20G30. (Translation) --Experiments were conducted using radioactive C^{14} in hermetic chambers. The 38 species studied differed greatly in ecological type and taxonomic position (Psilophytineae, Pteridophyta, Gymnospermae, Angiospermae). The value of the saturating concentration of CO_2 varied from 0.06% to 0.4%, was not related to the ecology and taxonomic position of the plants, did not depend on the age of the plant as a whole, and was constant for mature leaves of each species. In young or very old leaves saturation of photosynthesis can occur at higher or lower CO_2 concentrations than in middle-aged leaves. The intensity of illumination had no effect on the value of the saturating CO_2 concentra-

20556. MILLBANK, J. W. (Brewing Indust. Res. Found., Nutfield, Surrey, England.) The oxidation and fermentation of sugars by yeast protoplasts. Exptl. Cell Res. 29(3): 422-429. 1963.--Protoplasts of 3 strains of brewing yeasts (2 of Saccharomyces carlsbergensis, 1 of S. cerevisiae) were tested on glucose, fructose, sucrose and maltose and compared with intact cells. The use of protein N as a basis for determin- ing the parameters Q_{O_2} and Q_{CO_2} enabled direct comparison to be made. All 4 sugars were oxidized by protoplasts at rates equal to or greater than those of the corresponding intact cells. The fermentation rates were also similar in 2 of the strains; protoplasts of 1 strain of S. carlsber- gensis fermented more slowly than the corresponding cells. Cells and protoplasts of 1 strain normally able to metabolize maltose lost this ability when incubated for 2 hours in media lacking this sugar. The distribution of invertase was studied in 1 strain; 76% was found associated with the cell wall. The rest, associated with the protoplast, was active and adequate for the metabolic requirements of the yeast. --Author.

20557. PARKS, L. W. (Dept. Microbiol., Oreg. State Univ., Corvallis, Oreg., USA.), and PATRICIA R. STARR. A relationship between ergosterol and respiratory competency in yeast. Jour. Cell. and Comp. Physiol. 61(1): 61-65. Illus. 1963.--The effect of various metabolic inhibitors have been studied with regard to suppression of sterol synthesis and the induction of respirationally deficient forms of Saccharomyces cerevisiae. By limiting sterol for- mation a greater probability of respiratory deficiency was observed. Exogenously supplied ergosterol partially prevented this loss of respiration in the progeny. Various cytological, enzymic and genetic reports on loss of respiration in yeast are discussed in light of the reported observations. A theory on the role of sterols in regulating functional respiratory particle synthesis is presented.--Authors.

20558. SEMIKHATOVA, O. A. Izuchenie dykhaniya efemerov i efemeroidov Yuzhnykh Kyzylkumov. [Effect of respiration of ephemera and ephemeroids in the Southern Kyzylkums.] In: Pastbishcha Uzbekistana. [Pastureland of Uzbekistan.] Akad. Nauk Uzbek. SSR: Tashkent. 150-159. 1961; Referat. Zhur., Biol., 1962, No. 19G18. (Translation)--The intensity of respiration was studied by a manometric method (using a Warburg apparatus with special manometric vessels for leaves) during the flowering phase in 23 species of ephemera and ephemeroids growing under various ecological conditions in the Southern Kyzylkums. All of the plants were found to respire at a high level, which was almost unchanged during abrupt changes in environmental factors. Certain differences were found in these plants with respect to the critical temperatures. Galium verticillatum and Fumaria vaillantii (critical temperature of 45°C and higher) were found to be functionally the most resistant, while Goldbachia laevigata and Alyssum desertorum (critical temperature of 40°C) were the least resistant. In the case of the ephemera and ephemeroids, an increase in temperature is a factor which limits the growth period.

20559. SEMIKHATOVA, O. A., and E. I. DEN'KO. O vozdeistvii temperatury na dykhanie list'ev rastenii. [Effect of temperature on leaf

Figure 17 *Page from the subject index of* Biological Abstracts.

2804 [Vol. 43] Y **Y** YIELD

RMENTATION OF SUGARS BY YEAST PROTOPLASTS/ THE OXIDATION AND 20556

I-SUPINE POSITION IN X,	Y AND Z AXES/ SHORT-TIME TOLERANCE A	17394
RUSH TYPE FORMED BY THE	Y CHROMOSOME IN DROSOPHILA-HYDEI AND	17181
ON MEIOTIC LOSS OF THE	Y CHROMOSOME IN THE MALE DROSOPHILA/	193
TAGENETIC ACTION OF THE	Y HEXACHLORO CYCLOHEXANE/ THE MU	195
E OF THE MOLTING GLAND□	Y-ORGAN□ IN OVARIAN DEVELOPMENT OF T	12447
CROSS BREEDING WITH	YAK/	6480
□ AS EXEMPLIFIED IN THE	YAKHROMSKOE RESERVOIR OF THE MOSKVA-	4548
CT PESTS OF THE CENTRAL	YAKUTIA FORESTS/ INSE	3542
ND SOIL□ IN THE CENTRAL	YAKUTIAN LOWLAND/ THE PROBLEM OF CLA	4386
LEPTIDOPTERA OF CENTRAL	YAKUTIYA/ DATA ON FOREST PEST	12053
ASSOCIATIONS IN CENTRAL	YAKUTIYA/ THE SPORE POLLEN SPECTRUM	408
CCOSIS□ CESTODA□ IN THE	YAKUTSK-SSR/ EPIZOOTOIOLOGY OF ALVEO	25227
S IN THE FORESTS OF THE	YALTA FORESTRY FARM/ ROOT GRAFTING B	7750
OREST-ZONE AT GASSAN IN	YAMAGATA-PREFECTURE/ THE AOMORITODOM	20744
E BEDS IN AKAKURA AREA,	YAMAGATA-PREFECTURE, JAPAN/ A PALYNO	7272
NG IN A RURAL DISTRICT□	YAMAGATA, JAPAN□ EPIDEMIOLOGICAL AS	15562
CCOSIS□ CESTODA□ ON T		
OF FISHING IN THE LOW		
THE WESTERN PART OF THE	YANA RIVER-BASIN/ DESCRIPTION OF THE	4394
NT OF TIMBER STACKED AT	YARD AND CONTROL OF TRYPODENDRON LIN	7910
ES WHICH ARE NEW TO THE	YAROSLAVSK-OBLAST/ A NUMBER OF PLANT	15855
O BOTANICAL DATA ON THE	YARYRO INDIANS/ ETHN	15978
ACCELERATION ABOUT THE	YAW AXIS OF A FLIGHT SIMULATOR. TRES	4195
O OSCILLATION ABOUT THE	YAW AXIS/ VASTIBULAR RESPONSES T	17336
OF SERBIA IN THE FIRST	YEAR AFTER THE EPIZOOTIC DISEASES OF	16480
HE 1959-60 AGRICULTURAL	YEAR AND THE AUTHENTICITY OF THE PRO	11989
FIRST INDIAN DAIRY	YEAR BOOK 1960/	6430
E NUMERICAL-STRENGTH OF	YEAR CLASSES/ EARLY LIFE HISTORY OF	489
OSPHATE SOLUTION. A TWO	YEAR EXPERIENCE/ A STUDY OF ACIDULAT	18753
CLINICAL ENIGMA□ A 1-7	YEAR FOLLOW-UP STUDY AND EVALUATION□	9930
NFECTIOUS HEPATITIS. 10	YEAR FOLLOW-UP STUDY/ THE TREATMENT	9410
TERS OF THE SECOND LIFE	YEAR IN BREEDING/ USE OF SOME SUGAR	11693
F THE LIVER. A THIRTEEN	YEAR OBSERVATION/ GIANT CAVERNOUS HE	19510
S□ IN A DISPENSARY/ ONE	YEAR OF COPROCULTURE□ OF FECAL MICRO	24481
ICROORGANISMS□ IN A ONE	YEAR OF COPROCULTURE□ OF FECAL MICRO	24481
DETERMINATION OF STAGE,	YEAR OF DEVELOPMENT AND PUPATION DAT	8046
ERVOIR DURING ITS FIRST	YEAR OF EXISTENCE// OLIGACHAETOUS WO	8020
ES IN FIBER FLAX IN THE	YEAR OF HERBICIDE APPLICATION AND IN	11681
METHIONINE DURING FIRST	YEAR OF LIFE/ PERSISTENCE IN BLOOD O	15251
RINO LAMBS IN THE FIRST	YEAR OF LIFE/ THE GROWTH OF THE POLI	15070
LIVER WITHIN THE FIRST	YEAR OF LIFE/ VARIABILITY OF THE INF	10693
ITH SEAT-BELTS DURING A	YEAR OF PROGRAM EFFORTS/ INCREASE IN	2952
UTRITION, PRAGUE/ TENTH	YEAR OF THE INSTITUTE FOR STUDIES IN	22478
RESERVOIRS IN THE 20TH	YEAR OF THEIR EXISTENCE/ A HYDROBIOL	4604
RING STORAGE OVER A TEN	YEAR PERIOD/ QUANTITATIVE STUDY OF D	24369
UNION HOSPITAL. A FIVE	YEAR STUDY/ THE DEVELOPMENT AND FUNC	23590
JAPAN□ A NATION-WIDE 5	YEAR SURVEY□/ SKIN CANCERS IN	15556
OF CARP OF THE CURRENT	YEAR TO COMMERCIAL SIZE IN UZBEKISTA	8632
, NEW DELHI, DURING THE	YEAR 1959 TO MAY, 1961/ SALMONELLAE	6547
URE DURING THE ACADEMIC	YEAR 1960-1961/ SCHOLASTIC PERFORMAN	17033
UTE OF TUNIS DURING THE	YEAR 1961/ REPORT ON THE ACTIVITIES	17076
INFLUENZA THIS	YEAR□ EPIDEMIOLOGY□/	24591
BACTERIOLOGYS GREAT	YEAR□ FOR ACCOMPLISHMENTS□ 1882/	17081
ND PRACTICAL ASPECTS OF	YEAR-ROUND FERTILITY OF CERTAIN WOOD	3428
FACTOR, IN THE LIGHT OF	YEAR-TO-YEAR AND LONG-TERM FLUCTUATI	21934
HERIES FOR THE CALENDAR	YEAR-1959/ REPORT OF THE BUREAU OF C	21953
ERIES. FOR THE CALENDAR	YEAR-1960/ REPORT OF THE BUREAU OF C	21954
IFFERENT SEASONS OF THE	YEAR/ DISTRIBUTION OF PHOSPHORUS-32	815
O WEANING/ ESTIMATES OF	YEAR, SEX, AGE OF DAM, AGE AND IN BR	15149
TIONS OF LUCIOPERCA AND	YEARLINGS OF ABRAMIS-VIMBA/ ADAPTATI	8700
FEEDING CALVES VS. LONG	YEARLINGS/ RETURNS FROM	6447
COTIC DRUG ADDICTS FIVE	YEARS AFTER HOSPITALIZATION/ FOLLOWU	7068
RC OMA OF THE LIVER, 25	YEARS AFTER INJECTION OF THOROTRAST	19519
Y TUMORS IN THE RAT TWO	YEARS AFTER PARTIAL THYROIDECTOMY/ T	2270
R DISEASE MORE THAN TWO	YEARS AFTER SERUM□ POST-TRANSFUSION□	9508
SYCHIATRIC□ PATIENT. 10	YEARS AGO AND NOW/ THE VETERAN NP□ N	14249
KNEW BILHARZIASIS 5000	YEARS AGO/ THE EGYPTIANS	25223
ANUS/ 13	YEARS CAMPAIGN AGAINST UMBILICAL TET	2869
□ OF RYBIN RESERVOIR IN	YEARS CHARACTERIZED BY DIFFERENT FEE	21931
ESSIVE PEMPHIGUS OF ONE	YEARS DURATION. PRESENT CONDITION AF	6224
ORIGINAL TECHNIQUE/ ONE	YEARS EXPERIMENT WITH A DERIVATIVE O	10158
UGE/ 2 MORE	YEARS FOR BOMBAY HOOK□ WILDLIFE□ REF	15
ERA OUTBREAKS IN RECENT	YEARS IN WEST PAKISTAN/ EPIDEMIOLOGI	2864
DIES ON, ECZEMA□ A FOUR	YEARS OBSERVATION□ 58-61□ ACCORDING	18691
ISEASE IN PERSONS FIFTY	YEARS OF AGE AND YOUNGER/ DEATHS FRO	11078
CE IRRADIATED AT-1-TO-2	YEARS OF AGE/ AGE OF EXPOSURE AND TH	17489
CASES BETWEEN 18 AND 25	YEARS OF AGE/ CHOLECYSTITIS AND CHOL	5061
QUACY OF GIRLS 12 TO 14	YEARS OF AGE/ FACTORS RELATED TO THE	994
LY NOURISHED MEN, 60-69	YEARS OF AGE/ SERUM LIPID LEVELS AND	13785
BJECTS BETWEEN 7 AND 70	YEARS OF AGE/ SPIROMETRIC STUDIES IN	18529
DREN FROM BIRTH TO FIVE	YEARS OF AGE/ THE NATURAL HISTORY OF	6900
S/ THE RESULTS OF THREE	YEARS OF EXPERIMENTATION IN THE CHEM	7728
DEVIATIONS IN THE FIRST	YEARS OF LIFE. THE PEDIATRIC ASPECT	10706
NETIC PARAMETERS IN TEN	YEARS OF MILES-CITY R.O.P. STEER DAT	19692
L PATIENTS DURING SEVEN	YEARS OF OBSERVATION/ INTESTINAL PAR	25202
□/ EIGHTEEN	YEARS OF SOIL POISON TESTS□ ISOPTERA	12034
SKAYA-OBLAST DURING THE	YEARS OF SOVIET REGIME/ STUDIES OF T	17610
APSE□ STUDY BETWEEN THE	YEARS OF 1955-AND-1961□/ RESISTANCE	24466
NORMAL CHILD UNDER TWO	YEARS OLD AND IN SOME SUBJECTS□ CHIL	19611
10	YEARS PHARMACO PSYCHOTHERAPY/	19116
TURE FARM AT NITRA/ TEN	YEARS RESULTS ON BREEDING OF WALACHI	6484
TION. OBSERVATIONS ON A	YEARS WORK/ DIMINUTION OF INFANTILE	11098
CENTER OF CREMA IN THE	YEARS 1951-1960/ ANALYSIS OF CASES O	11082
ED IN MEXICO DURING THE	YEARS 1959, 1960, 1961/ STUDY OF CAS	11074
N SITU DATING BACK 5-10	YEARS. POSSIBLE SIGNIFICANCE OF THE	19471
MOSIS PROGRESSING FOR 8	YEARS. THERAPEUTIC ACTIVITY OF AMPHO	11265
N DURING A PERIOD OF 20	YEARS□ 1938-1957□/ OBSERVATIONS ON F	7009
T OF THE RHONE DURING 5	YEARS□ 1957-61□, AND DOCTORS DECLARA	6999
DISEASE OBSERVED FOR 9	YEARS/ A CASE WITH STEIN-LEVENTHAL S	6253
GENEVA DURING THE LAST	YEARS/ ASPECTS OF TUBERCULOSIS AT TH	11067
TIENTS OBSERVED OVER 30	YEARS/ DEGREE OF FIXATION OF THOUGHT	23553
OCI PERSISTING FOR MANY	YEARS/ DIAPAUSE OF THE COLORADO BEET	16427
WEST PAKISTAN IN RECENT	YEARS/ EPIDEMIOLOGY OF CHOLERA IN	24550
CARCIN OMA AFTER SEVEN	YEARS/ FATAL RECURRENCE OF PARATHYRO	6226
GES ONE MONTH AND SEVEN	YEARS/ PARENT-CHILD CORRELATIONS FOR	4191
OD FOREST DURING DROUTH	YEARS/ SOIL MOISTURE DEPLETION BY A	16216
ANGES OVER THE LAST 100	YEARS/ THE SCARABAEOID□ COLEOPTERA□	3755
HUKCHI SEA IN DIFFERENT	YEARS/ VARIATIONS IN NUMBERS OF WHAL	4629
STORAGE FOR TWENTY-ONE	YEARS/ VIABILITY AND BEHAVIOR OF LYO	3069
THEM OVER THE PAST TEN	YEARS, FROM 1951 TO 1961/ CASPIAN FO	4507
DIET, FOLLOWED FOR FOUR	YEARS, ON TOTAL CHOLESTEROL AND THE	4826
THE AMINO ACYL GROUP IN	YEAST AMINO ACYL S RNA□ SOLUBLE RIBO	8866
OSITIVE MICROORGANISMS□	YEAST AND BACILLUS□/ SITE OF GRAM ST	15177
AMINO-ACID TRANSPORT IN	YEAST AND EFFECTS OF NYSTATIN/	3031
TE DEHYDROGEN ASES FROM	YEAST AND RABBIT MUSCLE/ SUBUNIT STR	8948
ON/ DIFFERENCES BETWEEN	YEAST AND RAT LIVER AMINO-ACID-SPECI	719
ON-DEFICIENT MUTANTS IN	YEAST BY ACRIFLAVINE/ METHYLENE BLUE	8475
FLAVIN SYNTHESIS BY THE	YEAST CANDIDA-TROPICALIS-VAR.-RHAGII	11480
T OF HIGHER ALCOHOLS ON	YEAST CELLS AND ON CELL FREE YEAST E	7511

HNIQUE TO DETECT VIABLE	YEAST CELLS IN PASTEURIZED ORANGE DR	20407
/ THE FINE STRUCTURE OF	YEAST CELLS IN THE ELECTRON MICROSCO	21555
ACTS FROM PROLIFERATING	YEAST CELLS/ ULTRACENTRIFUGAL STUDIE	12783
EINS OF RATS FED TORULA	YEAST DIETS/ INCORPORATION OF VALINE	943
ATE ENZYME COMPOUNDS OF	YEAST DPN□ DIPHOSPHOPYRIDINE NUCLEOT	20588
NFORMATIONAL CHANGES OF	YEAST ENOL ASE IN SOLUTION/ CO	8990
CELLS AND ON CELL FREE	YEAST EXTRACTS/ THE EFFECT OF HIGHER	7511
HE TWO/ OBSERVATIONS ON	YEAST FERMENTATION IN DEFINED MEDIA	13476
CHNIQUES□ BACTERIAL AND	YEAST FERMENTATION□ ON THE PERFORMAN	20405
NSIS IN CULTURES OF THE	YEAST FORM PHASE/ ULTRA STRUCTURES O	11038
ISTICS OF SOME RACES OF	YEAST FROM DISTILLERIES PRODUCING PR	22671
CTURAL PECULIARITIES OF	YEAST GLUCANS SHOWING ACTIVITY IN TH	11493
IMMUNOLOGY OF THE	YEAST HANSENULA-WINGEI/	6733
HE PROSTHETIC GROUPS OF	YEAST L□ PLUS□ LACTATE DEHYDROGEN AS	7539
/ ON SOME PROPERTIES OF	YEAST L□ PLUS□ LACTATE DEHYDROGEN AS	7540
S. KINETIC STUDIES WITH	YEAST L□ PLUS□ LACTATE DEHYDROGEN AS	4722
	HYDROGEN AS	4723
	DROGEN ASE	8959
	ETERMINATIO	17168
ION USING N-15 LABELLED	YEAST PROTEIN□ AFTER GLUTEN-FREE DIE	9420
ION OF ADENYLIC-ACID IN	YEAST RIBO NUCLEIC-ACID/ POLAROGRAPH	18265
FOR THE GERMINATION OF	YEAST SPORES/ THE NUTRITIONAL REQUIR	7495
PORATION IN A CELL-FREE	YEAST SYSTEM/ POLY NUCLEOTIDE-DEPEND	20582
MALIC-ACID METABOLIZING	YEAST TO WINE PRODUCTION/ THE APPLIC	9242
ON OF CEREBRIN FROM THE	YEAST TORULOPSIS-UTILIS/ CONSTITUTI	24902
PURINE COMPOUNDS IN THE	YEAST VACUOLE/ ULTRAVIOLET MICROSCOP	11482
ON-DEFICIENT MUTANTS OF	YEAST. GENETICS□ CYTOPLASMIC INHERIT	17255
FERMENTATION OF CULTURE	YEAST. GLYCEROL AND LACTIC-ACID/ THE	18266
ARBOXYL ASE FROM BAKERS	YEAST. PROPERTIES OF ENZYME/ PHOSPHO	13088
N OF SELENITE BY INTACT	YEAST□ CANDIDA-ALBICANS AND BAKERS Y	20417
IDA-ALBICANS AND BAKERS	YEAST□ CELLS AND CELL-FREE PREPARATI	20417
IDA-ALBICANS AND BAKERS	YEAST□ REDUCTION OF SELENITE/ ENZYMA	20422
OF TREHALOSE IN BAKERS	YEAST□ SACCHAROMYCES-CEREVISIAE□/ FU	11477
F AUTOLYSATES FROM FOOD	YEAST□ TORULOPSIS-UTIILIS, CANDIDA-A	15743
DOPLASMIC RETICULUM□ IN	YEAST□/ ORIGIN OF THE EN	8429
TYL CARBINOL BY VARIOUS	YEAST-SPECIES/ PRODUCTION OF PHENYLA	7530
SUPER SUPPRESSORS IN	YEAST/	17239
SPIRATORY COMPETENCY IN	YEAST/ A RELATIONSHIP BETWEEN ERGOST	20557
CORPORATING SYSTEM FROM	YEAST/ AN ACTIVE CELL-FREE AMINO-ACI	20585
RODUCING PRESSED BAKING	YEAST/ CHARACTERISTICS OF SOME RACES	22671
NE REQUIRING MUTANTS IN	YEAST/ COMPLEMENTATION BETWEEN ADENI	8472
OF RESERVE DEPOSITS IN	YEAST/ ENDOGENOUS METABOLISM	7535
LLELIC RECOMBINATION IN	YEAST/ EVIDENCE FOR TWO TYPES OF A	21585
A CELLULAR PH OF BAKERS	YEAST/ INTR	7542
UCLEIC-ACID FRACTION IN	YEAST/ METABOLIC PROPERTIES OF A RIB	15928
A DIALYZABLE FACTOR OF	YEAST/ POSSIBLE PHOSPHORYLATION OF S	20586
IC GLYCOLYSIS IN BAKERS	YEAST/ REGULATION OF AEROB	15891
N ASE CRYSTALLIZED FROM	YEAST/ THE HYDROLYSIS OF P NITROPHEN	4774
N REVERSED BY X-RAYS IN	YEAST/ ULTRAVIOLET-RAY, X-RAY-AND NI	21619
CT OF VITAMIN-B ON THE□	YEAST, FROG□ CARBOHYDRATE-METABOLISM	22584
TI PYRETIC ACTIVITY OF□	YEAST, RAT□ SALICYLIC AND AURINTRI C	23937
BACTERIAL BIOTINID ASE□	YEAST, STREPTOCOCCUS-FAECALIS, PROPI	6611
C METABOLIC PRODUCTS OF	YEASTS AND FUNGI/ CARIOGENI	23481
IC-ACID□ AGAINST MOLDS,	YEASTS AND LACTIC-ACID BACILLI□/ INV	3028
ING CULTURES□ BACTERIA,	YEASTS AND TRUE FUNGI□/ GENERAL METH	20424
OF SELECTION OF SHERRY	YEASTS FOR ALCOHOL RESISTANCE/ METHO	1054
OOTH AND ROUGH FORMS OF	YEASTS IN THE PRESENCE OF ETHANOL OR	7547
IN THE CULTURE MEDIA OF	YEASTS OF THE GENUS CANDIDA/ COMPARA	2831
TATION OF PALATINOSE BY	YEASTS OF THE GENUS SACCHAROMYCES/ C	20555
OR AND PENICILLIUM, AND	YEASTS RHODOTORULA AND TORULOPSIS□ Q	7210
SENSITIVITY OF HAPLOID	YEASTS TO DENSELY IONIZING PARTICLES	17495
ORGANISMS□ BACTERIA AND	YEASTS□ UNDER STRESS/ BIOSYNTHETIC R	11285
ISMS.□ BACTERIA, FUNGI,	YEASTS□/ DEGRADATION OF NUCLEIC-ACID	24813
□ NOCARDIA, PROTEUS AND	YEASTS□/ DISTRIBUTION AND SUBSTRATE	11200
US, METHANOBACTERIA AND	YEASTS□/ NEW FREE-LIVING NITROGEN-FI	20435
REMOTE HYBRIDIZATION OF	YEASTS/ NUCLEIC-ACIDS AND	7502
ARABITOL BY OSMOPHILIC	YEASTS/ STUDIES ON THE FORMATION OF	3226
ONIZATION OF BUDDING OF	YEASTS/ SYNCHR	15893
, SPOREFORMING BACILLI,	YEASTS, MOLDS AND ACTINOMYCES□ OF HA	24802
DIATION ON SEEDS OF THE	YELLOW ACACIA/ THE EFFECTS OF COBALT	11972
ROWN GRANULAR LOAMS AND	YELLOW BROWN LOAMS OF THE WAIKATO-DI	7626
DING OF RED, ORANGE AND	YELLOW DELPHINIUMS/ THE BREE	3423
WHEAT AND OAT	YELLOW DWARF RESISTANCE/	20824
, BELGIAN CONGO/ JUNGLE	YELLOW FEVER AND ITS CONTROL IN GEME	24573
VIRUSES. PERSISTENCE OF	YELLOW FEVER ANTIBODIES FOLLOWING VA	10944
THE EXISTENCE OF SYLVAN	YELLOW FEVER IN ARGENTINA/ INVESTIGA	20193
ER INOCULATION WITH-17D	YELLOW FEVER VACCINE/ A FOLLOW-UP OF	2707
INATION WITH 17D STRAIN	YELLOW FEVER VACCINE/ IMMUNOLOGICAL	10944
NICULUS-L INFECTED WITH	YELLOW FEVER VIRUS/ FINE STRUCTURE O	11018
EPIDOPTERA□ INCLUDING A	YELLOW FORM OF THE LARVA/ SOME NOTES	8130
ONED BAIT IN CONTROL OF	YELLOW GOPHERS□ RODENTIA□ IN THE ALM	17621
VINE FANLEAF, GRAPEVINE	YELLOW MOSAIC AND ARABIS MOSAIC VIRU	16303
E FANLEAF AND GRAPEVINE	YELLOW MOSAIC VIRUSES/ HOST RANGE AN	16302
NATION AND FRUIT SET OF	YELLOW PASSIONFRUIT IN SOUTHERN FLOR	7654
/ A COLOR MUTANT OF THE	YELLOW PERCH□ PERCA-FLAVESCENS□ FROM	25546
PROTEIN COMBINING WITH	YELLOW PIGMENTS□ DIHYDRO PTERIDINE□	21243
ERTIES OF THE WHITE AND	YELLOW PORTIONS OF THE ADDUCTOR IN F	12562
SYNTHESIS OF THE	YELLOW PTERIDINE ISOSEPIAPTERIN/	8867
ANITOBA/ NESTING OF THE	YELLOW RAIL□ COTURNICOPS-NOVEBORACEN	25579
TEM OF PINK THISTLE AND	YELLOW SOWTHISTLE/ EFFECT OF THE SOD	20693
THE FIRST RECORD OF THE	YELLOW-BROWED WARBLER□ PHYLLOSCOPUS-	4007
MENTS RESPONSIBLE FOR A	YELLOW-FLOWERED MUTANT HYBRID FROM L	16182
PENINSULA OF MICHIGAN/	YELLOW-HEADED BLACK BIRDS NESTING IN	4023
EIGHT GROWTH OF PLANTED	YELLOW-POPLAR□ LIRIODENDRON-TULIPIFE	16242
Y MYO GLOBIN SOLUTIONS□	YELLOWFIN TUNA AND BEEF□/ EFFECT OF	13379
VIRUS/ SUGAR BEET MILD	YELLOWING VIRUS. A PERSISTENT APHID□	7825
JERSEY/ SITE QUALITY OF	YELLOWPOPLAR IN RELATION TO SOIL FAC	7719
SUGAR BEET	YELLOWS IN GREAT-BRITAIN,-1961/	20804
CONTROL OF VIRUS	YELLOWS IN SUGAR BEET CROPS/	7860
CONTROL/ THE NATURE OF	YELLOWS IN SUGAR BEETS AND MEASURES	20803
ICAL DIAGNOSIS OF VIRUS	YELLOWS OF SUGAR BEET/ SEROLOG	7823
OF INFECTION CAUSED BY	YELLOWS-TYPE VIRUSES IN TRIFOLIUM-RE	11937
TREES WITH SOUR CHERRY	YELLOWS/ FRUIT SET REDUCTIONS IN CHE	25041
LIPID IN MEATS/ ON THE	YELLOWTAIL OIL□ SERIOLA-GUINGUERADIA	4986
IN ISRAELIS OF BEDOUIN,	YEMENITE, AND EUROPEAN ORIGIN/ A STU	22602
BERIAN PLAIN AND OF THE	YENISEY-RIDGE/ FOSSIL FUNGI OF THE W	15769
TWO RARE LAND SLUGS IN	YERSEKE/ MILAX-GAGATES AND LIMAX-VAL	3857
ECT OF SENSITIZATION ON	YERSIN TYPE TUBERCULOSIS IN RABBITS/	24725
ANT HELMINTICS OF	YESTERDAY AND TODAY/	15733
UBSTANCES ON GROWTH AND	YIELD ALFALFA/ EFFECT OF IONIZING RA	20646
T OF FERTILIZERS ON THE	YIELD AND CHEMICAL COMPOSITION OF RE	20640
ON SOIL SOLUTION AND ON	YIELD AND COMPOSITION OF ALFALFA AND	11633
RVESTING FOR MAXIMIZING	YIELD AND DETERMINATION OF OPTIMUM D	12076
HE GROWTH, DEVELOPMENT,	YIELD AND ECONOMIC CHARACTERS OF WES	16019
OCIATIONS/ DRY MATTER	YIELD AND EVALUATION OF DOMINANT ASS	13039
CID□ ON PHOTOSYNTHESIS,	YIELD AND GRAIN QUALITY IN OATS/ THE	11553
URIAL TREATMENTS ON THE	YIELD AND MINERAL COMPOSITION OF RUN	11855
CONTAINING SCRAP ON THE	YIELD AND QUALITY OF FEED CROPS/ THE	11612
ELOPMENT OF FLAX AND ON	YIELD AND QUALITY OF FIBER/ INFLUENC	11687

Figure 18 Page from the subject index of Biological Abstracts.

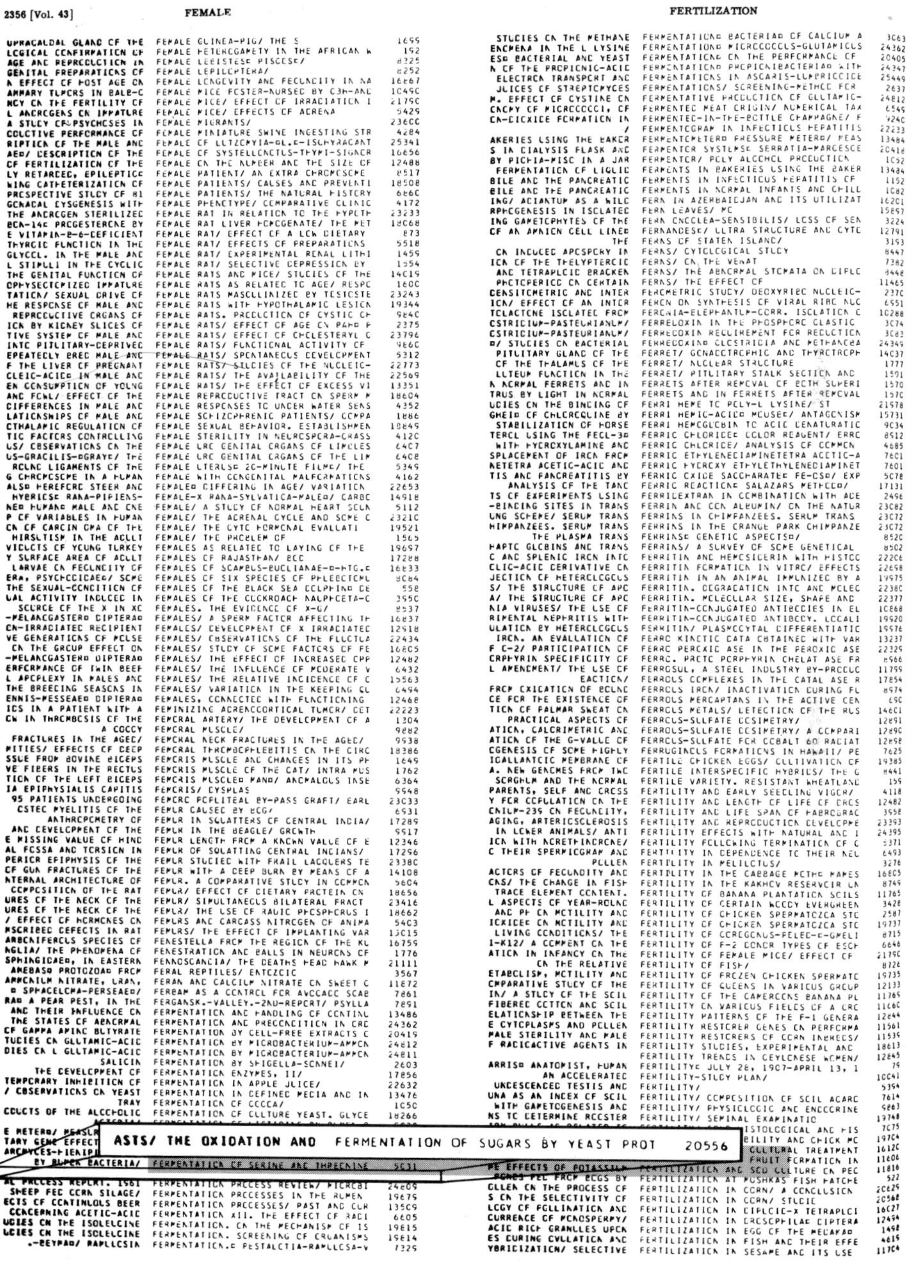

2356 [Vol. 43] FEMALE FERTILIZATION

URHACALDAL GLAND OF THE	FEMALE GUINEA-PIG/ THE S	1695
LOGICAL CONFIRMATION OF	FEMALE HETEROGAMETY IN THE AFRICAN W	192
AGE AND REPRODUCTION IN	FEMALE LEBISTES& PISCES/	8325
GENITAL PREPARATIONS OF	FEMALE LEPIDOPTERA/	8252
N EFFECT OF HOST AGE ON	FEMALE LONGEVITY AND FECUNDITY IN NA	16867
MAMMARY TUMORS IN BALB-C	FEMALE MICE FOSTER-NURSED BY C3H-AND	10490
NCY ON THE FERTILITY OF	FEMALE MICE/ EFFECT OF IRRADIATION I	21790
L ANDROGENS ON IMMATURE	FEMALE MICE/ EFFECTS OF ADRENA	5425
A STUDY OF PSYCHOSES IN	FEMALE MIGRANTS/	23600
COLCTIVE PERFORMANCE OF	FEMALE MINIATURE SWINE INGESTING STR	4284
RIPTION OF THE MALE AND	FEMALE OF LUTZOMYIA-AL.E-ISCHYRACANT	25341
AED/ DESCRIPTION OF THE	FEMALE OF SYSTELLONOTUS-THYMI-SIGNOR	16656
OF FERTILIZATION OF THE	FEMALE ON THE NUMBER AND THE SIZE OF	12488
LY RETARDED, EPILEPTIC&	FEMALE PATIENT/ AN EXTRA CHROMOSOME	8517
WING CATHETERIZATION OF	FEMALE PATIENTS/ CAUSES AND PREVENTI	18508
PROSPECTIVE STUDY OF 81	FEMALE PATIENTS/ THE NATURAL HISTORY	6860
GONADAL DYSGENESIS WITH	FEMALE PHENOTYPE/ COMPARATIVE CLINIC	4172
THE ANDROGEN STERILIZED	FEMALE RAT IN RELATION TO THE HYPOTH	23233
BCN-14C PROGESTERONE BY	FEMALE RAT LIVER HOMOGENATE/ THE MET	18068
E VITAMIN-B-6-DEFICIENT	FEMALE RAT/ EFFECT OF A LOW DIETARY	873
THYROID FUNCTION IN THE	FEMALE RAT/ EFFECTS OF PREPARATIONS	5518
GLYCOL. IN THE MALE AND	FEMALE RAT/ EXPERIMENTAL RENAL LITHI	1455
L STIMULI IN THE CYCLIC	FEMALE RAT/ SELECTIVE DEPRESSION BY	1554
THE GENITAL FUNCTION OF	FEMALE RATS AND MICE/ STUDIES OF THE	14019
OPHYSECTOMIZED IMMATURE	FEMALE RATS AS RELATED TO AGE/ RESPO	1600
TATION/ SEXUAL DRIVE OF	FEMALE RATS MASCULINIZED BY TESTOSTE	23243
HE RESPONSE OF MALE AND	FEMALE RATS WITH HYPOTHALAMIC LESION	19344
REPRODUCTIVE ORGANS OF	FEMALE RATS. PRODUCTION OF CYSTIC OH	9840
ION BY KIDNEY SLICES OF	FEMALE RATS/ EFFECT OF AGE ON PAH& P	2375
TIVE SYSTEM OF MALE AND	FEMALE RATS/ EFFECT OF CHOLESTERYL C	23796
INTO PITUITARY-DEPRIVED	FEMALE RATS/ FUNCTIONAL ACTIVITY OF	9860
EPEATEDLY BRED MALE AND	FEMALE RATS/ SPONTANEOUS DEVELOPMENT	5312
F THE LIVER OF PREGNANT	FEMALE RATS/ STUDIES OF THE NUCLEIC-	22773
CLEIC-ACID& IN MALE AND	FEMALE RATS/ THE AVAILABILITY OF THE	22569
EN CONSUMPTION OF YOUNG	FEMALE RATS/ THE EFFECT OF EXCESS VI	13351
AND FOWL/ EFFECT OF THE	FEMALE REPRODUCTIVE TRACT ON SPERM M	18604
DIFFERENCES IN MALE AND	FEMALE RESPONSES TO UNDER WATER SENS	4352
LATIONSHIPS OF MALE AND	FEMALE SCHIZOPHRENIC PATIENTS/ COMPA	1886
CTHALAMIC REGULATION OF	FEMALE SEXUAL BEHAVIOR. ESTABLISHMEN	10849
TIC FACTORS CONTROLLING	FEMALE STERILITY IN NEUROSPORA-CRASS	4120
US/ OBSERVATIONS ON THE	FEMALE URO GENITAL ORGANS OF LIMULES	6467
US-GRACILIS-BGRAYE/ THE	FEMALE URO GENITAL ORGANS OF THE LIM	6468
ROUND LIGAMENTS OF THE	FEMALE UTERUS& 20-MINUTE FILM&/ THE	5349
G CHROMOSOME IN A HUMAN	FEMALE WITH CONGENITAL MALFORMATIONS	4162
ALSO HEREFORD STEER AND	FEMALE& DIFFERING IN AGE/ VARIATION	22653
HYBRIDS& RANA-PIPIENS-	FEMALE-X RANA-SYLVATICA-MALE&/ CARBO	14918
NE& HUMAN& MALE AND ONE	FEMALE/ A STUDY OF NORMAL HEART SOUN	5112
P OF VARIABLES IN HUMAN	FEMALE/ THE ADRENAL CYCLE AND SOME C	23210
ON OF CARCIN OMA OF THE	FEMALE/ THE CYTO HORMONAL EVALUATI	19521
HIRSUTISM IN THE ADULT	FEMALE/ THE PROBLEM OF	1565
VIDUCTS OF YOUNG TURKEY	FEMALES AS RELATED TO LAYING OF THE	19697
Y SURFACE AREA OF ADULT	FEMALES OF RAJASTHAN/ BOD	17288
LARVAE ON FECUNDITY OF	FEMALES OF SCARABUS-EUCLIANAE-B-HTG.C	16833
ERA, PSYCHODIDAE&/ SOME	FEMALES OF SIX SPECIES OF PHLEBOTOMU	8064
THE SEXUAL-CONDITION OF	FEMALES OF THE BLACK SEA DOLPHIN& DE	558
UAL ACTIVITY INDUCED IN	FEMALES OF THE COCKROACH NAUPHOETA-C	3550
SOURCE OF THE X IN XO	FEMALES. THE EVIDENCE OF X-G/	8537
-MELANOGASTER& DIPTERA&	FEMALES/ A SPERM FACTOR AFFECTING TH	16837
ON-IRRADIATED RECIPIENT	FEMALES/ DEVELOPMENT OF X IRRADIATED	12518
VE GENERATIONS OF MOUSE	FEMALES/ OBSERVATIONS OF THE FLUCTUA	22434
ON THE GROUP EFFECT ON	FEMALES/ STUDY OF SOME FACTORS OF FE	16805
-MELANOGASTER& DIPTERA&	FEMALES/ THE EFFECT OF INCREASED OPP	12482
ERFORMANCE OF TWIN BEEF	FEMALES/ THE INFLUENCE OF MODERATE V	6432
L APOPLEXY IN MALES AND	FEMALES/ THE RELATIVE INCIDENCE OF C	15563
THE BREEDING SEASONS IN	FEMALES/ VARIATION IN THE KEEPING QU	6494
ENNIS-MESSEAE& DIPTERA&	FEMALES. CONNECTED WITH FUNCTIONING	12468
ICS IN A PATIENT WITH A	FEMINIZING ADRENOCORTICAL TUMOR/ OBT	22223
ON IN THROMBOSIS OF THE	FEMORAL ARTERY/ THE DEVELOPMENT OF A	1304
A COCCY	FEMORAL MUSCLE/	9882
FRACTURES IN THE AGED/	FEMORAL NECK FRACTURES IN THE AGED/	9538
MITIES/ EFFECTS OF DEEP	FEMORAL THROMBOPHLEBITIS ON THE CIRC	18386
SSUE FROM BOVINE BICEPS	FEMORIS MUSCLE AND CHANGES IN ITS PH	1649
VE FIBERS IN THE RECTUS	FEMORIS MUSCLE OF THE CAT/ INTRA MUS	1762
TION OF THE LEFT BICEPS	FEMORIS MUSCLE& MAN&/ ANOMALOUS INSE	6364
IA EPIPHYSIALIS CAPITIS	FEMORIS/ DYSPLAS	5548
95 PATIENTS UNDERGOING	FEMORO POPLITEAL BY-PASS GRAFT/ EARL	23033
OSTEO MYELITIS OF THE	FEMUR CAUSED BY ECG/	6531
ANTHROPOMETRY OF	FEMUR IN SQUATTERS OF CENTRAL INDIA/	17289
AND DEVELOPMENT OF THE	FEMUR IN THE BEAGLE/ GROWTH	9517
E MISSING VALUE OF HIND	FEMUR LENGTH FROM A KNOWN VALUE OF E	12346
AL FOSSA AND TORSION IN	FEMUR OF SQUATTING CENTRAL INDIANS/	17296
PERIOR EPIPHYSIS OF THE	FEMUR STUDIED WITH FRAIL LACOLERS TE	23380
OF GUN FRACTURES OF THE	FEMUR WITH A DEEP BURN BY MEANS OF A	14108
NTERNAL ARCHITECTURE OF	FEMUR. A COMPARATIVE STUDY IN COMMON	5604
COMPOSITION OF THE RAT	FEMUR/ EFFECT OF DIETARY PROTEIN ON	18656
URES OF THE NECK OF THE	FEMUR/ SIMULTANEOUS BILATERAL FRACT	23416
URES OF THE NECK OF THE	FEMUR/ THE USE OF RADIO PHOSPHORUS I	18662
/ EFFECT OF HORMONES ON	FEMURS AND CARCASS NITROGEN OF ANIMA	5403
MSCRIBED DEFECTS IN RAT	FEMURS/ THE EFFECT OF IMPLANTING VAR	13015
ARBONIFEROUS SPECIES OF	FENESTELLA FROM THE REGION OF THE KU	16759
NGLIA/ THE PHENOMENA OF	FENESTRATION AND BALLS IN NEURONS OF	1776
SPHINGIDAE&, IN EASTERN	FENNOSCANDIA/ THE DEATHS HEAD HAWK M	21111
AMEBAS& PROTOZOA& FROM	FERAL REPTILES/ ENTOZOIC	3567
AMMONIUM NITRATE, UREA,	FERAN AND CALCIUM NITRATE ON SWEET C	11872
& SPHACELOMA-PERSEAE&/	FERBAM AS A CONTROL FOR AVOCADO SCAB	7861
MAN A PEAR PEST, IN THE	FERGANSK.-VALLEY.-2ND-REPORT/ PSYLLA	7891
AND THEIR INFLUENCE ON	FERMENTATION AND HANDLING OF COCONUT	13486
THE STATES OF ABNORMAL	FERMENTATION AND PRECONDITION IN CRC	24362
OF GAMMA AMINO BUTYRATE	FERMENTATION BY CELL-FREE EXTRACTS O	20419
TUDIES ON GLUTAMIC-ACID	FERMENTATION BY MICROBACTERIUM-AMMON	24812
DIES ON L GLUTAMIC-ACID	FERMENTATION BY MICROBACTERIUM-AMMON	24811
SALICIN	FERMENTATION BY SHIGELLA-SONNEI/	2603
THE DEVELOPMENT OF	FERMENTATION ENZYMES, II/	17856
TEMPORARY INHIBITION OF	FERMENTATION IN APPLE JUICE/	22632
/ OBSERVATIONS ON YEAST	FERMENTATION IN DEFINED MEDIA AND IN	13476
TRAY	FERMENTATION OF COCOA/	1050
DUCTS OF THE ALCOHOLIC	FERMENTATION OF CULTURE YEAST. GLYCE	18266
E METERO/ MEASUR		
TARY GENE EFFECT		
ARCHYCES-HIERIP		
BY ... BACTERIA/	FERMENTATION OF SERINE AND THREONINE	5031
ASTS/ THE OXIDATION AND	FERMENTATION OF SUGARS BY YEAST PROT	20556
AL PROCESS REPORT. 1961	FERMENTATION PROCESS REVIEW/ MICROBI	24609
SHEEP FED CORN SILAGE/	FERMENTATION PROCESSES IN THE RUMEN	19675
ECTS OF CONTINUOUS BEER	FERMENTATION PROCESSES/ PAST AND CUR	13509
CONCERNING ACETIC-ACID	FERMENTATION XII. THE EFFECT OF RACI	6605
UDIES ON THE ISOLEUCINE	FERMENTATION. ON THE MECHANISM OF IS	19815
UDIES ON THE ISOLEUCINE	FERMENTATION. SCREENING OF ORGANISMS	19814
.-BEYMA&/ PAECILOMYCIN	FERMENTATION.& PESTALOTIA-RAMULOSA-V	7325

STUDIES ON THE METHANE	FERMENTATION& BACTERIA& OF CALCIUM A	3063
ENCHEMA IN THE L LYSINE	FERMENTATION& MICROCOCCUS-GLUTAMICUS	24362
ES& BACTERIAL AND YEAST	FERMENTATION& ON THE PERFORMANCE OF	20405
N OF THE PROPIONIC-ACID	FERMENTATION& PROPIONIBACTERIA& WITH	24347
ELECTRON TRANSPORT AND	FERMENTATIONS IN ASCARIS-LUMBRICOIDE	25449
JUICES OF STREPTOMYCES	FERMENTATIONS/ SCREENING-METHOD FOR	2637
M. EFFECT OF CYSTINE ON	FERMENTATIVE PRODUCTION OF GLUTAMIC-	24812
ONOMY OF MICROCOCCI, OF	FERMENTED MEAT ORIGIN/ NUMERICAL TAX	6545
ON-DIOXIDE FORMATION IN	FERMENTED-IN-THE-BOTTLE CHAMPAGNE/ F	9240
/	FERMENTOGRAM IN INFECTIOUS HEPATITIS	22233
AKERIES USING THE BAKER	FERMENTOMETER& PRESSURE METER&/ MEAS	13484
S IN DIALYSIS FLASK AND	FERMENTOR SYSTEMS& SERRATIA-MARCESCE	20418
BY PICHIA-MISC IN A JAR	FERMENTOR/ POLY ALCOHOL PRODUCTION	1052
FERMENTATION OF LIQUID	FERMENTS IN BAKERIES USING THE BAKER	13484
BILE AND THE PANCREATIC	FERMENTS IN INFECTIOUS HEPATITIS OF	1152
BILE AND THE PANCREATIC	FERMENTS IN NORMAL INFANTS AND CHILD	1082
ING/ ACTANTUM AS A WILD	FERN IN AZERBAIDJAN AND ITS UTILIZAT	16201
RPHOGENESIS IN ISOLATED	FERN LEAVES/ MC	15897
ING GAMETOPHYTES OF THE	FERN ONOCLEA-SENSIBILIS/ LOSS OF SEN	3224
OF AN AMNION CELL LINED	FERNANDES&/ ULTRA STRUCTURE AND CYTO	12791
THE	FERNS OF STATEN ISLAND/	3153
ON INDUCED APOSPORY IN	FERNS/ CYTOLOGICAL STUDY	8447
ICA OF THE THELYPTEROID	FERNS/ ON THE VENAT	7382
AND TETRAPLOID BRACKEN	FERNS/ THE ABNORMAL STOMATA ON DIPLO	9448
PHOTOPERIOD ON CERTAIN	FERNS/ THE EFFECT OF	11465
DENSITOMETRIC AND INTER	FEROMETRIC STUDY/ DEOXYRIBO NUCLEIC-	2370
ICA/ EFFECT OF AN INTER	FERON ON SYNTHESIS OF VIRAL RIBO NUC	6551
TOLACTONE ISOLATED FROM	FERONIA-ELEPHANTUM-CORR. ISOLATION O	10288
OSTRIDIUM-PASTEURIANUM/	FERREDOXIN IN THE PHOSPHORO CLASTIC	3074
OSTRIDIUM-PASTEURIANUM/	FERREDOXIN REQUIREMENT FOR REDUCTION	3083
&/ STUDIES ON BACTERIAL	FERREDOXIN& CLOSTRIDIA AND METHANOBA	24349
PITUITARY GLAND OF THE	FERRET/ GONADOTROPHIC AND THYROTROPH	14037
OF THE THALAMUS OF THE	FERRET/ NUCLEAR STRUCTURE	1777
LUTEUM FUNCTION IN THE	FERRET/ PITUITARY STALK SECTION AND	1591
N NORMAL FERRETS AND IN	FERRETS AFTER REMOVAL OF BOTH SUPERI	1570
TRUS BY LIGHT IN NORMAL	FERRETS AND IN FERRETS AFTER REMOVAL	1570
UDIES ON THE BINDING OF	FERRI HEME TO POLY-L LYSINE/ ST	21978
GHEI& OF CHLOROQUINE BY	FERRI HEMIC-ACID& MOUSE&/ ANTAGONISM	15731
STABILIZATION OF HORSE	FERRI HEMOGLOBIN TO ACID DENATURATIC	9034
TEROL USING THE FECL-3&	FERRIC CHLORIDE& COLOR REAGENT/ ERRO	8512
WITH HYDROXYLAMINE AND	FERRIC CHLORIDE/ ANALYSIS OF COMMON	4685
SPLACEMENT OF IRON FROM	FERRIC ETHYLENEDIAMINETETRA ACETIC-A	7601
NETETRA ACETIC-ACID AND	FERRIC HYDROXY ETHYLETHYLENEDIAMINET	7601
TIS AND PANCREATITIS BY	FERRIC OXIDE SACCHARATE& FE-OS&/ EXP	5078
ANALYSIS OF THE TANO	FERRIC REACTION& SALAZARS METHOD&/	17131
TS OF EXPERIMENTS USING	FERRILEXTRAN IN COMBINATION WITH ACE	2496
-BINDING SITES IN TRANS	FERRIN AND CON ALBUMIN/ ON THE NATUR	23082
UNG SCHEME/ SERUM TRANS	FERRINS IN CHIMPANZEES. SERUM TRANS	23072
HIMPANZEES. SERUM TRANS	FERRINS IN THE ORANGE PARK CHIMPANZE	23072
THE PLASMA TRANS	FERRINS& GENETIC ASPECTS&/	8520
HAPTO GLOBINS AND TRANS	FERRINS/ A SURVEY OF SOME GENETICAL	8502
C AND SPLENIC IRON INTO	FERRITIN AND HEMOSIDERIN WITH HISTOC	22206
CLIC-ACID DERIVATIVE ON	FERRITIN FORMATION IN VITRO/ EFFECTS	22658
JECTION OF HETEROLOGOUS	FERRITIN IN AN ANIMAL IMMUNIZED BY A	19975
S/ THE STRUCTURE OF APO	FERRITIN. DEGRADATION INTO MOLEC	22380
A/ THE STRUCTURE OF APO	FERRITIN. MOLECULAR SIZE, SHAPE AND	22377
NIA VIRUSES/ THE USE OF	FERRITIN-CONJUGATED ANTIBODIES IN EL	10868
RIMENTAL NEPHRITIS WITH	FERRITIN-CONJUGATED ANTIBODY. LOCALI	19920
ULATION BY HETEROLOGOUS	FERRITIN/ PLASMOCYTAL DIFFERENTIATIC	19976
IRON. AN EVALUATION OF	FERRO KINETIC DATA OBTAINED WITH VAR	13237
F C-2/ PARTICIPATION OF	FERRO PEROXID ASE IN THE PEROXID ASE	22329
ORPHYRIN SPECIFICITY OF	FERRO. PROTO PORPHYRIN CHELAT ASE FR	8966
L AMENDMENT/ THE USE OF	FERROSUL, A STEEL INDUSTRY BY-PRODUC	11799
EACTION/	FERROUS COMPLEXES IN THE CATAL ASE R	17854
FROM OXIDATION OF BOUND	FERROUS IRON/ INACTIVATION DURING FL	8974
CE FOR THE EXISTENCE OF	FERROUS MERCAPTANS IN THE ACTIVE CEN	690
TION OF PALMAR SWEAT ON	FERROUS METALS/ DETECTION OF THE RUS	14601
PRACTICAL ASPECTS OF	FERROUS-SULFATE DOSIMETRY/	12891
ATION, CALORIMETRIC AND	FERROUS-SULFATE DOSIMETRY/ A COMPARI	12890
ATION OF THE G-VALUE OF	FERROUS-SULFATE FOR COBALT 60 RADIAT	12858
OGENESIS OF SOME HIGHLY	FERRUGINOUS FORMATIONS IN HAWAII/ PE	7625
ICALLANTOIC MEMBRANE OF	FERTILE CHICKEN EGGS/ CULTIVATION OF	19385
A. NEW GENOMES FROM TWO	FERTILE INTERSPECIFIC HYBRIDS/ THE G	8441
SORGHUM AND THE NORMAL	FERTILE VARIETY. RESISTANT WHEATLAND	159
PARENTS, SELF AND CROSS	FERTILITY AND EARLY SEEDLING VIGOR/	4118
Y FOR COPULATION ON THE	FERTILITY AND LENGTH OF LIFE OF CROS	12482
CHIUM-235 ON FECUNDITY,	FERTILITY AND LIFE SPAN OF HABROBRAC	3658
AGING, ARTERIOSCLEROSIS	FERTILITY AND REPRODUCTION DEVELOPME	23393
IN LOWER ANIMALS/ ANTI	FERTILITY EFFECTS WITH NATURAL AND I	24395
ICA WITH NORETHINDRONE/	FERTILITY FOLLOWING TERMINATION OF C	5371
C THEIR SPERMIOGRAM AND	FERTILITY IN DEPENDENCE TO THEIR NEU	6493
POLLEN	FERTILITY IN MELILOTUS/	3276
ACTORS OF FECUNDITY AND	FERTILITY IN THE CABBAGE MOTHS MAMES	16805
ONS/ THE CHANGE IN FISH	FERTILITY IN THE KAKHOV RESERVOIR ON	8749
TRACE ELEMENT CONTENT.	FERTILITY OF BANANA PLANTATION SOILS	11765
L ASPECTS OF YEAR-ROUND	FERTILITY OF CERTAIN WOODY EVERGREEN	3428
AND PH ON MOTILITY AND	FERTILITY OF CHICKEN SPERMATOZOA STO	2587
ICKIDEE ON MOTILITY AND	FERTILITY OF CHICKEN SPERMATOZOA STO	19737
LIVING CONDITIONS/ THE	FERTILITY OF COREGONUS-PELED-E-GMELI	8715
1-K12/ A COMMENT ON THE	FERTILITY OF F-2 DONOR TYPES OF ESCH	6646
ATION IN INFANCY ON THE	FERTILITY OF FEMALE MICE/ EFFECT OF	21790
ON THE RELATIVE	FERTILITY OF FISH/	8726
ETABOLISM, MOTILITY AND	FERTILITY OF FROZEN CHICKEN SPERMATC	19735
COMPARATIVE STUDY OF THE	FERTILITY OF QUEENS IN VARIOUS GROUP	12133
IN/ A STUDY OF THE SOIL	FERTILITY OF THE CAMEROONS BANANA PL	11765
FIBERED COTTON AND SOIL	FERTILITY ON VARIOUS FIELDS OF A CRC	11660
ELATIONSHIP BETWEEN THE	FERTILITY PATTERNS OF THE F-1 GENERA	12644
E CYTOPLASMS AND POLLEN	FERTILITY RESTORER GENES ON PERFORMA	11561
MALE STERILITY AND MALE	FERTILITY RESTORERS OF CORN INBREDS/	11535
F RADIOACTIVE AGENTS IN	FERTILITY STUDIES, EXPERIMENTAL AND	18613
	FERTILITY TRENDS IN CEYLONESE WOMEN/	12845
ARRIS& ANATOMIST, HUMAN	FERTILITY& JULY 26, 1907-APRIL 13, 1	79
AN ACCELERATED	FERTILITY-STUDY PLAN/	10041
UNDESCENDED TESTIS AND	FERTILITY/	5354
UNA AS AN INDEX OF SOIL	FERTILITY/ COMPOSITION OF SOIL ACARC	7614
WITH GAMETOGENESIS AND	FERTILITY/ PHYSIOLOGIC AND ENDOCRINE	9863
NS TO DETERMINE ROOSTER	FERTILITY/ SEMINAL EXAMINATIO	13748
	... ISTOLOGICAL AND HIS	7675
	... EILITY AND CHICK MC	19704
	... CULTURAL TREATMENT	16120
	... FRUIT FORMATION IN	11606
FE EFFECTS OF POTASSIU	FERTILIZATION AND SOD CULTURE ON PEC	11816
RGNES FEL FROM EGGS BY	FERTILIZATION AT MUSHKAS FISH HATCHE	522
OLLEN ON THE PROCESS OF	FERTILIZATION IN CORN/ A CONCLUSION	20625
S ON THE SELECTIVITY OF	FERTILIZATION IN CORN/ STUDIE	20568
LOGY OF POLLINATION AND	FERTILIZATION IN DIPLOID-X TETRAPLOI	16027
CURRENCE OF MONOSPERMY/	FERTILIZATION IN DROSOPHILA& DIPTERA	12454
ACID RICH GRANULES UPON	FERTILIZATION IN EGG OF THE MEDAKA&	1498
ES DURING OVULATION AND	FERTILIZATION IN FISH AND THEIR EFFE	4615
YBRIDIZATION/ SELECTIVE	FERTILIZATION IN SESAME AND ITS USE	11704

Figure 19 *Page from the author index of* Biological Abstracts.

Miki-Morales [Vol. 43] 2100

MIKI S 19488
MIKI Y 15556
MIKKELSEN W M 15559
MIKKOLA A V V 21101
MIKKOLA K 25403
MIKLEVICH A V 10381
MIKOELYAN A L 9615
MIKOL C 1695
MIKOLAJCZYK J 211
3286
11607
17245
MIKUL SKA E I 21556
MIL SHTEIN G I 23643
MIL SHTEIN V V 8707
MILAD A A 18164
MILAKHINA M A 15873
MILANI M 14336
MILBLED G 22771
MILBURN T R 947
MILCH R A 2402
2403
MILCH S 8807
MILCU S M 23264
MILCU V 23171
MILEIKOVSKII S A 4566
21163
MILES A A 6054
13823
MILES R A 12174
MILES R S 8338
MILES W R 21841
MILEVSKAYA L 7195
MILEWSKA Z 22784
22785
MILFORD M H 3358
MILGRAM N 1950
MILGROM F 19946
MILHAUD F 10459
MILHORAT A T 23376
23377
MILIC-EMILI J 13962
MILKMAN R 16841
MILKOWSKA J 7491
MILL P J 25503
MILLAR D B S 22389
MILLAR D G 12853
MILLAR J H D 22202
MILLAR R H
MILLARD D G
MILLARD W W 17446
MILLEDGE H J 9027
MILLEN J E 9782
MILLEN J W 826
MILLER A 13859
14811
MILLER A A 11010
14305
MILLER A I 19090
MILLER A J 18302
22997
MILLER B B 21164
MILLER B F 4979
15016
MILLER B L 18343
MILLER C A 25135
MILLER C L 13428
MILLER C S 21885
MILLER D 2244
5021
9334
MILLER D E 20264
20701
MILLER E C 6513
MILLER E F II 17401
MILLER E K 14710
MILLER E L 1916
MILLER E R 792
793
1099
9747
MILLER F 25412
MILLER F K 10577
MILLER F S 10432
MILLER G E 17040
MILLER G V 14766
MILLER H 22139
MILLER H T 2511
MILLER H W JR 21177
MILLER J 13290
20098
MILLER J A 4048
MILLER J A JR 10432
MILLER J C 3396
24973
MILLER J D A 3124
10825
MILLER J F A P 6746
19953
19954
MILLER J H 11744
MILLER J J 17168
19075
MILLER J K 10766
MILLER J N 2849
10513
MILLER J Q 21683
MILLER J R 5576
21337
MILLER L 6806
MILLER L A 18482
MILLER L D 1148
MILLER L W 11868
MILLER M 10349
MILLER M C 2901
22203
MILLER M D 3291
18610
MILLER M H 5896
MILLER M R 17991
MILLER M W 7378
20495
MILLER N E 19026
MILLER O N 13290
17976

24833
MILLER P B 17402
MILLER P J 16919
MILLER P M 11468
MILLER R E 16293
MILLER R F 6511
13229
MILLER R H 21649
MILLER R J 3359
MILLER R O 16196
MILLER S 1828
MILLER S A 21765
MILLER S P 10610
MILLER T B 18516
MILLER T E 11728
MILLER T N 10284
MILLER W F 9787
15560
MILLER W H 8251
MILLER W J 10766
MILLER W L 6059
MILLER W T 6857
MILLER W W III 5454
MILLER-LIMMROTH W 1744
MILLES S S 10650
MILLETTE R L 1350
MILLICHAP J G 14220
18799
MILLIKAN C H 23048
MILLIKEN J A 14595
MILLINGTON J P 651
MILLINGTON R J 7608
MILLIS N F 20472
20484
MILLMAN B M 8303
MILLON R 1909/
MILLOY F J 13550
MILLS C F 13236
MILLS G C 13195
MILLS G L 13807
MILLS H L 25042
MILLS L W 19361
MILLS R P 144
MILLS S E 15199
MILMORE B K 2404
MILNE I G 18318
MILNE J S 20225
MILNE L J 40
MILLBANK J W 20556
MILNER A
MILNER B 1829
MILNER K C 2790
MILNOR W R 13606
18394
MILOKHIN A A 1779
MILOSERDOV N M 7737
MILOSLAVSKAYA N 4472
4473
MILOVANOVIC M 12178
MILROY S D 13801
MILSTEIN J M 18963
MILSTEIN P L S 12623
MILTON G W 6254
9329
9357
22741
MILYANOVSKII E S 8142
MILYAUSKAS V 3360
MILYUTIN V N 10869
MILYUTKIN A F 11734
MIMART J 19048
MIMS C A 1391
MINAKAMI H 23866
24225
24226
MINAKAMI S 13108
MINAMI M 2001
10285
18710
MINAMI T 10526
MINAMIKAWA K 19475
MINAMITANI K 22978
MINAMORI S 17274
MINAR J 11555
13551
25337
MINARD D 14661
MINC S 23586
MINCHINA R A 13917
MINCKLER L S 21886
MINDER I F 3532
MINDLIN S S 10648
MINER E J 10093
MINER J T 7674
MINESHITA T 23867
24105
MINESITA T 2102
MINESTAI T 14853
MING A L S 15399
MINICK O T 4067
MININNI D 6302
6303
6325
MINK G I 3493
MINKER E 14486
14487
14488
MINKEVICH I I 16276
MINKOWITZ S 1139
2836
MINKYAVICHUS A N 4567
MINOCHA J L 17246
MINOTAKIS C S 1515
MINOWADA J 10867
MINSKY R 19090
MINSON D J 15127
MINTER K W 8623
MINTON P R 17953
MINTZ D E 21842
MINYAEV N A 4372
MINYUSHEVA Z S 15724
MINZ B 18907
MIQUEL J 1819
MIRAGLIA G J 6897
MIRANDA C L 6200

MIRANDA M 15053
MIRCEVOVA L 9705
MIRCHAMSY H 2665
2669
MIRCHANDANI K W 6834
MIRCHINK T G 4373
MIRCIOIU C 5419
MIRIBEL 19054
MIRIMANYAN V A 7662
MIRKES L H 21424
MIRKIN B L 10286
9075
MIRKIN B M 8591
MIRONENKO A V 15961
MIRONOV N P 12085
MIRONOVA E V 3307
MIRONOVA I B 8805
MIRONOVA N V 8708
MIROSHINCHENKO M 4568
MIROSHNICHENKO M 6785
10941
MIROUZE J 17996
MIROVICH N I 1621
MIROWSKI M 13698
MIRRAKHIMOVA M 11657
MIRSKY A E 9072
13323
21565
MIRSKY J H 14496
MIRZOEV B M 23165
MISAKI A 4695
MISAKI H 9386
MISE J 1475
MISHCHENKO B A 15174
MISHELL D R JR 9837
MISHELL R 20099
MISHER A 9585
MISHIMA H 4693
MISHIMA K 2206
MISHINA A 24810
MISHRA H R 6429
MISHRA S S 10287
10288
MISHUSTIN E N 20607
24908
MISIEWICZ J J 9245
MISIK S B 1451
MISKIMEN M 21314
MISLIN H 18290
MISRA B 11159
MISRA G 11556
MISRA L P 7379
MISRA R C 8387
MISRA S K 11281
MISSIURO W 19622
MISTILES S P 13355
MISTILIS S 9490
MISTRUZZI L U 21198
MISTRY K B 7609
7610
11487
MISTRY S P 17998
MISU Y 23868
23997
MISUMI H 10028
MISZCZAK-LOCH T 4166
MITA M 5922
MITCHELL F G 4930
22638
MITCHELL G 1363
MITCHELL G E JR 6444
9299
9311
9324
MITCHELL H C 20248
MITCHELL I G 4002
MITCHELL J 22568
MITCHELL J C 21843
MITCHELL J E 16370
MITCHELL J H 19290
MITCHELL J P 8535
MITCHELL J R A 23075
MITCHELL J S 21783
MITCHELL J W 20571
MITCHELL M B 17247
MITCHELL M L 17953
MITCHELL P 15200
MITCHELL R A 8974
9794
18544
MITCHELL R E 1997
10449
MITCHELL R G 25136
MITCHELL R H 2534
MITCHELL R I 12907
MITCHELL R S 20381
MITCHELL T B 12333
MITCHELL W H 24904
MITCHELL W W 3168
MITCHENKO V P 11030
MITCHISON N A 20100
MITCHLEY B C V 2266
MITHOEFER J C 23189
MITIDIERI E 23869
MITRA D K 7143
MITRA G C 7379
MITRA S N 22647
MITRI T K 3840
MITROFANOV A M 7998
20972
MITROFANOV P I 7936
12123
MITROFANOV V S 6086
MITROFANOVA V G 9513
MITRONOVA R N 11298
MITROVIC S 1605
MITS A A 21102
MITSANYI A 19254
MITSCHER L A 23870
MITSCHERLICH G 7738
MITSKOVSKII I 20780
MITSUHASHI S 20203
MITSUI Y 10289
MITTELMAN A 9125
MITTLER T E 16807
MITYAEV I D 3530
3531
3533

20872
MIURA K 2853
MIURA N 2080
MIURA T 1594
1595
10649
MIURA Y 14137
21237
MIXTER G JR 13779
MIYA T S 23914
MIYAGI T 23871
23872
23943
23991
MIYAI K 22900
24811
24812
MIYAJI T 15556
MIYAJIMA Y 9386
MIYAKE H 17762
23873
MIYAKE T 17763
MIYAKEE T 14489
MIYAMOTO M 2101
MIYANAGA M 10445
MIYANISHI M 14786
MIYATA R 13230
MIYATA S 822
17951
23872
23991
MIYAWAKI M 25471
MIYAZAKI M 7575
18908
23873
MIYAZAKI S 17459
24203
MIYAZAKI Y 14591
23998
24114
MIYOKI T 2080
MIYOSHI Y 23792
MIZE D 1976
19092
MIZERES N J 15036
MIZIARA H 13730
MIZOCK B J 8975
MIZUNO Y 808
MIZUTANI A 22337
MIZUTANI H 15485
MKHITARYAN M A 11917
MKRTUMYAN K L 16386
MLADENOVA Z 18271
MLYNARYK P 9491
MNATSAKANOV T S 9817
MOBIUS G 2319
MOBLEY E M 10561
MOBLEY H M 7584
MOCHNACKA I 8262
MOCHRIE R D 15123
MOCK J 19111
MOCKEL S 24748
MOCZAR E 18419
MODEEN W R 17506
MODELL W 21352
MODERY M 4929
MODLIBOWSKA I 7634
MODLIN H C 14282
MODY N J 5268
MODY U 22569
MOEDE F 14352
MOELLER H C 14596
22895
MOELLER R W 7156
MOENS P B 17206
17248
MOERICKE V 11997
MOERTEL C G 19587
MOFFAT A D 6258
MOFFITT E A 15632
MOFFITT O P JR 10632
MOFTY A E 16544
MOGABGAB W J 15490
MOGAKI T 1492
MOGAMI T 17969
MOGG R A 10548
MOGHE R G 7168
MOGILEVCHIK L E 19861
MOGOSH I 10639
MOGUILEVSKY H C 1561
MOGUILEVSKY J A 12938
23319
MOHAMED A H 19955
MOHAMMAD M-B M 21048
MOHAMMAD W 16437
MOHAMMED A 19892
MOHD KHAN F 11365
MOHINDER P 20510
MOHLENBECK O 23636
MOHLENBROCK R H 7433
15865
MOHLENBROCK R 20511
MOHLER S R 17403
MOHME-LUNDHOLM E 856
857
2090
MOHNIKE G 22302
MOHONEY M C 17169
MOHR H-J 15702
MOHR J 12817
MOHR J L 12284
25284
25430
MOHR V 6572
MOHR W 7623
MOHRHAUER H 22533
MOHRI H 12584
MOHYUDDIN F 13363
MOINE G 20343
MOIR R Y 8829
MOIR T W 9571
9584
MOISAO R 9916
8417
15037
MOISEENKO F P 7739
MOISEEV A E 16409
MOISEEVA E M 11370

MOISEEVA T S 12102
MOISEICHENKO V F 20550
MOJONNIER L 13795
MOKADY R 7611
MOKAL A 24255
MOKHOV L A 8806
22204
MOKHOVA N I 20605
MOKRASCH L C 13289
MOKRIEVICH G L 7853
MOKRONOSOV A T 15884
MOLANDER D W 24160
MOLCHANOV S G 24669
MOLCHANOVA L V 5206
MOLCHANOVA V A 12500
MOLD K 9905
MOLDAVE K 13095
MOLDAVS KA S I 5724
MOLDENKE H N 7416
7417
15842
15843
20512
20513
MOLDOVANYI M 23403
MOLE-BAJER J 21492
MOLELLO J A 23440
MOLENAT M 15158
MOLENDA T 6
MOLFI A 3613
3614
MOLINA R R 22778
MOLINIER A 17764
MOLINIER R 20561
MOLINO G 22876
MOLL T 24705
MOLLARET H 2595
MOLLENHAUER H H 17170
17172
MOLLER F 6546
MOLLER G 6807
MOLLER I 25509
MOLLER T 25253
MOLLER T G H O 22170
MOLLISON B C 4003
MOLLISON P L 20052
MOLNAR F 2268
MOLNAR G 1121
2245
9636
MOLNAR G D 9544
MOLNAR L 9666
MOLNAR W 23011
MOLOMUT N 20101
24106
MOLOTKOVS KYI H 15895
MOLTHAN H D 11789
MOLTKE E 18545
MOMMAERTS W F H 726
MOMOSE K 21237
MOMOSE T 22205
MOMOT A G 2855
MOMOT Y G 11708
MOMOTOV I F 11428
MOMSTASTNY P 2737
MONACO C A F 13651
13652
13653
MONAKOV A V 3733
MONAN G E 8709
MONCADA R 5143
MONCHENKO V I 3734
4569
MONCKTON G 5594
21501
MONDER C 700
MONDON C E 22267
MONDOVI B 4711
MONDZAIN M L 10035
23545
MONEKOSSO G L 24603
MONELLO L F 4813
MONEY J 281
5871
14283
MONGE C C 25006
MONGE F S 3385
MONGIN M 14848
MONK I 13657
MONK R W 16197
MONKHOUSE F C 22481
MONLUX A W 20321
MONNE L 8221
25452
MONNEROT E 23644
MONNET 19907
MONNET J 11790
MONNIER J 14577
MONNIER M 1743
MONNIER P 17996
MONNIOT C 16618
MONOD T 3735
MONRO P 10290
MONROE C W 13985
MONROE M J 13494
MONROE R E 12501
MONROY A 3975
MONROY G 9653
9667
MONSAINGEON A 1059
14685
MONSELISE S P 16113
MONSERRAT J 13777
MONSTVILAITE Y 20693
MONSUR K A 20001
MONTAG B J 33
MONTAGNA W 1686
1696
1697
5632
5633
5634
6409
9960
MONTAGNIER L 15486
MONTALDI E R 11698
MONTANARI R 10291
MONTANO G 14772

MONTEIL H 2181
MONTEIRO E 2801
4275
6962
MONTEITH J L 11509
MONTEITH L G 25137
MONTELARO J 24970
24971
MONTEMAYOR F 8539
8553
MONTEMURRO D G 19344
MONTES M 2837
MONTESTRUC E 2802
MONTEVERDE J J 6705
MONTGOMERIE J Z 9751
MONTGOMERY D W 22721
22839
MONTGOMERY D A D 23760
MONTGOMERY H 15500
MONTGOMERY J B 18631
MONTGOMERY J A 22024
MONTGOMERY M W 13516
MONTGOMERY P O 14711
MONTGOMERY R D 5589
22579
MONTGOMERY W A 18257
MONTI A 13223
13237
MONTI F 24670
MONTI G 20387
MONTO A V 2952
MONTUORI E 10292
MONTY K J 6640
10813
MONTZKA T A 23874
MOODY I 13593
MOODY P A 124
MOOG E 23863
MOOK D G 1080
MOOKERJEA S 18049
MOOMAW C R 9330
MOON R C 5503
19417
MOONA J C 8339
MOONEN W A 5308
MOONEY C M 24649
MOONEY D P 13598
MOORE A E 24254
MOORE B 6898
MOORE B P 16842
MOORE C J 3463
MOORE C V 9157
MOORE D 13699
20168
22912
MOORE D V 15348
MOORE E J 3145
MOORE E L 1028
1032
MOORE E N 9577
9585
MOORE F D 2123
MOORE G E 2673
6168
10549
10867
MOORE H B 4471
MOORE H E JR 15811
MOORE J 15309
MOORE J C 8401
MOORE J H 19596
MOORE J J 13052
MOORE J M 2695
10907
MOORE J N 20713
20820
MOORE J W 18909
MOORE K E 19255
MOORE K M 3796
3797
MOORE L D 3462
MOORE L E 10084
MOORE M 6709
MOORE M B JR 11216
MOORE M E 13281
MOORE M H 16359
MOORE M T 19490
MOORE R A 5897
MOORE R B 9128
MOORE R C 21178
21179
MOORE R D 19379
MOORE R E 23809
MOORE R H 17672
MOORE R O 21264
25540
MOORE R T 2955
11371
MOORE R V 8912
MOORE R W 15071
MOORE S 640
687
709
4672
4728
MOORE W E C 19760
MOORE W M III 5393
MOORES R G 4821
MOORHOUSE D E 23225
MOORHOUSE J A 6013
MOORHOUSE J E 16819
MOOR-JANKOWSKI J 21647
MOORTHY B P 11439
MOOS R H 23587
MOOS W S 12939
MOOSE J W 12172
25214
MOOSE M G 5519
MORA E C 1390
MORA G 17090
MORA J 6621
MORAES M A P 11041
MORAES N 14601
MORAES W B C 16364
MORAITOPOULOU-DASSIMATI E 25550
MORALES D 9600
13637

In looking at the actual pages of a subject index, we can learn how the system works. Two pages from the subject index are shown on pages 92 and 93. On page 92, which lists the titles of articles that deal with yeasts, we find Millbank's paper listed, and its abstract number (20556) at the end of the line. You will note that the few words both *before* and *after* "yeast" are shown, so that the reader can get a good idea of what the article is about. If a scientist wanted to find out more about this paper, he would look up the abstract. There he would find the complete title, the author and his address, and the journal issue in which the paper originally appeared.

On page 93 we see another page of the subject index. In this case Millbank's article is listed under "fermentation." In the actual subject index, this article is also listed under the key words "oxidation," "sugars," and "protoplasts." A scientist interested in any of these aspects of Millbank's work would be directed to this paper by the abstract number.

The subject index to *Biological Abstracts* (called *B.A.S.I.C.* which stands for "Biological Abstracts Subjects in Context") appears twice a month. A scientist can check every paper abstracted that deals with yeast, fermentation, oxidation, or any other topic in which he is interested. This valuable aid in keeping up with recent work in science is widely used around the world.

Biological Abstracts also provides other indexes to aid the scientist. There is an author index (see page 94, which shows Millbank's name and the abstract number) which permits scientists to easily check articles written by a particular scientist. There is also a "systematic index" which lists the papers written about particular groups of organisms—protozoa, fungi, and so on.

As the scientific literature grows, the problems of abstracting and indexing all articles published becomes increasingly great. Without modern data-processing and computer techniques, such as those used by *Biological Abstracts,* it would be almost impossible to provide this important service to scientists.

Personal Records. Scientists are engaged in a continuous search for papers relating to their own work. With the help of the abstracting services, an investigator can search the literature for information about a particular topic or problem. Many different systems are used for keeping personal files of significant papers. Some scientists keep a file of titles and authors on 3″ x 5″ or 4″ x 6″ cards, alphabetized by author and date, so that they can be referred to quickly. Others have worked out a system on "punched cards," which permits them to retrieve in a short time all the papers written either by a particular person, or between certain years, or on a particular subject, and so on. Each system is quite personal, since in most cases it is designed to meet the needs of an individual scientist.

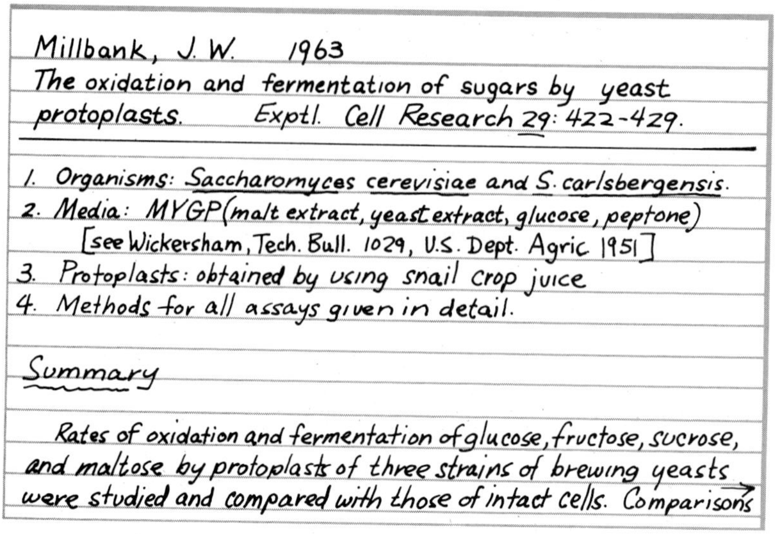

Millbank, J. W.   1963
The oxidation and fermentation of sugars by yeast
protoplasts.   Exptl. Cell Research 29: 422-429.

1. Organisms: _Saccharomyces cerevisiae_ and _S. carlsbergensis._
2. Media: MYGP (malt extract, yeast extract, glucose, peptone)
   [see Wickersham, Tech. Bull. 1029, U.S. Dept. Agric 1951]
3. Protoplasts: obtained by using snail crop juice
4. Methods for all assays given in detail.

Summary

   Rates of oxidation and fermentation of glucose, fructose, sucrose,
and maltose by protoplasts of three strains of brewing yeasts
were studied and compared with those of intact cells. Comparisons

*Figure 20   File card used to
record information about a single
scientific paper.*

Until a system to your liking is worked out, use index cards to record information about the papers you read. This method is similar to that used by many scientists and students. In Figure 20 is shown a card that a student might make if he were to come across the same paper by Millbank on yeasts that you read earlier in the chapter.

You will see that the person who made this reference card noted certain details about the organisms used, the media, and the procedures, and finally wrote a brief summary of the paper. Each person would make out a card that contained somewhat different information, depending on the interests of the individual.

It is important, at this time, to realize that the responsibility for reading in the literature and for keeping adequate records of what you have read is your own. This is the way scientists work. You can easily gain the habit of browsing through scientific journals, reading and making notes on articles of interest or relevant to work you are doing. Do not expect to be told to go to a library to read the journals. This is up to you. The value of the library depends entirely on how much use you make of it.

INVESTIGATIONS FOR FURTHER STUDY

As a rule, larger colleges and universities have extensive collections of scientific journals. Public libraries in the larger cities also subscribe to many of these journals. Smaller public libraries and high school libraries, on the other hand, may subscribe to but a few journals.

1. If possible, visit a large public library or a university library. Make a list of the journals they receive that deal with a science in general. Then list some journals dealing primarily with one or more of the biological sciences.

2. Go to the card catalog and determine how these journals are cataloged in the library.

3. In one issue of a journal, scan each paper and determine its structure. Construct a chart which compares all the articles in this one issue. Now do the same thing for an issue of an entirely different journal. Do all papers have about the same organization (structure), or is this determined in part by the journal in which they appear?

4. Listed below are the names of some of the journals which are published in foreign countries. Can you translate the titles and determine the biological subject matter with which each journal deals?

La Cellule   *Embryologia*
Zeitschrift für Botanik   *Crustaceana*
Cytologia   *Chromosoma*
Hereditas   *Insectes Sociaux*
Hydrobiologica   *Zoologischer Anzeiger*

5. In what field of science would you place each of the following journals?

The Journal of Biological Chemistry
The Bulletin of Mathematical Biophysics
Biochimica et Biophysica Acta
Journal of Molecular Biology

SUMMARY

In the preceding sections of this book we have discussed the meaning of science and the processes of biological investigation. By this time you have had considerable experience in working with these processes, and it may be profitable now to take a second look at them. With your added experience, it may be possible to grasp better the ways in which ideas and experiments interact to produce new explanations and understandings of biological phenomena. In other words, your experience can help you to understand better the way in which biological science grows.

Problems Questions which could form part of a successful experimental design occur to each of us nearly every day. Which route is the shortest distance between my home and my school? What brand of soap in our store is the most destructive to microorganisms on my skin? Which of the gasolines in my neighborhood will give the best mileage in my car over a given road test? Many of these questions you probably will leave unanswered. Science, however, if it is to progress, must constantly seek the answers to its questions.

How does the research worker select the questions which he will attempt to answer? Occasionally, he may experiment merely *to discover* whether or not something happens, with little previous experience, either of his own or of others, to guide him. More often, though, the scientist draws from previous experience with either the current or related problems in order to make an educated guess (hypothesis) that a predicted event can be confirmed by new data.

Competent research workers gain the insight necessary to make logical hypotheses through a constant study of the problems in which they are interested. This study began in some small sense on the day they were born, acquired momentum during their formal schooling, and finally approached maturity when they assumed the role of active researchers. The fascination of science is that complete mastery of knowledge is never attained. The more a scientist learns, the more he realizes how much he does not know. It is this realization, plus the desire to probe the unknown, which have paved the way for human progress.

While a laboratory investigator draws heavily upon his personal experience to frame hypotheses, an even *more important* part of his total experience is his familiarity with the knowledge of others. Knowledge of the contributions of other scientists can be gained in several ways; however, it is most important that the scientist be familiar with scientific literature, especially as it pertains to his particular problem. Perhaps someone has already answered his question. Perhaps someone asked his question before but came to a different conclusion than the one which now seems plausible. Perhaps new insights to his question can be gained by study of the experiments of others concerning related questions. Let there be no underemphasis of this point: the scientist, if he is to frame useful and effective hypotheses and avoid wasting time in testing them by collecting new data from nature or by experiments, must be familiar with the literature pertaining to his problem.

What kinds of questions can be answered or evaluated by new data which is collected? How does one frame a particular hypothesis in order that it may be most successfully tested? The common sense born of experience has shown that the most essential element of a good question for experimental design is *keeping it as simple and direct as possible.*

Suppose you intend to experiment with mileage from different gasolines. Don't ask what is the best gasoline to use in cars. To work a question
stated in this manner into an experimental design would involve the impossible task of testing all the effects of all gasolines upon all cars. Rather
decide what you want to know about gasoline and cars and stick to it. You
may, for instance, wish to ask which of the gasolines available in your
neighborhood will give the best mileage in your car at 60 miles per hour
over a given stretch of road. Now you have something you can work with.
If you wish to expand the findings of this experiment in future experiments,
you may, but keep your current question a *workable one.*

It must be stressed, however, that the simplicity of the questions which
have proven to be good ones for experimentation is a very misleading
simplicity. They are not simple in the sense that you bite off one little piece
of a problem and ignore all the other aspects that surround it. This can
only lead to unrelated little pieces of knowledge that nobody could really
consider good science.

Let us consider again the value of different gasolines for automobiles.
Of course, what you really want to know is all the different effects of all
the different gasolines upon an automobile. How much mileage you can
get from a gallon of fuel is an important aspect of this question, but you
wouldn't want to get more mileage from a gallon of fuel if that fuel was
one which burned up your engine. However, when you design experiments,
you want to break up your large question into smaller, workable ones, and
you ask each of these, one at a time. Remember, however, that the answer
to any one of these questions is only a part of the answer to the initial important question, "Which is the best gasoline?" So, in the end, what is
wanted is a way of putting all the questions and their answers together
again.

You will find many opportunities to express the questions being asked
in the remainder of the investigations in this course. Express them well.
They are the reasons for doing the experiments. Without an understanding
of its purpose, one can neither profitably design nor evaluate the results
of an experiment.

**Design of
Experiments**   It has become commonplace to consider science
and experiments reasonably close synonyms. This
is not true, for as it was pointed out earlier, many
scientists do little or no experimentation, but it is true that in most areas
of biological science today, experimentation is a major tool of the scientist.

Experimentation is a broad term that covers what scientists do in both
the field and the laboratory during the process of inquiry: asking questions,

gathering data, and evaluating these data. An experiment is not a hap-hazard trial; it is a well-planned attack on a specific problem. Experiments are designed to ask one or more questions within a framework which will yield possible answers. To design an experiment is to prepare an investigation from which data may be gathered and critically evaluated.

In former days, when modern science was just beginning, much scientific work was done in the field, where nature could be observed first hand, and, indeed, much biological work must still be done in the field. As time passed, however, it became more and more apparent that more precise measurements and more accurate observations could be made in the laboratory, because the scientific worker could then so control conditions that a comparison could be made between situations which differed in only one significant respect. That was the beginning of experimentation (the experiment of the single variable), which made possible such logical certainty in drawing a conclusion that it has become the preferred method of science wherever possible.

Conclusions. The technique of drawing conclusions from a set of data is seldom as obvious as it may seem at first. An important consideration in scientific procedure is to recognize that no results are ever completely unequivocal. No matter how closely the conditions of an experiment are controlled, variations do occur, and these variations can lead to error in the conclusions. Thus, the conclusions of the scientist must take into account the ego-deflating fact that his deductions may be wrong. To minimize this possibility, the scientist often repeats his experiments to be sure he can get similar results from trial to trial.

Often, too, the difference in the results from the control and the treated specimens may be small, causing one to wonder if a difference actually exists or if the apparent difference is just chance variation between the two samples. These problems in drawing conclusions have been greatly alleviated by the techniques of data analysis developed by statisticians.

If the data obtained are adequate, the scientist may be able to discard his hypothesis or to say that the data are consistent with it. It may never be possible to *prove* a hypothesis, but, at least until other data indicate that we should not do so, we may *accept* the hypothesis. Then we can look for another which may be a refinement of the earlier hypothesis, or one which combines several hypotheses. More data may be necessary for the proper evaluation of this new hypothesis. It may call for a new experiment, and thus the cycle continues, not as a circle, but as a spiral, leading to greater and greater understanding of nature.

PART TWO EXPERIMENTS
AND IDEAS IN BIOLOGICAL
INVESTIGATIONS

GROWTH AND INTERACTIONS
OF POPULATIONS

SECTION NINE

POPULATION DYNAMICS

Study of Populations by the Use of Microbes

Unicellular forms of life are convenient for studying population growth. Each cell division results directly in an increase in the population of individuals, and many cells reproduce themselves every few hours or even every few minutes. Such short generation times permit the production of millions or billions of individuals in a few hours or days.

Numerical changes in populations are *best* estimated by actually counting the individuals in a population at different times. The sociologist often does this by measuring the population growth of a country over ten-year intervals. This information is available from the national census. From these data, he can plot a population growth curve such as that seen in Figure 21. Understanding the nature of this curve helps the sociologist make certain hypotheses about future populations: what their needs will be, and how these needs may be met.

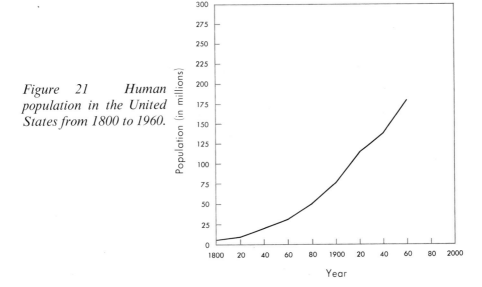

Figure 21 Human population in the United States from 1800 to 1960.

Microbiologists use two methods of counting the individuals in a population. The choice is determined by whether one wishes to measure only *viable* microbes (those which are able to reproduce) or all the organisms in the culture (both *viable* and *nonviable*). The inability to reproduce is, in practice, the criterion by which microbes are said to be "dead."

Viable microbes may be counted by distributing a suspension of the organism in a suitable liquefied agar culture medium. When the agar hardens, each of these microscopic individuals is then separated in space by the agar. During incubation, each of the viable microbes produces enough cells to form a visible colony. Each colony is then assumed to have originated from a single viable cell. Of course, the nonviable cells fail to reproduce in the agar, and therefore cannot be detected.

The individuals in a microbial population can also be counted by direct microscopic observation of the culture. Most methods of direct microscopic counting of the cells in a microbial suspension measure *both* viable and nonviable cells. Hence, a direct microscopic enumeration of microbes is sometimes called the "total count." Ideally, then, the difference between the total count and the viable count would equal the nonviable count. The curve obtained by plotting the increase of a population of microbes during its growth will differ, depending on the technique used for counting.

Understanding the growth of populations is simplified if the mathematics of their growth is understood. The growth of microbes can demonstrate the application of these mathematics to population growth in general.

Exponential or Logarithmic Growth. A microbial cell grows to a certain size and divides to become 2 cells; the 2 new cells repeat this process to become 4; the 4 become 8, and so on. Each doubling of the population by cell division is known as a *generation* of the microbe. During periods of maximum growth, the time required for each successive doubling of a population remains constant; this time is called the *generation time.*

Since the population doubles with each generation, its numbers can be expressed by exponents of the number 2. Thus, 1 cell can be expressed as 2^0 cells, 2 cells can be written as 2^1 cells, 4 cells as 2^2 cells, and so on. Such progressions in populations are called *exponential growth,* or *logarithmic growth.*

Table 11 illustrates exponential growth during the development of a population from a single microbe with a generation time of one hour. Note the following four points in this table:

(1) The time between successive generations (generation time) is constant during exponential growth.

(2) With each generation the population doubles. Compare the constant factor of increase in *geometric progressions*—1, 2, 4, 8, 16, and so on—with the constant difference of increase in *arithmetic progressions* —2, 4, 6, 8, 10, and so on.

(3) Exponents may also be expressed as *logarithms.* A logarithm is an exponent to which power a fixed base must be raised in order to yield

TABLE 11.   **Exponential Growth of Microorganisms**

Population age (hours)	0	1	2	3	4	5	6	7	$n*$
Population growth	o →	o o →	oo oo →	oooo oooo →	oooo oooo oooo oooo oooo →	etc. →	→	→	
Actual number of cells	1	2	4	8	16	32	64	128	x
Number of generations	0	1	2	3	4	5	6	7	n
Number of cells expressed as powers of 2	2^0	2^1	2^2	2^3	2^4	2^5	2^6	2^7	2^n
Number of cells expressed as logarithms of the base 2	0	1	2	3	4	5	6	7	n

* In this example we are assuming that the generation time is 1 hour. As a result, the population age in hours is equal to the number of generations; x = number of cells in n generations. For example, the logarithm to the base 2 of 16 is 4; that is, the base 2 must be raised to the 4th power (2^4) to equal 16. "The logarithm to the base 2 of 16 is 4" may be stated in shorthand as follows: $\log_2 16 = 4$.

a certain number. Since microbes double with each generation, a handy base to use with our table is 2. This relationship may be expressed mathematically as:

$$\log_2 x = n \text{ (read as "log to the base 2}$$
$$\text{of } x \text{ equals } n\text{")}$$
$$\text{where } x = \text{actual number of cells produced}$$
$$\text{in } n \text{ generations, and}$$
$$n = \text{the number of generations.}$$

(4) The number of generations (n) between any two measurements in an exponentially growing population is the difference between the exponents of the two measurements. By following the arrows, it can be seen that it took two generations for 4 cells to become 16 cells. Quick

arithmetic shows that the difference in exponents of $4 = 2^2$ and $16 = 2^4$ is $4 - 2$, or 2. In like manner, the number of generations which occurred between 8 or 2^3 cells and 128 or 2^7 cells is $n = 7 - 3 = 4$.

Logarithms and the Calculation of Growth. Since logarithms are also exponents, the number of generations can also be computed by the difference in logarithms to the base 2. Using the data of the last problem,

$$n = \log_2 128 - \log_2 8$$
$$\log_2 128 = 7 \text{ and } \log_2 8 = 3$$
$$n = 7 - 3 = 4 \text{ generations between 8 cells and 128 cells.}$$

This relationship between logarithms and the number of generations can be expressed as a generalized mathematical formula. If B is the number of microbes present after a certain period of exponential growth, and b is the number present at an earlier age of the population, then

$$\text{number of generations} = n = \log_2 B - \log_2 b.$$

The logarithms to the base 2 of the foregoing examples can be computed mentally; however, it would be helpful to have a table of logarithms for any number. Tables for $\log_2$ are not readily available, but fortunately there are tables for logarithms to the base 10 ($\log_{10}$). Logarithms based upon 10 are called common logarithms. A biologist can convert from $\log_{10}$ to $\log_2$ if he is familiar with common logarithms.

A logarithm usually is not a whole number; rather, it consists of two parts: an integer, called the *characteristic,* and a decimal, called the *mantissa.* To find the logarithm of a number, we determine the characteristic by noting the position of the number's decimal point. The following are three rules for determining the characteristic of a logarithm:

(1) If the decimal point of a number immediately follows its first digit, the characteristic of its log is 0. Thus, the characteristic of the log of any number from 1 to 10, but not including 10, is 0.

(2) If the decimal point appears after the second digit, the characteristic of its log is 1; if it appears after three digits, it is 2; if it appears after four digits, it is 3, and so on. Thus, the characteristic of 711.58 is 2.

(3) If the decimal appears immediately before the first non-zero digit, the characteristic of its log is -1, usually written $\bar{1}$; if there is one zero between the decimal point and the first digit, the characteristic is $\bar{2}$, and so on. Hence, the characteristic of 0.008 is $\bar{3}$.

Using common logs, state the characteristics of the following numbers:

a. 100
b. 274
c. 1000
d. 0.4790
e. 7,456,132
f. 0.000002
g. 8.561
h. 0.0479

In this list, the characteristic of the logs of both 100 and 274 is 2; the characteristic of the $\log_{10}$ 1000 is 3. Note that the exponential expression 10^2 exactly equals 100 and that 10^3 exactly equals 1000, but that neither the digit 2 nor the digit 3 can alone express the logarithm (exponent), to the base 10, which represents 274. This logarithm is a number somewhere between 2 and 3 and is expressed as 2 plus a decimal. This decimal is called the mantissa of the logarithm.

Therefore, a logarithm is incomplete until its mantissa is determined. This is done most easily by consulting the table of common logarithms in Appendix F. The first two digits of the number for which you want to find the mantissa are listed in the left-hand column; the third digit is listed in the top horizontal column.

As an example of how the logarithm of a number is found, follow through the calculation of the common logarithm of 274.

$$\text{characteristic of } 274 = 2$$
$$\text{mantissa} = .4378 \text{ (found in the table at the}$$
$$\text{junction of the row for the}$$
$$\text{number ``27'' with the column}$$
$$\text{for the number ``4'')}$$
$$\log_{10} 274 = 2.4378 \text{ or in exponential terms,}$$
$$10^{2.4378} = 274$$

Our second example will be to calculate the log of 1,378,000. You may have some difficulty in finding the logarithm of this number. Notice that 1,378,000 lies between 1,370,000 and 1,380,000. The logarithm we wish to find lies somewhere between the logarithms of these two numbers in our table. We will adopt the convention of rounding our numbers off to 3 significant digits before finding the logarithm. (There are methods of finding the logarithm more accurately, but we do not need this much accuracy for our data.) To find the logarithm of 1,378,000 we would first round off to 3 significant digits (1,380,000), and then look in the tables where we would find the logarithm 6.1399.

PROBLEM

What is the logarithm of 0.00458?

    The table of logarithms can also be used to convert a logarithm to its original number. The original number is called the *antilogarithm.* As an example, find the antilogarithm of $\bar{2}.6812$. The logarithm table shows that the mantissa (0.6812) represents the digits 480. The characteristic is $\bar{2}$, so the antilogarithm of $\bar{2}.6812$ is 0.0480. Expressed as a power of 10, $10^{\bar{2}.6812}$ is 0.0480.

    Suppose we were asked to find the antilogarithm of $\bar{2}.6818$. We can determine that our antilog lies between 0.0480 and 0.0481, but $\bar{2}.6818$ is closer to the logarithm of 0.0481 than it is to the logarithm of 0.0480. The value 0.6818 is only .0003 from the logarithm of 0.0481, while it is 0.006 from the logarithm of 0.0480. Therefore, we shall take as the antilog the value 0.0481. As stated before, it is possible to get a more accurate value, but this is not considered necessary for our purposes.

PROBLEM

What is the antilog of 6.9243? of $\bar{4}.7634$?

    We can use our knowledge of logarithms and antilogarithms in a handy method for doing multiplication and division. As an example, consider a procedure for finding the product of 100 and 100,000. We could write 100 as 10^2 and 100,000 as 10^5. Therefore, $\log_{10} 100 = 2$ and $\log_{10} 100,000 = 5$. We know that $10^2 \cdot 10^5 = (10 \cdot 10) (10 \cdot 10 \cdot 10 \cdot 10 \cdot 10) = 10^{2+5} = 10^7$. Notice that we have added the exponents of our factors to get the exponent of our product. Because these exponents are logarithms, we have actually added the two logarithms to get the logarithm of our product. Finally, if we can find out what number is represented by 10^7—in other words, what number has a logarithm of 7 when the base is 10—we will have our answer. This is exactly what we have done above, except that this time we do not need a table to determine that the number which is the antilogarithm of 7 is 10,000,000.

    Using a similar argument, we could show that division involves the subtraction of logarithms. Carefully review the following two rules:

(1) To multiply, add the logs of the numbers, and take the antilog of this sum. Thus, to multiply 339×864, add $\log_{10} 339$ to $\log_{10} 864$; the antilog of this sum is the product of 399×864. Compute the answer.

(2) To divide, subtract the logs of the numbers, and find the antilog of this difference. Thus, to divide 2557 by 450, round 2557 to 2560 and

then subtract $\log_{10}$ 450 from $\log_{10}$ 2560; the antilog of this difference will be the quotient. Compute the answer.

A knowledge of logarithms permits one to perform computations involving the logarithmic nature of growth. You will observe this phenomenon in the next Investigation. To illustrate, use 10 as a base to find the answer to the following problem.

Suppose a culture starts with 10 cells/ml which reproduce without interruption until 1,000,000 cells/ml are present. How many generations (n) will have elapsed? Remember from the previous discussion of generations that n may be expressed by:

$$n = \log_2 B - \log_2 b$$
$$B = 1{,}000{,}000 \text{ and } b = 10$$

Remember also, however, that from generation to generation, microbes double rather than increase by a factor of 10. Thus, we must convert our common logs to $\log_2$. To do this, we divide the common logs by $\log_{10}$ 2.

As another illustration, consider the following problem. Suppose B represents the total number of cells present at a given time all having originated from a single cell. If we can determine the exponent of 2 so that $B = 2^n$, then, as before, n is the number of generations required to produce B cells. Therefore, we must devise a method for finding n if we know B.

If $B = 2^n$, then certainly $\log_{10} B = \log_{10} 2^n$, because if two numbers are equal they can both be represented by 10 raised to the same power. For example, suppose $B = 10^{2.3142}$. If $B = 2^n$, then 2^n would also have to be equal to $10^{2.3142}$. In other words, their logarithms to the base 10 are equal. For our next step we will show that $\log_{10} 2^n = n \cdot \log_{10} 2$. To do this, first look at $\log_{10} 2^3$. Recall that $\log_{10} 2 = .3010$; that is, $10^{.3010} = 2$. We can then write 2^3 as $(10^{.3010})^3$, but $(10^{.3010})^3 = 10^{.9030}$. (Recall from algebra that $(2^3)^4 = 2^{12}$, and so on.)

We now have $2^3 = 10^{.9030}$, or in other words, $\log_{10} 2^3 = .9030$. Since $\log_{10} 2 = .3010$, we observe that $\log_{10} 2^3 = 3 \log_{10} 2$. This is a *specific* example, but it is *always* true that $\log_{10} 2^n = n \cdot \log_{10} 2$.

We have previously shown that if $B = 2^n$, then $\log_{10} B = \log_{10} 2^n$. We can now state that $\log_{10} B = n \cdot \log_{10} 2$. Dividing both sides of the equation by $\log_{10} 2$, we have

$$\frac{\log_{10} B}{\log_{10} 2} = n$$

where n is the number of generations. This is the method we will use to find the number of generations (n) if we know the number of cells present (B) at a given time.

For example, suppose we start with a single cell. How many generations will have elapsed when we have 10,000,000 cells? We want to express

10,000,000 as 2^n where n is the number of generations. As we explained,

$$\frac{\log_{10} 10,000,000}{\log_{10} 2} = n.$$

$\log_{10} 10,000,000 = 7.0000$ and $\log_{10} 2 = .3010$ so that,

$$\frac{\log_{10} 10,000,000}{\log_{10} 2} = \frac{7.0000}{.3010} = 23.3 \text{ generations.}$$

Of course, .3 generations is meaningless since generations are represented by whole numbers.

Apply this reasoning to another problem. Suppose a culture begins with 10 cells/ml and reproduces without interruption until 1,000,000 cells/ml are present. How many generations (n) will have elapsed?

Remember that n may be expressed as

$$n = \log_2 B - \log_2 b$$

where
$$B = 1,000,000 \text{ and}$$
$$b = 10.$$

Now,
$$\log_2 B = \frac{\log_{10} B}{\log_{10} 2} \text{ and } \log_2 b = \frac{\log_{10} b}{\log_{10} 2}$$

therefore,
$$n = \frac{\log_{10} B}{\log_{10} 2} - \frac{\log_{10} b}{\log_{10} 2} = \frac{\log_{10} B - \log_{10} b}{\log_{10} 2}$$

$$n = \frac{\log_{10} 1,000,000 - \log_{10} 10}{\log_{10} 2}$$

$$= \frac{6.0000 - 1.0000}{.3010} = \frac{5.0000}{.3010}$$

$$= 16.6 \text{ generations}$$

The *growth rate* of the population is a measure of its increase in numbers during a given time and can be expressed as $r = \frac{n}{t}$, where r is the growth rate, n is the number of generations, and t is the time required to produce that number of generations. The time required for the population to produce a new generation is called the *generation time* (g) and can be expressed by:

$$g = \frac{\text{total time between } B \text{ and } b}{\text{number of generations between } B \text{ and } b}$$

If in our example the lapsed time between 10 and 1,000,000 cells was 10 hours, then

$$g = \frac{10}{16.6} = 0.6 \text{ hour, or 36 minutes.}$$

In other words, this population doubled in number every 36 minutes.

Its growth rate is $r = \dfrac{16.6}{10}$ or 1.66 generations per hour.

Plotting the Microbial Growth Curve. Now consider the graph of a microbial population of 100 microbes having a generation time of 1 hour and immediately starting to multiply by cell division. The graph of this population may be plotted by using the actual number of organisms (y-axis) as a function of culture age (x-axis). However, as the plot in Figure 22A shows, the actual number of microbes soon attains immense values requiring a huge sheet of graph paper for accurate plotting. More important, the population increase is really not a direct arithmetic function of culture age. The resulting line is a curve rather than a straight line.

Figure 22A and B   Comparison of plots of microbial growth using arithmetic and logarithmic scales to express the number of individual organisms.

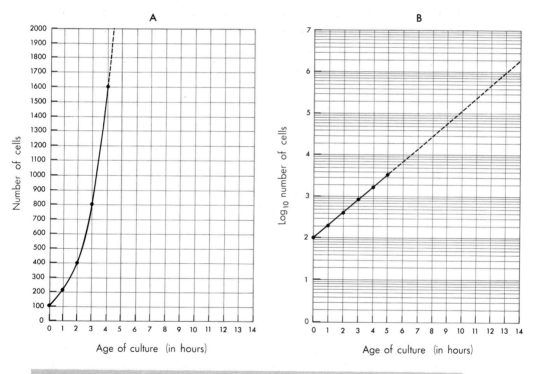

Age of culture (hours)	0	1	2	3	4	5
Number of cells (A)	100	200	400	800	1600	3200
Log_{10} (Number of cells) (B)	2.00	2.30	2.60	2.90	3.20	3.51

However, population growth will become a straight-line function of culture age if the data are plotted on a semi-logarithmic graph. In this graph, the population is plotted by logarithms of the number of organisms (see Figure 22B), while the culture age remains on an arithmetic scale. By the proper scaling of these logarithms, enormous numbers of individuals may be plotted on ordinary semi-logarithmic graphing paper. By extrapolation, it can be seen that up to 10,000,000 (or 10^7) organisms involving 14 generations can be plotted on semi-log graph paper. The arithmetic scale, on the other hand, will not permit us to graph even the fifth generation of 3200 organisms.

Characteristics of the Microbial Growth Curve. Population growth cannot continue indefinitely. It is limited by space, food, and other factors. A "typical" microbial culture develops in a way remarkably similar to other expanding populations of living things. Figure 23 shows the rise and fall of a population of microbes in a defined environment.

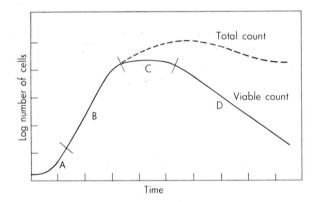

Figure 23   Idealized microbial growth curves as determined by viable and total counts of the same population.

Some rather definite phases (A, B, C, and D) can be recognized in this idealized plot of the growth curve. Do not be surprised if your results fail to reproduce this plot exactly. If deviations from this "typical" growth curve are found, they will be understood better by a recognition of those factors which influence population development.

First, note Phase A. This period, called the *lag* period, is often found in populations. It appears before newly developing populations enter into the period of logarithmic (exponential) growth (Phase B). One explanation for the static lag period is that the cells must adjust to their new environment before division begins. Perhaps new enzymes must be synthesized before growth occurs. Another explanation for the lag phase in certain cases is that a mutant cell is naturally selected from the population at large as the dominant organism of the culture. In this case, most of the cells inoculated at the beginning (zero time), fail to reproduce in the new environment of the culture medium, while the mutant strain may be highly successful. Some investigators suggest that although cell division may lag in Phase A, syntheses of several important constituents in the individual cells do occur at this time. Thus, individual cells may grow during the lag period, but there is little or no increase in the number of individual organisms.

Now note Phase B in Figure 23. This is the exponential or logarithmic *growth* phase. It represents the time during culture development when a constant rate of increase in the number of microorganisms is maintained. Nearly all the cells are viable and reproducing. This constant increase in numbers of individuals per unit of time eventually leads to the maximum population of the culture. When sufficiently large numbers of microbes have accumulated, food shortages, lack of space, the accumulation of toxic products, and so on, cause the population to enter the next phase.

Phase C is known as the *maximum stationary* phase of a culture. A population may remain in this phase for some time. Note that the total count (viable plus nonviable cells) continues to increase beyond the beginning of the stationary growth phase for viable cells. The explanation for this is that the production of new cells in the viable-cell curve is counterbalanced by the death of old cells.

Phase D is called the *death* phase. The ratio of viable to nonviable cells becomes less and less. The death rate, like the logarithmic growth rate, attains a constant value. Later, the curve for the death phase may undergo considerable change. Mutant cells, resistant to the harmful effects of the old environment, may appear and give rise to new populations. Old cells may disintegrate, causing the total count and the viable count to decrease. On the other hand, the products of cell breakdown may serve as the substrate for forming new cells. (Watch for these phenomena when plotting your results for Investigation 8 which deals with the growth of a yeast population, *Saccharomyces cerevisiae*.)

PROBLEMS

1. Starting with one bacterium with a generation time of one hour and assuming that all cells remain viable, how many individuals would be present after 24 hours? after 4 days? Express these numbers of cells as exponents of 2.
2. Assume that an increase in the temperature of incubation for the culture described in question 1 reduced the generation time to 30 minutes. How would this affect your answers to the question?

3. Examine the following family of curves demonstrating parts of the growth curves from four cultures, A, B, C, and D.

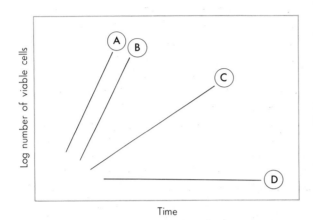

Figure 24   Family of growth curves.

   Which of the following statements are correct and which ones are incorrect? Give the reasons for your answers.

a. Culture A has a more rapid rate of growth (generation time) than does Culture C.

b. Culture A has a more rapid rate of growth than does Culture B.

c. Culture D may be in either the initial lag or maximum stationary phases of the growth curve.

d. Cultures A and C will both attain the same populations in the maximum stationary phase.

e. Cultures A, B, and C are each in the logarithmic phase of growth.

Microbial Methods and Techniques

Biologists had to solve many problems in order to grow microbes for study in the laboratory. One such problem was the nutritional requirements of bacteria. Different sorts of organisms require different foods. You would not think of feeding the same food to a fish, a dog, and a cow; each requires a special food. The different species of microbes are just as demanding in their nutritional requirements: some will grow in a medium containing simple inorganic molecules; others require complex organic molecules for growth.

   Culturing Microorganisms. If a pinch of soil and all the substances needed for growth of microbes were placed in a container, the result would be a tremendous hodgepodge of species. Many kinds of bacteria, yeasts, and molds would grow and form colonies, and it would be impossible to learn much about any single species. Serious work in microbiology was difficult until methods were developed for growing a single species in pure culture.

During the earlier career of Louis Pasteur (Figure 25) and German microbiologist Robert Koch (Figure 26), it was difficult to obtain pure cultures. The standard practice was to grow microbes in a culture solution containing all the substances necessary for their growth. When Pasteur was interested in the microbes involved in wine production, he would place a tiny drop of wine in a culture solution. The original drop would frequently contain more than one species of microbe. It was difficult, therefore, to obtain a pure culture.

The problem of separating one species of microbe from its neighbors so that it could be grown in pure culture was finally solved in the laboratories of Robert Koch. Koch and several other biologists discovered that a solid, rather than a liquid culture medium, could be used to isolate pure cultures of microbes. As is often the case in science, the discoveries of Koch and his group were based on the observations of another investigator, Karl Schroeter.

In 1872, Schroeter noted that bacteria would grow on the surface of several materials such as that of a cut potato. The bacteria formed large masses, called *colonies*. When these individual colonies were examined under a microscope, each was found to consist of great numbers of indi-

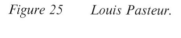

Figure 25   Louis Pasteur.

Figure 26   Robert Koch.

viduals. More important, however, all organisms in a single colony were usually of the same species. Apparently single cells had landed on the surface of the potato and had then multiplied into millions of cells. These colonies thus became visible to the naked eye, and because all the individuals in a single colony were derived from one cell, they formed a pure culture.

Koch then tried spreading dilute suspensions of several species of microbes over a solid culture medium. The individual cells would stick at different locations on the surface, and the invisible single cells would start to multiply. Eventually, as Schroeter had noted, millions of cells resulted to produce a colony from each original cell. Each colony was a pure culture.

Koch, however, was dissatisfied. The potato is not an adequate food for all species of microbes; in fact, only a few kinds will grow on a slice of potato. The potato slice had another serious disadvantage: it was difficult to keep sterile. When it was sliced, microbes from the knife, or even from the air, would become attached to its surface. These, too, would grow and form colonies. One could not be sure whether the colonies came from accidental contamination of the potato or from the microbes placed on the potato by the investigator. It was necessary, therefore, to develop a culture medium that would (1) have all the substances necessary for the growth of microbes, and (2) be sterile.

Koch had already made a culture medium known as *nutrient broth.* His nutrient broth contained meat extract and partially hydrolyzed protein (peptone). These products served as sources of amino acids, vitamins, carbohydrates, and other essential nutrients. To solidify the broth he added gelatin. Then he boiled the mixture in order to kill any microbes that were present.

To solidify the liquid mixture, Koch poured it into sterile, specially constructed dishes, known as *petri dishes* or *petri plates,* so named because one of Koch's students, Petri, designed them. Each half of a petri dish is a round, flat-bottomed glass dish with vertical sides. The culture medium is poured into the bottom half of the dish; the other half serves as a lid to prevent microbes in the air from getting on the culture medium. The closed dishes can be sterilized by heating in an oven or sterilizer.

Koch's nutrient medium contained materials necessary for the growth of many species of microbes. It was also possible to keep the medium sterile. He could smear microbes across the medium, a process known as *streaking.* The streaking separated individual cells, and from each cell produced a pure colony.

Koch discovered, however, that gelatin has its disadvantages. It melts at 28°C; this is below the best temperature for the growth of many microbes. In addition, many microbes synthesize an enzyme, *gelatinase,* which digests gelatin, causing the medium to liquefy. Whenever the medium liquefied, the separate, pure colonies would run together and mix.

It required the experience of Frau Hesse, the wife of one of Koch's students, to solve Koch's problems with gelatin. On her suggestion, Koch replaced gelatin with an extract of seaweed known as *agar.* Agar proved to be ideal for the special purpose of making a solid culture medium. It is attacked by only a few microbial species, and, in a solid state, it does not soften until it reaches a temperature of about 90°C. Liquid agar does not solidify until it is cooled to 42°C. The fact that it remains liquid until cooled to this temperature makes possible a refinement of the methods of obtaining pure cultures. Instead of streaking mixed cultures to isolate pure ones, the researcher can mix the culture with melted, but cooled, agar and pour the mixture into sterile petri dishes. When the agar sets, the individual bacteria are trapped at different locations in the agar where they develop into separate colonies.

Today, the pure culture techniques of Koch are still used in microbiology laboratories. When cultivating microbes in the laboratory, microbiologists still use his old but completely adequate techniques. Koch was the first scientist to demonstrate convincingly that a particular disease is produced by infection with a specific bacterium. He could never have done this without first having developed a method of obtaining pure cultures.

When it became possible to grow microorganisms in pure culture, it also became possible to observe the effects of the environment (the physical and chemical surroundings) on the growth of microbes. Not all species of microbes were able to grow in the first medium developed by Koch. It was found that if different substances were added to the medium, different species would be able to grow. One species might grow well on a medium that contained only a few types of molecules; another species might require a medium with many kinds of molecules.

Other environmental conditions similarly affect each microorganism's ability to grow and multiply. Some species grow best at 20°C and others at 30°C. Some require acid conditions; others require basic conditions. Some need oxygen; others do not.

Laboratory Rules. The microbial attributes of small size and rapid reproduction are an advantage to the researcher who is using these organisms to study populations of living things. These attributes are, however, also of advantage to the microbe and help explain its success in the world. A trifling inoculation with microbes, inconspicuous though it may be at the start, may cause serious infections to develop.

If work with microbes is to proceed successfully and safely, the general rules which apply to all laboratory work (see page 14) must be carefully followed. A few additional rules which apply to the investigations in this section are:

1. *Never lay contaminated and used equipment (pipettes, inoculating loops, and so on) on desk tops—use pipette jars, trays, or other provided receptacles.*
2. *If a living culture is spilled, immediately notify the instructor and then disinfect your hands and the contaminated table area. (A 2% aqueous Lysol solution is convenient for this purpose.)*
3. *Liquid waste, agar, and contaminated materials should be discarded in special containers.*

Transfer of Agar Cultures. Before agar slant cultures of living organisms are used, each person should practice the following manipulations several times. Instead of using the culture of *Bacillus subtilis* suggested in step 1, use two sterile slants. Make a transfer from one tube to the other as if you were actually inoculating the second tube from the first. After using these sterile slants, incubate them for 3 days and observe. If any growth occurs, your techniques were not aseptic.

To transfer live cultures, use the operations that are outlined in the following steps and illustrated in Figure 27.

1. Hold the test tube containing an agar slant culture of *B. subtilis* and a tube containing a sterile agar slant in your left hand. Hold the inoculating loop in your right hand.

2. Heat the transfer loop in the burner until it glows orange. Allow it to cool for a period of approximately 30 seconds.

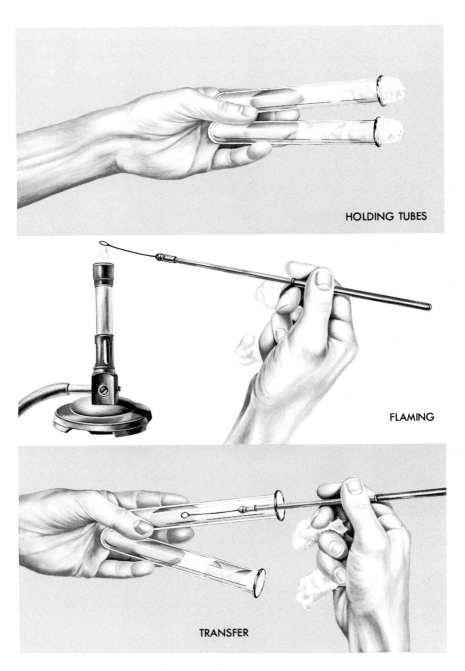

HOLDING TUBES

FLAMING

TRANSFER

Figure 27   Aseptic transfer techniques.

3. While the loop is cooling, open both test tubes by placing the plugs between the fingers of the right hand. Flame the mouths of the test tubes by passing them slowly through the flame 3 times.

4. Remove a small bit of bacterial growth from the surface of the agar culture and transfer it immediately to the surface of the sterile nutrient agar. Do not dig into the agar surfaces. The pressure of the needle is sufficient to remove and to apply the inoculum.

5. Flame the needle again and pass the mouths of the test tubes through the flame as before.

6. Replace the cotton plugs and stand the test tubes up in the rack provided for this purpose.

7. This transfer practice may be repeated using a tube of sterile nutrient *broth* and another tube of nutrient *broth* containing a culture of the bacterium, *B. subtilis.*

8. Incubate your culture for 48 hours at either 22°C or room temperature and observe it for growth.

Volumetric Transfer of Broth Cultures. A pipette will be used to transfer a known volume of a liquid culture of *B. subtilis* to a tube of sterile nutrient broth. Use the following procedure:

1. Unwrap a sterile 1.0 ml pipette. Take care that the 2 or 3 inches nearest the tip touches nothing that is not sterile. Hold the pipette between your thumb and second finger. This will leave your index finger free for easy manipulation over the end of the pipette (see Figure 28). Practice drawing up and measuring quantities of pure water before proceeding.

2. In your left hand, hold the tube of broth which you have just inoculated and a tube of sterile broth. Take a sterile pipette in your right hand.

3. Open both test tubes as you did when transfers were made with a loop. Flame the mouths of the test tubes by passing them through the flame 3 times.

4. Insert the sterile end of the pipette into the inoculated broth culture. Use *careful* mouth suction to fill the pipette to the 1.0 ml mark. Remove the end of the pipette from the inoculated broth to a position about 1 inch above the surface of the sterile broth. Keep your index finger firmly over the end of the pipette so that *no dripping occurs.*

5. Aseptically allow 0.1 ml of the inoculated culture to fall on the surface of the medium in the tube of sterile broth.

6. Immediately place the pipette and its remaining contents into a disposal cylinder containing 2% aqueous Lysol.

Figure 28 *Proper method of* holding the pipette.

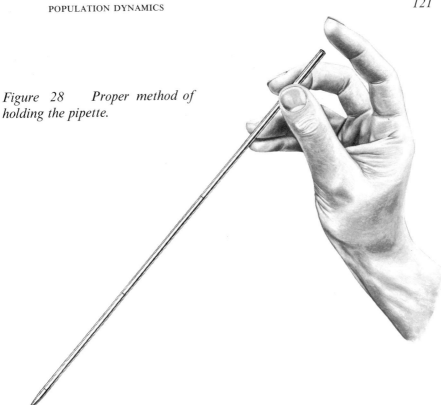

7. Flame the mouths of the test tubes and replace the cotton plugs. Stand both tubes of inoculated broth in the rack provided for this purpose.

8. Incubate cultures at room temperature or 37°C for 48 hours and observe for growth.

The Hemocytometer. A direct census of microbes in a given volume of liquid must necessarily be taken by microscopic examination. A common device for providing known small volumes of fluid for microscopic examination is the counting chamber or *hemocytometer* (so-called because it was developed originally for counting cells in the blood). The counting chamber is a microscope slide with regularly ruled chambers, each holding a known volume of liquid. A glass cover is placed over the slide before counting.

By counting the cells in samples of known volumes taken from a culture of a known volume, the population of the whole culture or any part thereof can be estimated. To justify such estimates, every effort must be made to be sure that the tiny volumes which are being counted are random samples of the larger culture volumes.

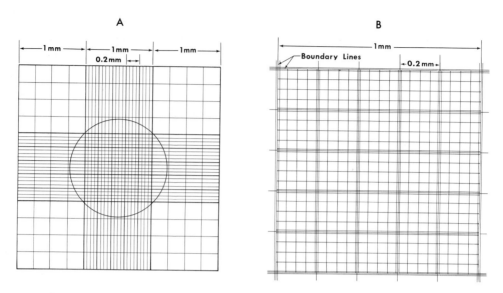

Figure 29A and B   *Two views of the rulings in the counting chamber.*

The figures show two views of the rulings in the counting chamber. Figure 29A shows the entire ruled area of the chamber. Note that it consists essentially of nine squares of one square millimeter (mm²) each. Each of these is subdivided into smaller units. Only one complete square millimeter area can be observed at a time in the low power (100×) field of your microscope. Such an area is indicated by the circle on Figure 29A. Since many of the populations of yeast and fungal spores you are to count will be counted in this center area, we should concentrate on it for a moment.

Figure 29B shows an enlargement of the rulings of the center, large square. Note that this 1 mm² area is subdivided into 25 squares which are 0.2 mm on a side (0.04 mm² in area). With these pictures clearly in mind, examine the counting chambers with the 100-power lens system of the microscope. Note the squares and rulings as outlined in Figures 29A and B.

Each large square has an area of 1 mm²; however, counting techniques are concerned with the number of individuals in a given volume rather than in a given area. The problem, then, is how can we calculate the volume of a liquid over a flat area of a known size? To do this, the third dimension must be considered—the depth of the liquid over the ruled area. The distance between the bottom of the counting chamber and the cover glass overlaying the chamber determines the depth, which in this case is 0.1 mm. The volume (length times width times depth) of a single large square can now be calculated as $1.0 \times 1.0 \times 0.1 = 0.1 \text{ mm}^3$.

Counts of microorganisms are commonly recorded as the number of individuals per cubic centimeter (also cm^3, cc, or ml). To estimate the number of cells per cm^3 from those present in a counted sample of 0.1 mm^3, one must know how many 0.1 mm^3 there are in 1 cm^3. Remember, $1 \text{ cm} = 10 \text{ mm}$, or, stated in another way, $1 \text{ mm} = 0.1 \text{ cm}$. The 1 mm^2 area of the large squares can then be converted to cm^2 as follows:

$$1 \text{ mm}^2 = 1 \text{ mm} \times 1 \text{ mm} = 0.1 \text{ cm} \times 0.1 \text{ cm} = .01 \text{ cm}^2$$

Next, to obtain the volume in cm^3 of the area represented by a large square, one may convert its depth of 0.1 mm to 0.01 cm. Then the volume represented by a large square becomes, as before, length times width times depth, or

$$0.1 \text{ cm} \times 0.1 \text{ cm} \times 0.01 \text{ cm} = 0.0001 \text{ cm}^3$$
$$= (1/10,000 \text{ cm}^3)$$

Thus, if the number of organisms in one large square is counted, the number in 1.0 cm^3 of the culture can be estimated by multiplying the count by $10,000$. Figure 30 compares the volume of 1 mm^3 with that of 1 cm^3.

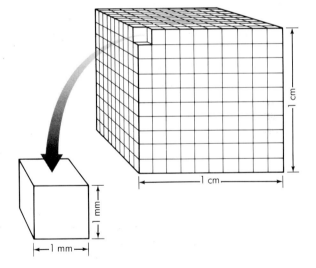

Figure 30   A comparison of the volume of a one-millimeter cube with that of a one-centimeter cube.

As an example, suppose that 210 yeast cells were counted in the large center square. Expressed in numbers of cells per cm^3, the original population contains,

$$210 \times 10,000 = 2,100,000 \text{ cells per cm}^3,$$

or, expressed as an exponential quantity, 2.10×10^6 cells per cm^3.

You should count about 200 to 300 cells in a specified area in order to obtain a reasonably accurate count. Some cultures will be populations which do not contain 200 to 300 cells in a single large square. In these cases, the other large squares or the smaller squares may be used to count volumes with approximately 200 to 300 cells.

Counting the Cells in a Yeast Suspension. Use the following steps for practice in counting:

1. Shake an aqueous suspension of yeast cells well and, before it settles, use a sterile pipette to remove 0.1 cc of the suspension.

2. Replace the first two drops of this suspension from the pipette into the original suspension. Work rapidly but carefully.

3. Immediately transfer enough of the cell suspension from the pipette to the counting chamber so that no air bubbles are formed. If air bubbles are formed, remove the cover glass and wash the slide before repeating the procedure.

4. Mount the counting chamber on your microscope and observe it under low power.

5. After the lines of the counting slide are in focus, find the large center square in your microscopic field and reduce the light until the small, oval, yeast cells are in focus.

6. When you start counting the cells in the large center square, use as a guide not the smallest but the medium-sized squares (0.2 mm × 0.2 mm). Start counting from the top row of these medium-sized squares and continue to the bottom row. Some cells will probably touch the lines forming these squares. Count these cells only if they are on the lines forming either the top or the right sides of the square. If a cell touches either the bottom or the left sides of a medium-sized square, do not count it; it will be counted with another square.

7. Count approximately 200 to 300 cells before determining the number of cells per cm^3. Four different situations may arise in your counting:

   a. There may be about 200 to 300 cells per large square (0.1 mm^3 or $1/10,000$ cm^3). In this case, multiply the cell count by 10,000 to obtain the number of cells per cm^3. (Recall from the discussion of exponents that 10,000 may also be expressed as 1×10^4.)

   b. There may be fewer than 200 cells visible in the large center square. It will then be necessary to count cells in several of the same size corner squares to obtain a total of about 200 cells. Divide the total number of cells counted by the number of squares involved to obtain the average for one square. Then multiply this number by 10,000 to obtain the number of cells per cm^3. For example, 240 cells were counted in four large squares. This is an average of 60 cells per square. Sixty cells per large square $\times 10^4 = 6 \times 10^5$ cells/cm^3.

c. There may be a much larger number of cells than 200 per large square. If all cells in a large square were counted, too much time would be spent. In this case, count 200 to 300 cells in the medium-sized (0.2 mm $\times$ 0.2 mm) divisions of the large square. (Remember that the large center square is divided into 25 medium-sized squares.) To get the average number of cells per medium-sized square, divide the total number of cells counted by the number of medium-sized squares counted. Multiply this average by 25 to estimate the number of cells per large square. This number times 10^4 equals the number of cells per cm^3.

Example: There was a total of 210 cells in three medium-sized squares. How many cells were there per cm^3 in the original culture?

$$\frac{210}{3} = 70 \text{ cells per medium-sized square}$$

$$70 \times 25 = 1750 \text{ cells}/0.1 \text{ mm } (1750 \text{ cells/large square})$$

$$1750 \times 10^4 \text{ } (10,000) = 17,500,000 = 1.75 \times 10^7 \text{ cells/cm}^3$$

d. The cell numbers may be too dense to count. The suspension must then be diluted before a count is made. Do not forget to multiply the final cell number by the amount with which your suspension was diluted.

Example: 1 cm^3 of a yeast culture was diluted with 99 cm^3 of water (1/100 dilution), before using the counting chamber. When counted, this dilution yielded 220 cells per 0.1 cm^3. How many cells were there per cm^3 of the original culture?

$$220 \times 10^4 \times 100 = 220,000,000 \text{ } (22 \times 10^7) \text{ cells/cm}^3$$

PROBLEMS

1. Suppose the center large square of your chamber contains 53 yeast cells. You count the four large corner squares and find that they contain 51, 54, 55, and 60 cells, respectively. What is the best estimate of the total number of yeast cells per cm^3 in your original culture? the best estimate of the total number of cells per liter in your original culture? (Use the relationship, 1000 cm^3 = 1 liter.)

2. You have a suspension of yeast cells suspected to contain approximately 300,000,000 cells per cm^3. How many cells is this per 0.0001 cm^3 (the volume of one large square)? How much should a sample of this culture be diluted before counting in order to obtain about 300 cells per large square?

INVESTIGATION 8   Growth of a Yeast Population

The yeast *Saccharomyces cerevisiae* has an oval shape and measures 50 microns (μ) in diameter. Asexual reproduction in this yeast comes about by a process of cell division known as budding. In budding, the mother cell forms a small outgrowth or bud at its surface. The bud enlarges until it is about the size of the mother cell. Then nuclear division occurs, and one new nucleus goes to each cell. Finally, a cross wall is laid down between the two cells and they separate into two daughter cells. Both of these may reproduce a third generation, and so on. A photograph showing the different steps involved in a single generation of a yeast cell is shown in Figure 31.

Some of the cells in our population studies will be in various stages of budding. This leads to the question, "Should budding cells be counted as two cells or as one cell?" Think this question over and make your decision before the experiment starts. Discuss the reasons for your decisions until the class reaches an agreement as to the best course of action for the group.

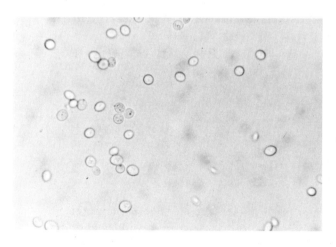

Figure 31   Budding and reproduction by the yeast,   Saccharomyces cerevisiae.

Materials (per class)

1. One 1000 ml flask
2. One package dry yeast

Materials (per team)

1. One microscope
2. One hemocytometer
3. One 250 ml flask
4. Two 150 ml flasks
5. One volumetric pipette, 1 ml accuracy

Procedure

1. Inoculate 1 liter of sterile water with a package of dry yeast.
2. After shaking the liquid to suspend the yeast cells uniformly, transfer 1 ml of this stock to a flask containing 99 ml of sterile water.
3. Shake the second dilution of yeast cells to form a uniform suspension. Transfer 1 ml of the second suspension to each of two flasks containing 49 ml of sterile *culture medium.*
4. Each student should determine the number of yeast cells per ml in the second (99ml) dilution flask by use of the hemocytometer counting chamber. How many cells per ml are to be found in each of your two culture flasks immediately after inoculation? This number represents the population count per ml in your cultures at the zero (starting) time of your study. Record it on a data chart similar to Chart A.

CHART A. Population Growth in Yeast Cultures Maintained
at 12° C and 22° C

Date	Time of day	Age of culture	Team average of cells per ml at	
			12° C	*22° C*
		0		
		24		
		48		

5. Each team now has two cultures of *S. cerevisiae.* Incubate one of these at 12°C and the other at 22°C.
6. Each student should count and record the number of yeast cells in each of the two cultures daily. Each count should be recorded in the notebooks of the individual students and the average number entered in the chart. For later ease in computations and graphing, these counts should be recorded as exponents of 10. For example, 1,400,000 cells per ml may be expressed 1.4×10^6 cells per ml. Continue the daily counts until the cultures are about 10 days old.
7. Graph your own and your team average on semilogarithmic graph paper. The exponential scale on the y-axis is used to indicate the numbers of organisms present at a particular time. The time is shown on the x-axis with an arithmetic scale.

8. The data from each team should now be pooled with data from the rest of the class. The mean values for the class at each temperature (12°C and 22°C) may be recorded in charts similar to Chart B.

CHART B. **Individual Counts by Teams Performing
Yeast Population Growth Studies at 12° C**

Age of culture (hours)	Number of cells per ml team number 1, 2, 3, 4, 5, etc.	Total	Mean ($\bar{x}$)	Standard deviation (s)
0				
24				
etc.				

9. Plot the yeast population for the class on the same semilogarithmic graph paper which was used for plotting individual and team data.

INTERPRETATIONS

1. Compare the charts and graphs of the pooled class data with those of your own team. Calculate the standard deviations of your team's data on different days. Compare these values with the standard deviations from the data of the class. Are there variations in the two? Discuss the reasons for any such variations.

2. Concentrate on a 48-hour period during the logarithmic period of growth. Calculate the following from your team's data and from the data of the class.

   a. How many generations occurred during this 48-hour period in the cultures grown at 12°C and 22°C?

   b. What was the generation time in each culture?

   c. Considering generation time as a *growth rate,* how much faster (or slower) was the rate of growth at 22°C than at 12°C?

   d. Do you think your answer for part c would hold for any 10°C difference in temperature? Explain.

3. Observe the period beyond the phase of logarithmic growth.

   a. Did the total number of individuals in your culture remain constant each day during this period?

   b. What are some explanations for the particular constancy or variations which your graphs show in this period? Did your results agree with those of the class?

   c. If you had determined viable cells, what may have been the general trend of the growth curve in its last few days? What procedures could be used to check this hypothesis? If time permits, check your hypothesis with results from another set of cultures.

PROBLEMS

1. Figure 21 (page 103), presents a population growth curve for the United States (1800–1960). From what you have seen in your yeast population studies, in what phase of growth do you think our national population is now?

2. Extrapolate the U. S. population curve to the year 2000. What are some possible events that may cause your extrapolation to be invalid?

3. The common and most reliable method for determining "live" microbes is by the somewhat cumbersome and lengthy plate count method. A principle of staining is that only "dead" cells take stain, a factor which could provide a rapid method of distinguishing viable cells from non-viable ones. How would you design an experiment to test how different stains A, B, C, and D might correlate with the plate count method in determining the number of viable cells in a culture?

4. Based on your results concerning the effect of temperature on CO_2 production (Investigation 5), how do you think temperatures of 5°C, 35°C, 45°C, and 55°C might affect the growth of yeast populations? Test your hypothesis.

5. The criterion for calling a microbe "living" is more commonly based on its ability to reproduce. This criterion is not used in judging many other "living things" as live or dead. Why is it a convenient one for microbes?

6. What probably happens to the shapes of yeast protoplasts when dry yeast is placed in pure water? Why?

PATTERN OF INQUIRY 5

Factors Affecting Population Development

A microbiologist was investigating the effects of an antibiotic on the inhibition of growth of a species of bacteria. He made a series of dilutions of the antibiotic in a culture medium and added the same amount of inoculum to each. After 24 hours, he counted the number of viable cells remaining in each concentration of the antibiotic. He obtained the following results:

EXPERIMENT 1

Concentration of antibiotic in micrograms per liter	Number of viable cells per ml after 24 hours of incubation
none	6×10^8
0.1	3×10^7
0.2	5×10^4
0.4	2×10^2
0.8	none
1.6	none
3.2	none

EXPÉRIMENT 2

Concentration of antibiotic in micrograms per liter	Number of viable cells per ml after 24 hours of incubation
none	8×10^8
0.1	6×10^8
0.2	2×10^8
0.4	9×10^7
0.8	4×10^7
1.6	7×10^6
3.2	8×10^3

A few days later, he wished to repeat the experiment, but found that his original culture of bacteria had become contaminated. He still had the plates which he used in making the counts, and he made a new isolation from one plate which had only a few colonies on it. Using routine procedures he found that he had managed to isolate a pure culture of the original species. Using this new culture, he repeated the first experiment and obtained the results in Experiment 2. What explanations can you give for the different results of the two experiments?

| **Mutation Frequency** | Many factors may also contribute to *mutation frequency* (proportion of mutants that exists in a culture at any given moment). Two inherent factors |

important in causing a marked increase in the proportion of mutants as new populations grow, are (1) reproduction of mutants, and (2) *mutation rate* of culture. *Mutation rate* is the probability for a mutation in a given gene per cell per unit time. This is often expressed as n mutation events per n number of cells per cell-generation for a given gene. Consider two generations of 100 bacterial cells with a mutation rate of $\frac{1}{10}$. This rate is convenient for demonstration purposes but is really too high. Table 12 considers 100 such cells. Since the proportion of mutants is 1:10, of the original 100 cells, 90 are wild types and 10 are mutants.

Note the first new generation in Table 12 (page 132). The mutants divide to produce 20 cells of their own type. Of the total number of wild cells, however, 90% (or a theoretical 81 cells) will divide to produce 162 wild-type cells, while 10% (or 9 cells) will mutate and divide to produce 18 new mutant cells. These 18 new mutants plus the 20 from the reproduction of the old mutants yield 38 mutants in this new generation of 200 cells. This same reasoning carried into the second generation yields a proportion of mutants in the population of 108.4:400 as compared with 1:10 in our original inoculum. The 108.4 is the sum from the reproduction of old mutants (38 × 2) plus the new mutants (32.4). (Although fractions of cells are mentioned, it should be remembered that this is a theoretical, mathematical calculation. Fractions of cells do not reproduce.)

The arithmetic becomes increasingly more complicated. Fill in the values for the third generation. Naturally, if this increase in the proportion of mutants were to continue, nearly the entire culture would soon be mutants. This condition may be prevented, however, by *back mutations* (the reversion of mutant genes to their original state). Back mutations, too, have their own characteristic mutation rates. When enough mutants have accumulated, back mutation may begin; the forward and backward mutations should reach an equilibrium and just balance each other. At this point, the culture should reach and maintain a *mutation equilibrium* (a constant proportion of mutated cells).

TABLE 12.   **Theoretical Increase in Proportion
of Mutants in a Population**

GENERATION	TOTAL CELLS	TOTAL NUMBER WILD CELLS	NUMBER OF NEW MUTANTS THIS GENERATION	TOTAL NUMBER MUTANTS	FREQUENCY MUTATION (mutants: Total population)
0	100	90	10	10	10:100
1	200	162	18 →	38	38:200
2	400	291.6	32.4 →	108.4	108.4:400
3	800				

10% or
9 cells mutate

81 or 90%
of wild cells

Reproduction
to give 20 cells

10% or
16.2 cells mutate

145.8 or 90%
of wild cells

Reproduction
to give 76 cells

10% or
cells mutate

or 90%
of wild cells

Reproduction
to give   cells

To illustrate the establishment of a mutation equilibrium, consider a mutation $A \rightarrow B$. We will start with all A-type cells. As the population increases, B-type cells will appear, and the proportion of B cells to the total number of cells increases. Eventually, however, enough B cells will accumulate to permit the regular occurrence of the $B \rightarrow A$ "back mutation." As is true in a chemical equilibrium, there will be as many $B \rightarrow A$ as $A \rightarrow B$ mutations. At this equilibrium point, the proportion of mutants in the population remains constant.

Suppose the experimenter starts with a small inoculum of all A cells. Some of the A's change to B. When enough B's accumulate, some start changing back to A. The more A's thus produced, the more B's can result until an equilibrium is finally reached where a constant amount of each type is present.

This discussion has ignored the important factor of variation in mutation rate and natural selection which may shift the proportion of live $A : B$ by favoring the survival of either type. Back mutations are important, however, in establishing a constant proportion of mutants in a given population.

INVESTIGATION 9   **Determining Mutation Frequency In Bacteria**

In this experiment we will attempt to determine the frequency of formation of mutants from cultures of the red pigmented bacterium *Serratia marcescens,* strain D1.

Materials (per team)

1. One stock culture of red *S. marcescens,* strain D1
2. Eleven tubes of *S. marcescens* broth
3. One sterile pipette (1.0-10.0 ml size)
4. Six sterile 9.0 ml water blanks in test tubes
5. One glass dally (a 5-inch piece of glass rod, 4 or 6 mm in diameter, bent to the shape of a hockey stick)
6. Eight sterile petri plates containing 15.0 ml each of *S. marcescens* agar
7. Wire loop

Procedure

1. Each team should inoculate a tube containing 10 ml of *S. marcescens* broth with a small inoculum from a stock slant of pigmented *S. marcescens,* strain D1. Incubate for 24 hours at room temperature.

2. Using a sterile pipette, aseptically make six serial 10-fold dilutions of the 24-hour broth culture in sterile 9.0 ml water blanks. Label the dilutions 1:10, 1:100, 1:1000, 1:10,000, 1:100,000, 1:1,000,000 (or 10^1, 10^2, 10^3, 10^4, 10^5, 10^6), respectively.

3. Place 0.1 ml of the 10^3 dilution on the surface of each of two petri plates each containing 15 ml of solidified *S. marcescens* agar. Spread the inoculum evenly over the surface of the plate with a cooled, alcohol-flamed, glass dally.

4. Repeat Step 3 with the 10^4, 10^5, and 10^6 dilutions of the culture. Be sure to flame the dally before and after each use. Label each plate with the appropriate dilutions.

5. Invert the plates and incubate for 24 hours either in a 27°C incubator (if one is available) or at room temperature.

6. If possible, select a pair of plates containing about 200 to 400 colonies for counting. Remember the discrete colonies on these plates are each assumed to have arisen from a single cell of *S. marcescens*, strain D1.

7. Count the total number of colonies on your plates; note the number which are red and the number which are white. Also note colonies of other colors.

8. Use a wire loop to transfer aseptically a small inoculum of from 5 to 10 of the white colonies to slants of sterile *S. marcescens* agar. Label each white isolate of *S. marcescens*. You may determine the naming procedure. Incubate these slants for 24 hours at room temperature. Now store the stock cultures of white mutants in the refrigerator.

9. Study the morphology and staining characteristics of *S. marcescens*. To do this, prepare fixed smears of several colonies, both white and red, as follows. (a) Place a drop of water on a clean microscope slide. (b) Use a cooled, sterile wire loop to transfer a small amount of cells from a slant to the water drop. (c) Spread the resulting cell suspension over about $\frac{1}{3}$ of the slide and *gently* heat to evaporate the water. The cells will be fixed to the slide, much as a fried egg sticks to an ungreased skillet.

10. These fixed smears will be stained by the most widely used stain in microbiology, Gram's stain. This technique imparts either a violet or a pink color to the bacteria of a given species, thus separating this species into one of two groups—Gram-positive or Gram-negative. The Gram stain technique is described as follows:

   a. Flood a fixed smear of the organism with Hucker's ammonium oxalate crystal violet stain for 1 minute.

   b. Drain off the excess stain and gently wash the slide under flowing tap water being careful not to wash away the fixed smear.

c. Flood the slide with Gram's iodine for one minute.

d. Rinse the iodine off with 95% ethanol until no more dye flows away (about 30 seconds).

e. Wash in tap water.

f. Counterstain by flooding the slide with safranin for 30 seconds.

g. Wash off the excess safranin in tap water, blot, and allow the slide to air dry.

h. Examine the slide using the oil immersion lens, if available. If it is not, use high power ($430\times$).

INTERPRETATIONS

1. Note the Gram reaction of *S. marcescens.* Is it violet (Gram-positive) or pink (Gram-negative)? Do both white and red colonies have cells with the same Gram reaction? Is *S. marcescens* shaped like a rod (bacillus), a sphere (coccus), or a corkscrew (spirillum)? Compare the Gram reaction and morphology of *S. marcescens* with those of stock cultures of other species of bacteria.

2. What was the viable count of red and white *S. marcescens* per ml in the original broth culture? CAUTION: *Note that each plate was inoculated with 0.1 ml rather than with 1.0 ml.* If 200 colonies were found on the plate inoculated with 10^6 dilution, the number of viable organisms per ml of original culture would be 200×10^7, or 2,000,000,000 per ml.

3. Was the loss in pigmentation by *S. marcescens* accompanied by a change in either its morphology or its Gram reaction? If such changes were noticed, how would they complicate the proper identification of the white colonies as mutants of the red forms?

4. What percentage of the total number of colonies represented white mutants? Pool the results of the class. Calculate the mean and standard deviation for percentage of white colonies obtained by the different teams in the class. This mean value will be used as the "mutation frequency" of *S. marcescens,* strain D1. In what way might the calculation of standard deviation be of value?

5. Did anyone notice single colonies with both red and white segments? How might such an occurrence be explained?

INVESTIGATIONS FOR FURTHER STUDY

1. Perhaps it would be possible to cause your white mutants to pigment again in a medium more complete in nutrients than

the *S. marcescens* medium. Supplement this medium with sources of mixed amino acids (peptone, for instance), sugar mixtures, purines and pyrimidines (yeast extract), mineral mixtures, and so on. If any one mixture is able to restore pigmentation, then determine by elimination what specific chemical or chemicals within the mixture are responsible.

2. If you have an available source of either ultraviolet light or X ray, use one of them to irradiate suspensions of *S. marcescens,* strain D1. Determine the ratio of red to white colonies produced by irradiated and nonirradiated suspensions of this organism.

3. Obtain a gram positive bacterium (*Bacillus subtilis,* for example), and use it along with *S. marcescens* to determine the specificity in the various reagents in the Gram's stain. Make several slides with a smear of both organisms (not mixed), and substitute other reagents for each step in the procedure. For example, will malachite green substitute for crystal violet? acetone for alcohol? hydrogen peroxide for Gram's iodine? You should try substitutions of your own choosing.

SECTION TEN

INTERACTION WITHOUT CELL CONTACT

The methods by which various kinds of organisms are able to communicate has long been a subject of intense investigation. Social organization depends upon communication. Porpoises appear to have a kind of language, bees communicate via sound vibrations and "dance" patterns, and termites have been demonstrated to possess some form of communication.

While it is extremely unlikely that any form of "language" exists between individual plants or microorganisms, there are various forms of complex chemical *interactions* which affect the existence of populations of countless thousands of individual organisms. The subject of chemical interaction between cells is enormously complex. One can approach this subject only by a careful study of interactions that can be investigated in the laboratory.

The next series of investigations centers on one general problem: the nature of an interaction between cells that results in visible changes within a population of a specific microbe.

INVESTIGATION 10	The Interaction of Two Mutants of a Bacterium

The results of Investigation 9 probably revealed the presence of a number of white (or various colored) mutants of *S. marcescens*. Two of these white mutants have been studied and given the code names of "933" and "WCF." The wild-type, red-pigmented bacteria is coded as D1.

The results of Investigations 10, 11 and 12, together with the parallel reading on pigmentation, present all of the data necessary to formulate a meaningful hypothesis to account for a puzzling interaction. It is possible for you to arrive at the same explanation as research biologists who are, at this writing, still continuing their efforts to learn more about bacterial pigmentation. At the conclusion of Investigation 12, your instructor may check your hypothesis against the hypothesis most generally accepted at present as our explanation of the interaction evident in these investigations.

Materials (per team)

1. Stock cultures of *S. marcescens*, strains 933, WCF, and D1
2. Wire loop
3. Four sterile petri plates, each containing 15 ml of *S. marcescens* agar
4. Four tubes of sterile *S. marcescens* broth

Procedure

1. Streak a loopful of 24-hour, *S. marcescens* broth cultures of strains 933 and WCF on the surface of one agar plate as shown in Figure 32. As controls, prepare three plates with a single streak of 933, WCF, and strain D1.

Figure 32   *Preparation of agar plates.*

2. Invert the plates and incubate them at room temperature.

3. Observe each of the plates daily and record evidence of any change either in the physical appearance of the growth or in the color. An accurate observation of each strain is important.

INTERPRETATIONS

1. Describe the differences between the experimental and control plates and between each streak on the experimental plate.
2. Formulate a hypothesis to account for the results of this investigation.
3. In what way do these results indicate interaction without cell contact?

Parallel Reading: Pigmentation in S. marcescens

Several compounds which contain the ring structure found in pyrroles are vital to the existence of both plants and animals. A pyrrole is the compound whose structure is indicated in Figure 33. Compounds which contain two, three, or four of these characteristic ring structures are called dipyrroles, tripyrroles, and tetrapyrroles, respectively.

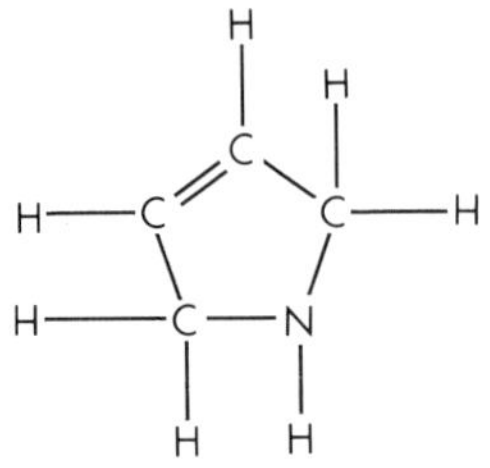

Figure 33   Ring structure of a single pyrrole.

Hemoglobin and chlorophyll are both examples of tetrapyrroles (4 pyrroles bonded together). The chemical structures of these two physiological pigments are shown in Figure 34. Note the positions of the 4 pyrrole rings in relation to one another.

The red pigment of the bacterium *Serratia marcescens* has interested biochemists because it is, uniquely, a tripyrrole with the name prodigiosin. The structure of prodigiosin may be described by using the symbols A, B, and C to represent its three pyrrole structures. A, B, and C must be present in a combined form to yield the red form of prodigiosin, A-B-C. Figure 35 gives the structural formula of prodigiosin and the parts of the molecule which we will represent by the symbols A, B, and C.

HEME

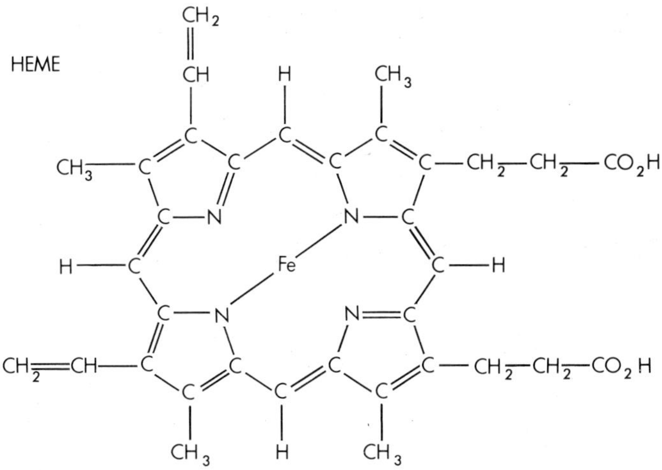

Figure 34   The tetrapyrroles of the pigments hemoglobin and chlorophyll.

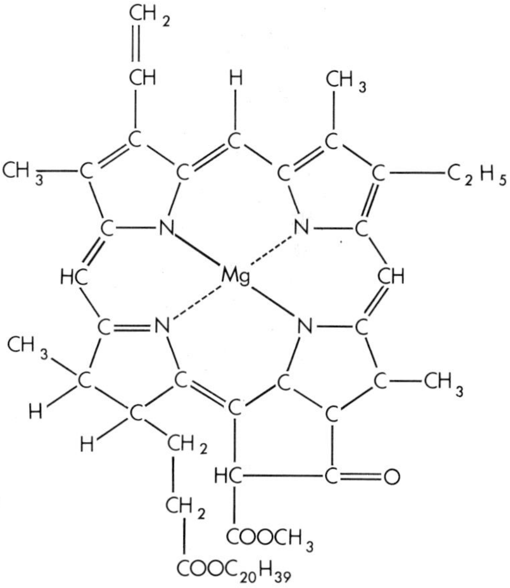

CHLOROPHYLL

Figure 35   Structure of prodigiosin.

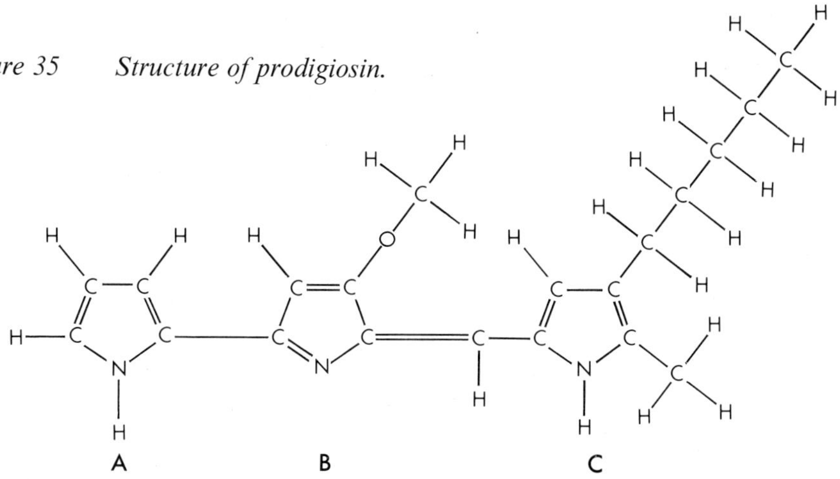

INVESTIGATION 11 — A Verification of Results

When a wild, prodigiosin-producing strain of *S. marcescens* is plated on a proper medium and incubated at 25–30°C, most of its colonies will have the red color of prodigiosin. Often, however, a few colonies are white, indicating that the cells in these colonies can no longer produce the complete molecule of pigment, A-B-C. This could be due to a mutated gene (or genes) in the cells of these white colonies. If the mutation resulted in the loss of the ability of some gene to direct the production of any of the series of enzymes involved in the conversion of medium constituents to prodigiosin, one could account for the loss in pigmentation.

Materials (per team)

1. Stock cultures of *S. marcescens,* strains 933 and WCF
2. Three tubes of *S. marcescens* broth
3. Glass dally
4. Three petri plates poured with *S. marcescens* agar in the manner described in the Procedure

Procedure

1. Pour 10 to 15 ml of cooled liquid *S. marcescens* agar into the bottom of 3 sterile petri plates. Allow it to harden. Invert the plates and pour enough agar into the petri plate covers to cover about one-half of their areas.
2. Inoculate the agar surface in the bottom half of one plate with 0.1 ml of a 24-hour broth culture of *S. marcescens,* strain WCF. Spread the inoculum evenly over the entire surface of the agar with an alcohol-flamed glass dally.
3. Repeat Step 2 using the agar in the same petri plate cover and a 24-hour broth culture of *S. marcescens,* strain 933.

Figure 36   Plating strains of S. marcescens *to check interactions.*

Agar inoculated with 933

Agar inoculated with WCF

4. Inoculate the bottom of one of the other plates with strain WCF and the top of the third plate with 933. These two plates with only one strain each are your controls.

5. Assemble the plates in the usual manner. (See Figure 36.) Incubate the dishes at room temperature. Observe daily and record the appearance of each culture.

INTERPRETATIONS

1. What reasons can you think of that might justify the experimental approach used here?
2. What conclusions did the experiment yield regarding your hypothesis?
3. How would you proceed further to test the validity of your conclusions?
4. What do you think the results of this experiment would be if the plates had been inverted during the incubation with strain 933 on the top and WCF on the bottom?
5. React to the following statement: the phenotypes of these strains can be changed at will without affecting their genotypes.

INVESTIGATION 12	A Study of Interaction Between Unknown Mutants

We have examined two known mutants of *S. marcescens*, WCF and 933, and found that an interaction occurs between these strains. Do all non-pigmented mutants of *S. marcescens* resemble either WCF or 933 in this respect, or may other genes and molecules be involved? Use the nonpigmented isolates from Investigation 9 to find an answer to this question.

Materials (per team)

1. Stock cultures of strains 933 and WCF and white isolates from Investigation 10
2. Tube of *S. marcescens* broth for each of the cultures from Step 1
3. Two sterile Pyrex cake pans with aluminum foil cover
4. Wire loop
5. 100 ml *S. marcescens* agar

Procedure

Test the ability of the nonpigmented mutants which you isolated in Investigation 9 to interact with each other and with strains 933 and WCF. A suggested method for this testing using two Pyrex cake dishes might be as illustrated in Figure 37.

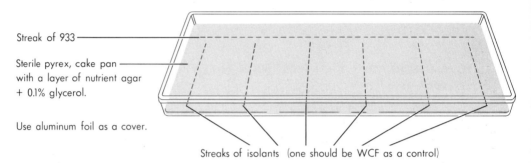

Streak of 933

Sterile pyrex, cake pan
with a layer of nutrient agar
+ 0.1% glycerol.

Use aluminum foil as a cover.

Streaks of isolants (one should be WCF as a control)

Figure 37   Suggested procedure for determining if certain unknown, non-pigmenting isolates (isolants) are complementary with either strain 933 or WCF of S. marcescens.

INTERPRETATIONS

1. Do you have any syntrophic combinations in your isolates? Do they correspond to either WCF or 933 or do they appear to be different kinds of mutants? Explain.
2. Why might streaks 10 mm apart interact syntrophically while the same streaks 10 cm apart fail to show this phenomenon?

INVESTIGATIONS FOR FURTHER STUDY

Do you think the red pigment from *S. marcescens* is a single, pure substance? Design and test methods of extracting the pigment and of testing its purity via paper chromatography.

INVESTIGATION 13   Preparation of a Scientific Paper

This investigation will differ from those that you have done previously. Instead of concentrating on a specific laboratory investigation, you will be asked to study the results of Investigations 10, 11 and 12 and to combine your interpretation into the construction of a scientific paper that meets the criteria discussed in the literature section of Part I.

You should feel free to develop your own ideas, exact details for the structure of the paper will not be given. It should, however, reflect the following points:

1. The nature of your problem and the hypothesis you set out to test should be clearly stated.
2. You should explain in very clear terms how you went about performing various aspects of your investigation so that someone else could repeat the same series of investigations.
3. You should state as clearly as possible the actual results obtained including data and such analyses of these data as you may have performed.
4. An interpretation of the experimental results based upon an evaluation of your data should be clearly stated.
5. A concluding statement should be made that reflects upon your original hypothesis and gives as much of a conclusion as you are able to give in light of your interpretations.

It might be well to study various articles in the literature as well as those reproduced in this book to give you some help in how to structure this paper. In essence, what you are asked to do is as follows: state a hypothesis that could account for the interactions which you have observed between various strains of *S. marcescens* during your work in Investigations 10, 11 and 12; describe the kind of experimentation you did in seeking to verify your hypothesis; and finally, express in your own words and with your own ideas, based upon your experimental work, what you believe to be the best possible explanation for these interactions between the several mutants of *S. marcescens.*

This is not going to be an easy task but it is typical of the problem that faces the researcher in that he must be able to communicate his work in as clear and concise a fashion as possible so that other investigators might carry on or verify his work by their own experimental techniques.

If your work has been careful, if you have been meticulous in keeping notes on each of these past three investigations, and if you have very carefully thought through each of the investigations, you might be able to write a paper that would be of significant interest to those people who are now conducting research into the pigmentation of various microorganisms.

You should keep in mind that there is no absolute answer as yet known to completely explain the nature of the interactions and the formation of pigments between these mutant strains of bacteria. There are, however, several hypotheses that have been advanced by researchers in this field that might be compared with your own on completion of this paper.

SECTION ELEVEN

INTERACTION FOLLOWING CELL CONTACT

Besides population interactions that work at a distance, as in antibiosis and syntrophism, there are others that require cell contacts, in which the contents of genetically different cells become mixed. Such intimacy, limited to cells of the same or closely related organisms, offers numerous opportunities for interactions that may increase or decrease the chance for survival. Two types of intracellular interactions are *heterokaryosis* (see Figure 38) and *complementation.* The first of these involves the transfer of dissimilar nuclei into a common cytoplasm; the second involves physiological interactions between dissimilar genetic material.

Nuclear fusion and genetic recombination in asexual or sexual reproduction are also examples of interactions inside cells that affect both individuals and populations. These interactions can enlarge upon the range of variability arising from mutation in separate individuals, alter the immediate effects of natural selection, and moderate the eventual course of evolution. The fungus *Aspergillus nidulans* provides suitable material for exploring several of these interactions.

Heterokaryosis in *Aspergillus* In contrast to the colonies of *Serratia* or *Saccharomyces,* which are masses of separate cells, the vegetative growth of *A. nidulans,* like that of most fungi, is a matrix of microscopic filaments. These branch and rejoin freely during growth. Although each filament is compartmented by crosswalls, the cytoplasm in adjacent compartments is continuous through a minute pore in this crosswall. Some biologists have proposed that the *whole patch* of cottony growth you see in the culture is one cell. For convenience, however, each compartment is still called a cell. An entire vegetative body of connected filaments is a *mycelium* (plural, *mycelia*). The open space between the filaments is part of the environment.

A mycelium with only one genome is a *homokaryon* (identical nuclei); one with two different genomes, arising from mutation in a homokaryon or from cell fusion between two different homokaryons (Figure 38), is a *heterokaryon* (nonidentical nuclei). The filaments are only a few microns in diameter. The even smaller nuclei number several to each cell. While streaming cytoplasm continuously mixes the cell contents, nuclei often bump one another and are pushed through the pores from cell to cell. Heterokaryons and diploids both offer appropriate conditions for the possibility of complementation, a type of interaction to be explained in Investigation 15.

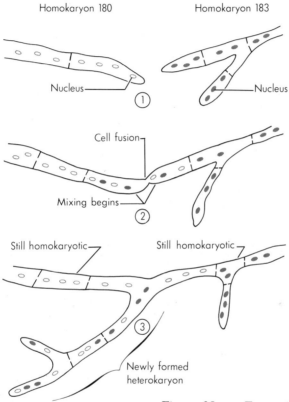

Figure 38   Formation of hetero-karyon by cell fusion.

Reproduction in *Aspergillus*   The mycelium grows partly in the agar medium, where nutrients are absorbed, and partly in the air, where many hyphae develop into *sporophores* (Figure 39). The sporophores produce asexual reproductive bodies called *mitospores*. Formed by mitosis, mitospores reproduce the vegetative mycelium. Whether from homokaryons or heterokaryons, the mitospores of *A. nidulans* contain one haploid nucleus. These spores are valuable as a ready means of isolating genetically pure strains, as the formation of a mitospore automatically dissociates the two genomes in a heterokaryon.

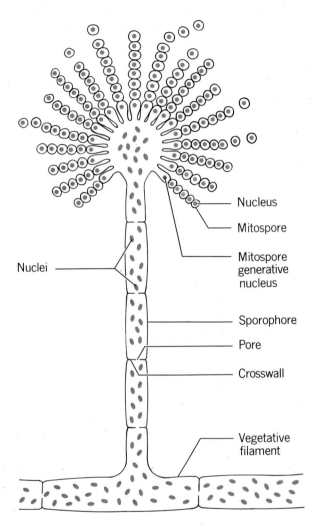

Figure 39   Sporophore of
Aspergillus *in long-section.*

Mitospores give color to the mycelium. You will use color as a quick clue to what goes on inside the spore and mycelium. The color developed by a mitospore is genetically determined by its nucleus. Mitospores of different colors may thus develop side by side. Some knowledge of spore-pigment genetics will help you interpret the clues. Wild-type mitospores are green, mutant alleles at the y locus determine yellow pigment, and those at the w locus prevent the formation of pigment (white mitospores). Although a mitospore that lacks the wild-type gene for green pigment

(y^+) will be yellow, as expected, one that lacks the wildtype gene for yellow pigment (w^+) will be white even in the presence of y^+. Why this is so may be rationalized from the abbreviated scheme of pigment biosynthesis given below. (If either the w or y mutant is present, the synthesis will stop at the step shown by the vertical line.)

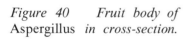

$$\text{metabolism} \longrightarrow \overset{\text{colorless}}{\underset{\text{substance}}{}} \Big|_\rightarrow \overset{w \text{ mutant}}{\underset{\text{pigment}}{\overset{\text{yellow}}{}}} \Big|_\rightarrow \overset{y \text{ mutant}}{\underset{\text{pigment}}{\overset{\text{green}}{}}}$$

Nuclei occasionally fuse in vegetative cells of heterokaryons, and therefore vegetative diploid strains can be formed. Mitosis usually serves to maintain genetic constancy, by duplicating the genetic material at each nuclear division. In heterozygous diploids, however, genetic recombination is a possible but rare event during mitosis. It has been found in several organisms, and its occurrence at low frequency is probably general.

In *A. nidulans*, sexual reproduction takes place in fruit bodies, which are produced less frequently than are sporophores. Nuclear fusion followed by meiosis occurs in special cells, called *meiosporangia*, within the fruit bodies. The progeny, like the adults (mycelia) of this fungus, are haploid. There are numerous meiosporangia in each fruit body, and each mature meiosporangium contains eight *meiospores* (Figure 40).

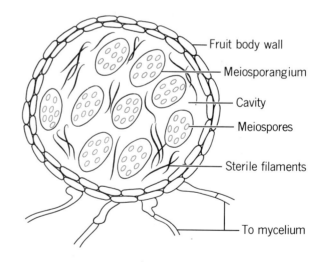

Figure 40   Fruit body of Aspergillus *in cross-section.*

The nucleus of a meiospore is a product of meiosis. Germination of the meiospore re-establishes the vegetative mycelium. The fruit bodies, which develop in the aerial mycelium near the agar surface, are small black spheres barely visible to the unaided eye.

QUESTIONS FOR DISCUSSION

1. Compare the colony and the mycelium as types of cell populations. What sorts of interactions between cells are possible in each?

2. Is a heterokaryotic mycelium, containing two different genomes, haploid or diploid?

3. Is nuclear fusion necessary for recombination of genetic material?

4. Why are interactions such as cell fusion, nuclear fusion, and genetic recombination limited to members of the same or closely related species?

5. What color mitospore would each of the following genotypes produce?

   a. $w^+ y^+$
   b. $w^+ y$
   c. $w^+ y/w \, y$ (diploid mitospore)
   d. $w \, y^+$
   e. $w \, y^+/w \, y^+$
   f. $w \, y^+/w^+ y$

INVESTIGATION 14   Confirmation of Strains and Genotypes

In science it is never necessary, in principle, to accept anything on faith. In keeping with this ideal, now is the time to satisfy yourself that the cultures given you for this set of investigations contain *Aspergillus nidulans* strains of the correct genotypes. Cultures can become contaminated accidentally by spores of bacteria or fungi ever present in air and dust. Spontaneous mutation, continuous at low frequency in all organisms, may back mutate a deficient gene to a wild type at any time. There is small chance of success in Investigations 15 through 18 if your starting materials are faulty.

Materials (per team)

1. Petri plate cultures (5 to 7 days old):
   a. One of *A. nidulans,* strain 180
   b. One of *A. nidulans,* strain 183

2. Microscope
3. Several slides and coverslips
4. Tissue paper
5. Bacterial inoculating needle
6. Glass marking pen or wax pencil
7. Two fine dissecting needles (Mount No. 13 sewing needles in sticks of balsa wood.)
8. 100 ml sterile distilled water
9. 50 ml sterile wetting solution in a 125 ml flask
10. Two sterile pipettes, 1 ml capacity
11. Two sterile Pasteur pipettes, fitted with rubber bulbs
12. Three sterile test tubes, 10 to 20 ml capacity, plugged with cotton, aluminum foil, or slip-on metal caps
13. One plate each of the 8 media in Table 13, page 151

Procedure Day I

1. Autoclave the sterile materials needed for Day II (20 minutes at 120°C).
2. Prepare the 8 media listed in Table 13. For convenience, each team may prepare one or two kinds for the whole class. See Appendix D, Preparation of Culture Media, for the simplest procedure.

Procedure Day II

1. The genetic characteristics of these strains are so specific that no special knowledge is required to distinguish them from all other fungi. View the cultures from above. If they are no more than 5 to 7 days old (they should be dated), strain 180 should be white and strain 183 light yellow. Correct color eliminates many possible contaminants.
2. The sporophore of *Aspergillus* is unique (see Figure 39). Examine a bit of aerial mycelium under the microscope. A wet mount will work best. Place one drop of wetting agent on a microscope slide, and with fine dissecting needles, add the bit of aerial mycelium, teasing it apart somewhat. Then add a cover slip (avoid trapping air bubbles under it), and take up excess liquid in a tissue held to the edge of the slip until it stops floating. The chain of mitospores can be seen in characteristic array under low power (100×). (See Figure 39.) Individual mitospores and crosswalls will be seen clearly under high power (440×). Nuclei are usually invisible without special staining or phase-contrast microscopy; the crosswall pores, not more than 100 mμ in

diameter, are seen best in an electron microscope. If you have trouble finding sporophores with mitospores still attached after mounting, try different aged materials from several locales of the same mycelium.

3. Growth responses on a series of appropriate test media (Table 13) will verify the presence of each specific deficiency. The two strains are supposed to have these genotypes:

Strain 180: $w\ y^+\ pdx\ bio\ met\ ade\ pab^+$
Strain 183: $w^+y\ pdx\ bio\ met^+\ ade^+\ pab$

Altogether, 7 loci are involved; their respective alleles are written above in parallel form. Symbols with the superscript ($+$) represent wild-type genes; the others represent mutations. The letters are abbreviations for the following mutant traits:

w: white mitospores
y: yellow mitospores
pdx: pyridoxine (required in the medium)
bio: biotin (required in the medium)
met: methionine (required in the medium)
ade: adenine (required in the medium)
pab: para-aminobenzoic acid (required in the medium)

a. Wipe the entire surface of your lab bench with 70% alcohol. Soap and water will do as well, but take longer to dry and are less likely to kill spores. Dust concentrated on the bench top is worse than air as a source of contaminants.

b. With a sterile pipette, aseptically transfer 2 ml of sterile wetting solution into a 5- to 7-day-old culture of strain 180. Suspend the mitospores by pumping the solution vigorously over the mycelium with a sterile Pasteur pipette and rubber bulb.

c. With the same Pasteur pipette transfer the spore suspension into a sterile tube. Dilute the suspension with sterile water until it is barely turbid when compared by transmitted light with a tube containing only wetting solution. If the filled tube is still too turbid, discard about half the suspension and add more sterile water.

d. With a bacterial inoculating loop, remove one loopful of diluted suspension and spot inoculate it near the edge of a plate of medium number 1. Now spot a fresh loopful on each of the other seven media in the same way.

e. Be sure each plate is labeled on the outside with its medium number, the strain number near the spot inoculated, and the date.

f. Now use strain 183 and repeat Steps b through e. Inoculate it on the opposite side of the same plates.

TABLE 13. Test for Each Specific Nutritional Deficiency

Test Medium Number	Strain	Specific deficiencies of strains					Growth responses			
		pdx	bio	met	ade	pab	Expected		Observed	
							180	183	180	183
	180w	pdx	bio							
	183y			met	ade	pab				
	Media									
1*	M+	—	—	—	—	—				
2	M+	—	bio	met	ade	pab				
3	M+	pdx	—	met	ade	pab				
4	M+	pdx	bio	—	ade	pab				
5	M+	pdx	bio	met	—	pab				
6	M+	pdx	bio	met	ade	—				
7*	M+	pdx	bio	met	ade	pab				
8*	YAG	pdx	bio	met	ade	pab				

* Control

Procedure Days III and V

1. Examine the plates after 3 and 5 days and record the results in Table 13. Proceed to the next investigation if the observed and expected results check.
2. If wild-type growth is observed where it is not expected, back mutation is not necessarily indicated. A trace of required supplement from YAG medium may have been carried over with the inoculum, especially if the inoculum was not adequately diluted. From the *edge* of the unexpected growth *in the test plate,* cut out a piece of inoculum no larger than 1 cu mm, and transfer it to a freshly made plate of the *same* test medium.
3. If wild-type growth is observed in the second test, loss of the deficiency must be presumed. The feasibility of attempting Investigations 15 through 18 should be thought over carefully in discussion with other students and the instructor.

INVESTIGATION 15	Heterokaryosis and Complementation

Complementation is probably more like genetic dominance than anything else encountered in your previous biology course. The added feature is that *complementation,* as the word suggests, involves a *mutual* compensation of genetic defects that neither of two genomes can overcome separately. Recall that a *genome* is one haploid set of chromosomes. Two different genomes are essential for complementation within cells. Combining the genomes into a fused, diploid nucleus is not necessary.

Recall also that many genes (DNA) act by specifying a particular gene product (messenger RNA), which in turn specifies the formation of a particular enzyme. The gene product is synthesized at the site of the gene in the nucleus; the enzyme is made in the cytoplasm. Each specific enzyme usually catalyzes one chemical reaction. If that reaction produces an essential substance, such as a vitamin, total loss of specific enzyme activity through gene mutation can block the reaction and cause the affected individual to die of starvation. Haploid individuals, with only one genome, are especially vulnerable.

Survival is possible through complementation, which may be viewed as the reappearance of lost enzyme activity by an interaction between nonidentical gene products and a common cytoplasm. Complementation is probably as general as life itself, and understanding the mechanism of complementation in detail is the object of intense current research.

Any gene dosage desired in a heterokaryon may be provided for in the mixture of mitospores used as inoculum. Since each mitospore contains a single nucleus, varying the ratio of mitospores varies the ratio of nuclei. The nuclear ratio, in turn, affects the gene dosage of any unlike alleles in the different nuclei. The way is open to explore how well specific genes act at different gene concentrations.

Anyone would expect good complementation in heterokaryons with 1:1 nuclear ratios. What happens, though, as certain wild-type genes become less and less frequent? The procedure outlined below is designed to determine if there is a threshold level of gene dosage (gene concentration) below which complementation is not initiated, as judged by the ability of an inoculum to initiate heterokaryotic growth. This is one of several uses for complementation tests.

The student who wishes to be carefully quantitative in approach must make sure that the chains of mitospores are broken up into a uniform suspension of single spores and that the freshly made, uniform suspensions of the two strains are equal in spore concentration. Only then should the student begin the diluting and mixing procedures.

Materials (per team)

1. Microscope
2. Hemocytometer (optional)
3. Bacterial inoculating needle
4. Glass marking pen
5. Cultures on YAG agar plates (5 to 7 days old):
   a. One of strain 180
   b. One of strain 183
6. Media (sterile):
   a. Six plates each of the 3 agar media listed for Day II, Step 9
   b. 50 ml *liquid* M medium plus all 5 supplements
7. 100 ml sterile distilled water
8. 50 ml sterile wetting solution in 125 ml flask
9. 22 sterile pipettes, 1 ml capacity
10. Two sterile Pasteur pipettes with rubber bulbs
11. 20 sterile test tubes, 10 to 20 ml, plugged but empty
12. One wire rack for test tubes

Procedure Day I

1. Sterilize equipment.
2. Prepare media.

Procedure Day II

1. Every team will be supplied with a heavily sporulated culture of each strain, 180 and 183. These should be 5- to 7-day-old cultures grown in petri plates of YAG agar medium. Practically the entire surface should be covered with sporulated growth.

2. Take up the spores of strain 180 as described in Investigation 14, Day II, Step 3. Transfer the 3 ml of suspension into a sterile, empty tube.

3. Add 2 ml of liquid M medium plus all 5 supplements.

4. Continue pumping the suspension in and out of the Pasteur pipette for several minutes. Then check one drop under the microscope. Pump some more if the suspension is not composed of a uniform distribution of single spores.

5. Now rework Steps 2 through 4 for strain 183.

6. Check spore concentration with a hemocytometer count (optional). If there is any *great* difference, make an appropriate dilution of the more concentrated suspension by carefully adding sterile, distilled water. (How large is *"great"*? What criterion would you use?)

7. Make serial dilutions of each strain separately by transferring 1 ml at each step into 9 ml of liquid M medium plus all 5 supplements. You should then have tubes of each strain at 1, 10^{-1}, 10^{-2}, 10^{-3}, and 10^{-4} times the concentration of the original suspension. (See Table 14.)

8. In another set of empty tubes, mix 0.5 ml of each dilution of the two strains (see Step 7) in the combinations listed below. Save the unmixed dilutions as inocula for controls.

9. Spot inoculate one loopful of each of these mixtures on the following media. Spot no more than two mixtures per plate, one spot each.

    a. M medium   b. M + *pdx* + *bio* medium   c. M + all 5 media

TABLE 14.

Dilutions of strain 183 mitospores	Dilutions of strain 180 mitospores	Input ratios of 183/180
10^{-4}	1	10^{-4}
10^{-3}	1	10^{-3}
10^{-2}	1	10^{-2}
10^{-1}	1	10^{-1}
1	1	1
1	10^{-1}	10^{1}
1	10^{-2}	10^{2}
1	10^{-3}	10^{3}
1	10^{-4}	10^{4}

10. Also spot undiluted inocula of strains 180 and 183 separately, as controls, on all three media. Label and date the plates, and circle the location of each spot.

Procedure Day III (and each day thereafter)

1. Check the plates every day. If none of the mixtures on M + *pdx* + *bio* have started growing by the time a response is observed on M + all 5 media, overspot each inoculum with one loopful of sterile M + all 5 liquid media. Why? Do not overspot more than once in two days. Stop overspotting when the first mixed inoculum begins to grow.

2. Transfer any complementing heterokaryons growing on M + *pdx* + *bio* medium, to YAG agar plates. Put only one inoculum in each plate. Should mitospores or pieces of mycelium be used here? Why?

3. Grow the heterokaryons on YAG medium for 10 to 14 days. Then note the numbers of white, yellow, and green patches.

4. Save the 2-week-old cultures on YAG medium for Investigations 16 and 17.

QUESTIONS FOR DISCUSSION

1. Did all mixtures of mitospores initiate equally good complementation, as judged by growth on M + *pdx* + *bio* medium compared to controls? Explain. How else could you measure complementation?

2. Were the mycelia uniformly heterokaryotic on all the kinds of media on which the mixtures of mitospores grew? Could they be uniformly heterokaryotic if the nuclear ratios were very disparate? What criterion is appropriate for uniform heterokaryosis?

3. How are you sure that the growth on M + *pdx* + *bio* is a complementing heterokaryon rather than syntrophic growth of intermingled but unfused homokaryons?

4. Since supplements were added to stimulate spore germination, how do you know complementation is effective, even if heterokaryosis is certain?

5. Do you imagine that the initial gene dosage persists during growth under various conditions? What might change the dosage? How could you test your ideas?

6. How can genes interact if they are not in the same nucleus?

7. How could complementation aid evolution?

INVESTIGATION 16   **Genetic Recombination at Meiosis**

Classical genetics is based upon analyzing genetic recombination at meiosis. The data needed for this purpose are the genotypes of the haploid nuclei which are produced by meiosis. The genes of Mendel and the genetic maps of chromosomes are deduced from the relative frequencies of these genotypes.

The progeny of haploid organisms, like *A. nidulans,* offer the advantage of direct analysis. The progeny of *A. nidulans* are the haploid meiospores, each containing a product of meiosis. The phenotype of the germinated meiospore usually corresponds exactly to its genotype. By contrast, deducing the genotypes of diploid progeny, as in *Drosophila,* is made difficult by the masking effects of the allelic interaction termed dominance. Analyzing a cross in a haploid organism, then, is similar to being able to determine directly the genotypes of sperm and unfertilized eggs in man. The combination of genes in each haploid nucleus produced by meiosis is immediately evident from the phenotype of each haploid progeny.

The purpose of this investigation is to construct a partial linkage map of the 5 loci with unlike alleles in strains 180 and 183. This is done by comparing the interactions during meiotic recombination of all possible pairs of loci. Before such comparisons may be made, however, normal segregation must be confirmed for each locus. Map only those loci that show normal segregation.

Different allelic genes, those genes which occur at the same locus and affect the same characteristic in the organism, should yield two kinds of haploid progeny in equal frequency. This is normal segregation. Exclude from the comparisons any loci that show abnormal segregation. This condition is detected as a significant deviation from a 1:1 ratio in the frequency of the mutant and wild-type alleles in the progeny and can be determined by using the chi-square test of significance.

Genes at different loci on the same chromosome are said to be linked. Linkage is detected and measured by the frequency of meiotic recombination between loci. The closer the loci, the less frequently their genes recombine. If two non-allelic genes at unlinked loci enter a cross in the same haploid nucleus, they have a random chance of appearing together (combined) in a haploid progeny. Any two unlinked, heterozygous loci should thus yield four kinds of progeny in equal frequency. Linkage is detected as a significant excess of parental genotypes, or combinations, in the progeny. Linkage distance is estimated by the following expression:

$$\text{map units} = \frac{\text{number of recombined progeny}}{\text{total number of progeny}} \times 100.$$

Materials (per team)

1. Dissecting microscope
2. Dissecting needle
3. Bacterial inoculating loop
4. Glass marking pen
5. Glass dally
6. 50 ml 95% alcohol (to flame-sterilize dally before each use)
7. Ten small tubes sterile 0.8% saline, 0.5 ml/tube
8. Media (sterile):
   a. One plate 3% aqueous agar
   b. YAG agar plates:
      Day II: 2 plates
      Day V: 4 plates
      Day XII: 4 plates
   c. Modified M media:
      Day XVII: 4 plates *each* of the five media listed for Day XVII, Step 1

One disadvantage of *A. nidulans* for meiotic analysis is that the fruit bodies may be either selfed (fusion of nuclei from the same parental strain) or crossed (fusion of nuclei from different parental strains). Only the latter will produce detectable meiotic recombination. The procedure below will explain how to select only the crossed fruit bodies. No progeny of selfed fruit bodies should be included in the data.

Tests for segregation and for detecting linkage and estimates of linkage should be done on data pooled from the teams.

Procedure Day I

1. Sterilize equipment.
2. Prepare media for Day II, Steps 2 and 5.

Procedure Day II

1. Remove the tops of the petri plates (from Investigation 15) containing the heterokaryotic cultures on YAG medium. Use a dissecting microscope to find the small black balls usually located just beneath the surface of the growth. These are the fruit bodies which contain the meiospores (sexual spores). The nucleus of each meiospore is a product of meiosis.
2. Use a sterile needle to transfer 10 large, black, fruiting bodies to a plate of sterile, 3% aqueous agar.

3. Use the sterile needle to roll the balls over the surface of the agar. Continue the rolling operation until the balls are shiny black, a process which will remove the mitospores.

4. Each cleaned fruit body is transferred to a numbered tube containing 0.5 ml of sterile 0.8% saline (8g NaCl in 1000 ml distilled water). Crush each fruit body against the inner side of the test tube to release the meiospores. Then shake the tube to suspend all of the meiospores in the saline. Each suspension is a random sample of meiospores from many meiosporangia. Each meiospore contains one nucleus.

5. Aseptically transfer a loopful of the spore suspension from each tube and streak it as a radius on a fresh plate of YAG medium. Label the streak to correspond to its tube number. Make 5 such streaks on each YAG plate, sterilizing the loop between each transfer. Figure 41 illustrates how your plates should look.

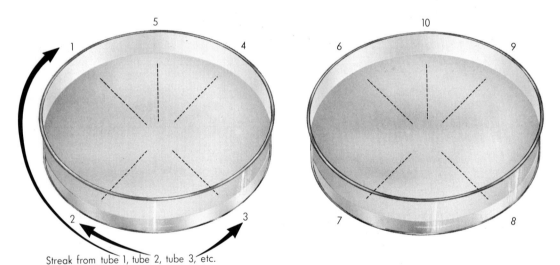

Streak from tube 1, tube 2, tube 3, etc.

Figure 41   Preparation of YAG plate.

6. Store the saline suspensions of the meiospores in the refrigerator. Incubate the plates for 3 days at room temperature.

Procedure Day V

1. Note very carefully which streaks have a uniform color and which of them are variegated.

2. Take a tube of meiospores which gave rise to a variegated streak and aseptically inoculate 0.1 ml (2 drops) onto each of 4 plates of fresh YAG medium. Spread the inoculum evenly over the surface of the agar using an alcohol-flamed, glass dally.

3. Incubate these latter plates at room temperature until the individual mycelia show color. Record the number of mycelia per plate of each color.

Procedure Day XII (probably)

1. Each group will now need four more plates of YAG medium. Mark off the bottom of each plate into ten "pie-shaped" sections. Number the plates 1 through 4 and the sections on each plate 1 through 10.

2. Using a freshly-flamed transfer needle each time, inoculate mito-spores from each of 40 mycelia (taken at random) in a separate sector. Transfer by stabbing the center of the mycelium and then the center of the sector at its broadest place. Refrigerate and save the original cultures on YAG medium.

3. Incubate until sporulating mycelia appear.

Procedure Day XVII (probably)

1. For the next step you will need four petri plates for each of the following five modifications of M medium:

Type of Medium	Modification of M Medium
MA	M + pyridoxine + biotin (controls)
MB	M + pyridoxine + biotin + methionine + adenine
MC	M + pyridoxine + biotin + methionine + para-aminobenzoic acid
MD	M + pyridoxine + biotin + adenine + para-aminobenzoic acid
ME	M + pyridoxine + biotin + methionine + para-aminobenzoic acid + adenine

All plates must be sectioned into ten pie-shaped areas. Number the sectors from 1 through 40. All plates must be labeled as to type of medium.

2. Use a flamed needle to transfer a sample from each mycelium on the YAG plates to a corresponding sector in a plate containing each kind of M medium. In other words, strain 1 on plate 1 will be transferred to sector 1 on *each* kind of medium (5 different kinds).

3. Incubate the plates at room temperature for 3 days.

Procedure Day XX (probably)

1. Score each strain for color and growth.
2. Determine the specific genotype of each.
3. Construct a linkage map for the loci that show linkage (see questions).

QUESTIONS FOR DISCUSSION

1. Was normal segregation demonstrated for the *w, y, ade, met,* and *pab* loci?

2. Which pairs of loci are linked?

3. What is the map distance between any linked pairs of loci? Do more than 2 of the loci belong to the same linkage group?

4. Why is it not permissible to include data from selfed fruit bodies in the analyses?

INVESTIGATION 17 Selection and Isolation of Diploids

The nuclei in homokaryotic mycelia of *A. nidulans* are mostly haploid. A few may be diploid, but these are not easily detected since they are homozygous for all loci. However, heterokaryosis and mitospores provide a system for detecting diploid nuclei formed by fusion of unlike nuclei in the heterokaryon. Such a diploid will be heterozygous for several of the gene mutations for nutritional deficiencies or color variations. A heterozygous diploid mitospore can yield a mycelium on M medium plus only pyridoxine and biotin (homozygous, nutritional deficiencies in the diploid). This medium would not support the growth of either haploid strain. Furthermore, since the color genes will complement in heterozygous diploids, diploid mycelia can be identified easily by the green mitospores.

Materials (per team)

1. Five cultures on YAG medium from Investigation 15
2. Media (sterile):
   a. Seven plates of M medium plus biotin and pyridoxine
   b. Eight plates fresh YAG medium
3. Dissecting microscope
4. Sterile wetting agent
5. Sterile test tube
6. Sterile Pasteur pipette
7. Inoculating needle

Procedure Day I

1. Sterilize equipment.
2. Prepare the media.

Procedure Day II

1. Each group will need the 5 cultures on YAG medium prepared in Investigation 15, 7 plates of M medium containing biotin and pyridoxine, and 8 plates of fresh YAG medium.
2. Under a dissecting microscope, examine the cultures on YAG medium to detect either sectors or spores with a deep green color. If green spores are found, use a sterile needle to streak some of them across the surface of two of the plates containing the M medium (plus biotin and pyridoxine).
3. Incubate the plates at room temperature for 3 to 5 days.
4. Now select a mycelium in a culture plate from Investigation 15, which did not have green spores. Add 3.0 ml of a sterile wetting agent to one of these plates. Tilt the plate gently back and forth until the soap solution contains a heavy concentration of spores.
5. Collect the suspension of spores carefully by tilting the plate and using a pipette to transfer it to a sterile test tube of water. Break up the chains of spores with a sterile Pasteur pipette equipped with a rubber bulb.
6. Transfer 0.1 ml (2 drops) of the spore suspension to the agar surface in each of the 5 plates of M medium. Spread the inoculum with the sterilized dally and incubate the plates at room temperature for 3 to 6 days.

Procedure Days III to V

1. Look for colonies with green spores in the cultures from Day II, Steps 3 and 6.
2. Transfer the green spores from *one* mycelium on the M medium to the center of each of the ten "pie-shaped" sectors on the four plates of YAG medium. Incubate and save these plates for Investigation 18.

INVESTIGATION 18   Genetic Recombination at Mitosis

The means of producing genetically novel individuals by the sequence heterokaryosis, diploidization, and somatic recombination (without the involvement of sex organs or fruit bodies) is termed a "parasexual cycle."

The main steps in this cycle of intracellular interactions may be summarized as follows:

1. Production of a heterokaryon, which may involve strains with different nutritional markers and visual markers (such as color), thus
   permitting the easy detection of the different steps in the cycle.
2. Production of a diploid nucleus by fusion of genetically different,
   haploid nuclei and the capture of the diploid nucleus in a mitospore,
   which may produce a diploid mycelium.
3. Production of recombined nuclei by (a) mitotic crossing-over or
   (b) haploidization.
4. Isolation of recombined diploid or haploid nuclei in mitospores.
   Mitotic crossing-over is equivalent to meiotic crossing-over, except
   that (a) meiotic crossing-over is ordinarily restricted to Prophase I of
   meiosis, (b) crossing-over at mitosis is much less frequent, and
   (c) multiple crossovers at the same mitosis are correspondingly rare.

Haploidization results from an accident of mitosis wherein the distribution of chromosomes during mitosis is not exact. Once a nucleus gets one
chromosome too few or too many, subsequent mitoses are irregular, and
the number of chromosomes diminishes in successive mitoses until a
haploid chromosome number is reached.

The green mycelia from Investigation 16 will yield either white or yellow
sectors on a green background. These sectors may result either from
mitotic crossing-over or haploidization. In mitotic crossing-over, a white or
yellow sector will contain recombinants within a linkage group. In haploidization, the white or yellow spores may include all possible combinations of linkage groups, but all genes on one chromosome will remain
in the parental combination. In one sense, haploidization is equivalent to
segregation without crossing-over for linked genes.

Only rarely will mitotic crossing-over occur in a diploid nucleus and
then be followed by haploidization of that recombinant nucleus prior to
its observation as a segregant for the visual marker. If a white or yellow
homozygous diploid colony is detected, it is possible to obtain haploid
products which can be tested. This, however, requires additional procedures not available with the material in question.

Materials (per team)

1. Four plates of YAG medium inoculated with green spores during
   Investigation 17
2. Dissecting microscope
3. Inoculating needle

4. Media (sterile):
   a. Seven plates of fresh YAG medium
   b. Seven plates of fresh M medium as prepared for Investigation 16

Procedure Day I

Prepare media.

Procedure Day II

Examine the 4 plates of YAG medium inoculated with green spores in Investigation 17. Under the dissecting scope, look for sectors in the mycelia with the yellow or white colors of the original strains. Use a sterile needle to streak these spores across the surfaces of plates of YAG medium. Each plate should have 10 streaks. Incubate 3 to 5 days.

Procedure Days III to V

1. Examine the plates for streaks with sectors of yellow or white. Green growths might also be seen as a contaminant in some streaks.
2. Next transfer spores from the yellow or white streaks to new YAG plates. Do not pick up any green spores this time. Incubate until each colony is sporulating.

Procedure Days VI to IX

Prepare the same kinds and number of plates of M medium as were used in Investigation 16. Incubate the plates until they can be scored for presence or absence of growth of each type of medium.

QUESTIONS FOR DISCUSSION

1. Which recombinants came about by mitotic crossing-over and which by haploidization? Were there any that were undeterminable?

2. Were there any double crossovers? If possible, compare the percentage of crossovers that were double in mitosis with those which were double in meiosis.

3. Would it be possible to construct a chromosome linkage map with mitotic crossing-over data alone? Explain.

4. What is the distinction between somatic recombination and mitotic crossing-over?

5. What are the irreducible elements of sexual reproduction? Compare them with the elements of the "parasexual cycle" in *A. nidulans.*

6. Diagram and compare the "parasexual cycle" of *A. nidulans* with the sexual cycle of man.

7. List and compare the types of interactions following cell contact that you have encountered in the investigations, readings, and discussions associated with this section.

GROWTH, DEVELOPMENT, AND BEHAVIOR OF INDIVIDUALS

SECTION TWELVE

GROWTH AND DEVELOPMENT IN PLANTS

Living things can reproduce their kind; perhaps this is their most characteristic property. Reproduction in most organisms is sexual and involves
the production of gametes, their fusion to form a zygote or fertilized
egg, and the development of an embryo from the zygote. But how does this
embryo develop from the single-celled zygote to a complex bean plant,
or to an even more complex organism such as a frog or a man? This is one
of the most baffling questions in biology. Attempts have been made to
explain these extraordinary events since the early history of man.

Meiosis Basic to sexual reproduction in any species is the
formation of gametes. Gametes have half as many
chromosomes as are found in the zygote. The reduction of the number of
chromosomes from the diploid number (2n) found in the zygote to the
haploid number (n) found in the gametes is accomplished during *meiosis*.

Meiosis may occur at various places in the life history of the many
species of organisms. In the moss plants and in ferns, the stage which
produces sperms or eggs is an independent, haploid plant, and, in some
cases, it may live for many years. In some plants and in nearly all animals,
the formation of sperms and eggs is the direct result of meiosis, although
some change in cell structure may follow the second meiotic division before the sperms or eggs are mature.

Meiosis results in two divisions of the nucleus accompanied by a single
division of the chromosomes. The process is outlined in Figure 42.
In this diagram, the diploid cell has six chromosomes and each of the four
daughter cells has three chromosomes.

Diploid cells have two sets of chromosomes; one set came from the male
parent through the sperm and the other from the female parent through
the egg. Early in the first meiotic division, the members of each homol-
ogous pair of chromosomes synapse (come together along their entire
lengths). Each chromosome of each pair then duplicates itself, yielding
a quartet or tetrad of chromosomes. This process is followed by two
successive divisions of the nucleus, with each of the four daughter nuclei
receiving one chromosome from each quartet. We call these two divisions
Meiosis I and Meiosis II.

**Life History
of a
Flowering Plant** Our study of the growth and development of a
flowering plant will be aided by a review of the life
history of such a plant, as shown in Figure 43.
The essential parts of a flower are the stamens and
the pistil. The most important part of the stamen is the anther, in which

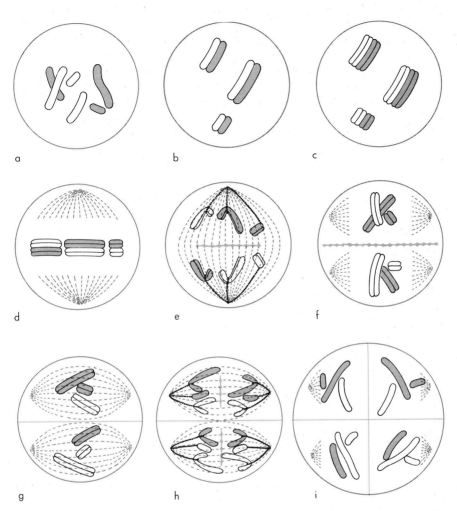

Figure 42   *Diagrammatic representation of the meiotic divisions of a diploid cell with three pairs of chromosomes. One set of three is shaded; the other is unshaded.*

the pollen grains are produced. Similarly, the most important part of the pistil is the ovulary (often called ovary) which produces ovules.

An anther usually produces four more or less cylindrical regions of tissue in which most of the cells produce microspores (little spores). Each microspore mother cell undergoes meiosis producing four microspores, each with one haploid nucleus which then undergoes one mitotic division. At the same time, the outer wall of the microspore thickens, often becoming sculptured in a pattern unique for the species. This two-nucleated structure is a pollen grain.

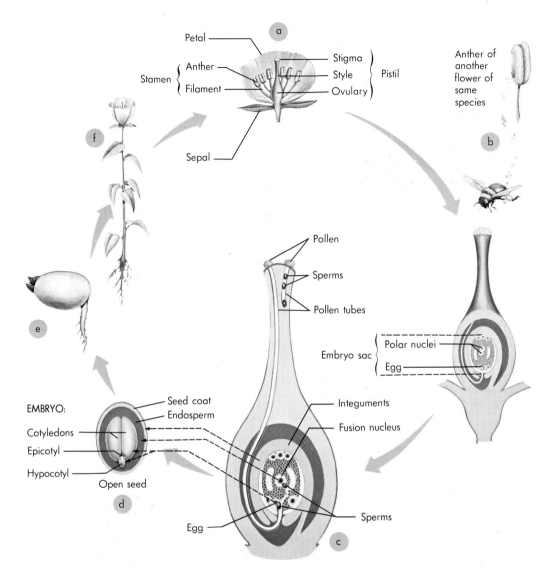

Figure 43 Shown in sequence for a generalized flowering plant are: (a) the flower; (b) pollination by an insect; (c) the interior of the pistil at the time of fertilization (a pollen tube has grown to the ovule, and double fertilization is about to take place); (d) the seed (the black arrows indicate that the seed coat is produced by the integuments of the ovule, the endosperm in the seed by the fertilized fusion nucleus, and the embryo by the fertilized egg); (e) the seedling (f) the mature plant, with flower.

At the same time that pollen grains are produced in the anther, a series of events which may lead to the production of eggs is taking place in the ovulary. Depending on the species, from one to many ovules are produced in a cavity (or cavities) in the ovulary. The ovules can first be seen as small protuberances which arise usually from definite regions of the ovulary wall. In each young ovule a diploid megaspore mother cell differentiates, divides by meiosis, and produces four haploid megaspores. Usually three of these spores disintegrate; the remaining megaspore may divide by mitosis and give rise to an eight-nucleated microscopic plant which lives within the ovule as a parasite. This is a megagametophyte, a plant which produces large gametes. In the flowering plants, it is often called the *embryo sac.* One of the eight nuclei with some surrounding cytoplasm becomes an egg. Two other nuclei, called the polar nuclei, come to rest near the middle of the megagametophyte.

The development of the egg in the megagametophyte takes place at about the same time as the development of the pollen grains in the anther. When the pollen grains are mature, the anther opens, and pollen grains may be carried to the stigma of the pistil by gravity, wind, or insects. There the pollen grains may germinate, forming a pollen tube which grows into the stigma and down through the style to the ovulary where it may enter one of the ovules.

Soon after germination of the pollen grain, one of its two nuclei divides to form two sperm nuclei. The other nucleus moves with the growing tip of the pollen tube and no doubt controls the synthesis of enzymes which digest the cells of the stigma and style in the pathway of the pollen tube. Since the pollen grain or pollen tube is a plant which produces sperms, what would you call this phase of the life cycle? The pollen tube grows into the megagametophyte. Here the end of the tube disintegrates, and the two sperms move into the megagametophyte where one of them fuses with the egg nucleus and the other fuses with the two polar nuclei. Fusion of sperm and egg results in a zygote; fusion of the other sperm with the polar nuclei results in what is called a triple fusion nucleus. The triple fusion nucleus then divides by mitosis and forms what is called an endosperm which is important as a food source for the developing embryo.

The zygote divides and forms a two-celled embryo which continues its development within the endosperm. In some species, by the time the seed is mature, the embryo will have completely digested the endosperm, using it as food. This happens in the common bean. In other plants such as the castor bean or corn (the corn grain is a fruit consisting of an ovulary with an enclosed seed), most of the food stored in the seed will be in the endosperm. In these species, the embryo will have used only a small part of the food present in the endosperm.

The development of the endosperm and embryo in the ovule of shepherd's purse (*Capsella bursa-pastoris*) is shown in Figure 44. An ovule containing an embryo is called a seed. The structures present in some mature seeds are shown in Figure 45.

It is often said that all of the parts of each embryo develop by cell division and cell growth. If we consider growth as simply an increase in size, it

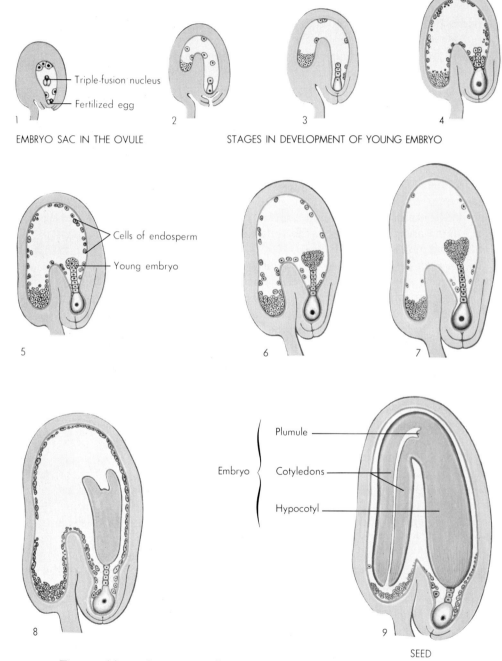

EMBRYO SAC IN THE OVULE   STAGES IN DEVELOPMENT OF YOUNG EMBRYO

*Figure 44   Diagrams illustrating growth of
embryo and endosperm in Shepherd's Purse.*

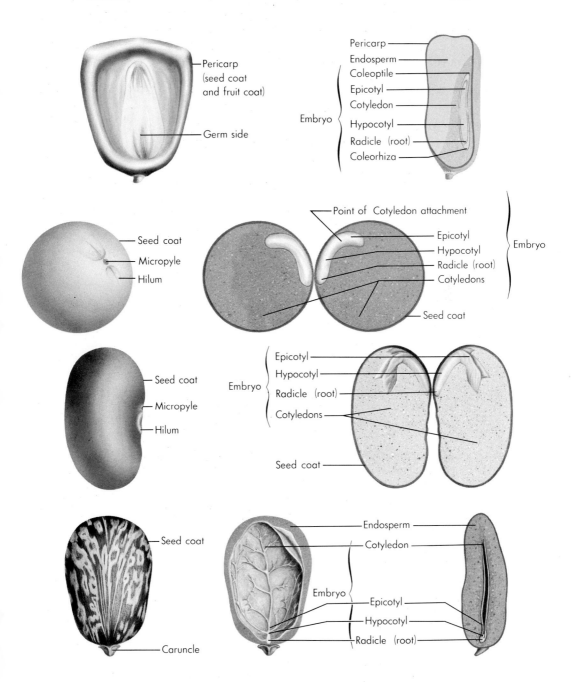

Figure 45   *Seeds and their parts. Starting from the top, these are corn, Alaska pea, Kentucky Wonder bean, and castor bean.*

is obvious that something else has happened. The cells of leaves, stems, and roots are not all alike. What is it that causes them to differentiate? This is a question which biologists have not yet answered. Some of the processes involved in the germination of seeds and the growth of plants are well understood; others are not. We will look at some of the problems in each of these two categories.

PATTERN OF INQUIRY 6

Developing Seedlings

It has been observed that as the shoot and root of the corn and castor bean grow, the endosperm becomes smaller. As the shoot and root of the bean plant grow in size and dry weight, there is a decrease in the dry weight of the cotyledons. What explanation can you give for such data? What was it that moved?

INVESTIGATION 19   Enzyme Activity in Germinating Seeds

Materials (per team)

1. Corn grains
2. Three petri plates
3. Starch agar
4. Razor blades
5. Iodine solution
6. Tes-Tape

Procedure (per team), Part One

1. Obtain 5 dry corn grains and 10 corn grains which have been soaked for 24 hours.
2. Prepare 3 culture dishes by pouring not more than 15 ml of melted starch agar into each of 3 petri plates or similar containers. Allow the agar to cool, then cover the dishes. Label completely as to team, class, experiment, date, and treatment.
3. With a sharp razor blade or scalpel carefully cut both the dry grains and the soaked grains lengthwise, as in the diagram (see Figure 46). Place 5 of the soaked grains (10 halves) in boiling water and boil for at least 20 minutes.

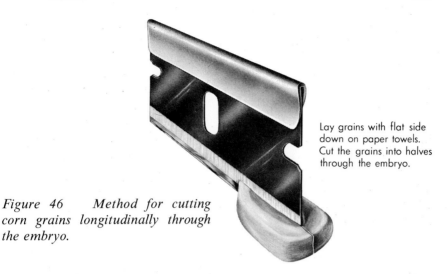

Lay grains with flat side down on paper towels. Cut the grains into halves through the embryo.

Figure 46   Method for cutting corn grains longitudinally through the embryo.

4. Place 5 half-grains from each group, dry, soaked, and boiled, in the appropriate dish so that the cut surface of the grain is in contact with the surface of the agar. Actually the embryo will be in contact with the agar. Space them wide apart but not too close to the edge of the dish (see Figure 47).

Place half grains on starch agar with cut surface of embryo in contact with agar.

Figure 47   Position of the split corn grains on the starch agar.

5. Leave the dishes at room temperature for 24 hours.
6. At the end of 24 hours, remove the grains from the agar and pour a few drops of iodine solution on the surface of the agar in each dish. Swish it around and immediately pour it off. Rinse the surface of the agar carefully with tap water.

QUESTIONS FOR DISCUSSION

1. What change, if any, has taken place in the starch agar where the corn embryos were placed?

2. How was this experiment controlled?

Procedure, Part Two

1. Dip one end of a Tes-Tape paper into the agar zone where the corn embryos were placed.
2. Allow the Tes-Tape paper to remain in the agar for 5 to 10 minutes. A color change in the paper indicates the presence of a simple sugar.
3. Set aside the agar plates for the tetrazolium test which will follow.

QUESTIONS FOR DISCUSSION

1. What might be a good control for the Tes-Tape investigation?

2. Explain the importance of formulating "if . . . , then . . ." statements to guide experimental design.

INVESTIGATION 20   **Isolation of an Enzyme**

The test just completed indicates that starch has been changed into sugar. Now consider an experiment which will give more evidence for the hypothesis that an enzyme is responsible for this change. If the enzyme diffused into the agar and changed the starch, then the agar found under the germinating embryo should contain some of the enzyme.

Design and carry out an experiment which will demonstrate the presence of an enzyme in the agar.

QUESTIONS FOR DISCUSSION

1. Do the results of this test indicate that you have been able to isolate the enzyme which is responsible for changing starch into sugar?

2. What further test would be necessary before you could say the substance is an enzyme?

INVESTIGATIONS FOR FURTHER STUDY

How can you test the rate of diffusion of the enzyme?

Another sugar test which can be applied to the clear area is the tetrazolium test. Colorless 2,3,5-triphenyltetrazolium chloride, when in the presence of reducing sugars, will be reduced to a pink color. Apply a solution of tetrazolium to the clear areas on the plates just tested and see if it indicates the presence of reducing sugars.

When a seed begins to sprout, we say it germinates, and we know it is viable. Imagine the disappointment and financial loss if a farmer or florist were to plant a batch of seeds and very few of them sprouted. To minimize such a possibility, many seed growers and the departments of agriculture of various states routinely test samples of seeds to determine what percentage will germinate. The germination test consists of planting a sample of seeds under standardized conditions and then determining the percentage which germinate. One drawback of this method is that it takes several days for the seeds to germinate. We may approach the problem from another angle, however, using the "if . . . , then . . ." statement. If a seed is alive, then enzymes should be changing starch to sugar in the seed. If reducing sugars are present, then the tetrazolium test should give a positive result. Thus the tetrazolium test should be an accurate indication of the percentage of live seeds in a sample.

| INVESTIGATION 21 | **Testing for Seed Viability** |

You are asked to provide the procedure for this Investigation. Using the "if . . . , then . . ." reasoning, design an experiment to test the hypothesis that there is no difference in the percentage of viable seeds as determined by the germination test and by the tetrazolium test. If you use pea seeds for the tetrazolium test, split them as shown in Figure 48. You may find a chart similar to Chart C, page 176, useful in recording your data.

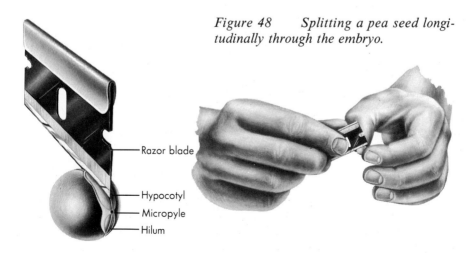

Figure 48   Splitting a pea seed longitudinally through the embryo.

Razor blade

Hypocotyl

Micropyle

Hilum

CHART C. **Comparison of Germination and Tetrazolium Tests as Measures of Seed Viability**

	Germination test	*Tetrazolium test*	
		Unboiled seeds	*Boiled seeds*
Total number of seeds			
Number of "viable" seeds			
Percent of "viable" seeds			

QUESTIONS FOR DISCUSSION

1. How does the percentage of viability, as determined by the tetrazolium test, compare with the percentage of viability, as determined by the germination test?

2. If you wished to know if the data showed any significant difference between the two tests, what test for significance would you use? Why?

3. Apply the test of significance which you have selected. Are the differences significant?

4. What does the tetrazolium test actually indicate?

5. In what part of the seeds examined was the chemical action greatest?

INVESTIGATIONS FOR FURTHER STUDY

Design experiments to answer the following questions:

1. Would similar results be obtained from dry seeds?

2. What is the minimum time that seeds must be soaked to bring about the tetrazolium reaction?

3. Would similar results be obtained with a piece of raw potato cut from a point near a growing sprout? How near the growing sprout must it be cut so that the reaction may be observed?

The tetrazolium test makes use of our knowledge of some of the chemical reactions which take place in active cells as a basis for a seed viability test which is much quicker than germination tests. There are, however, many cases in which neither the tetrazolium test nor the germination test will tell us whether or not the seeds are capable of germinating. Many species produce seeds which will not germinate even though they are placed in an environment which we would expect to be favorable for them, and in which at some other time, they may germinate well. We call this condition in which seeds will not germinate *dormancy*. In many cases dormancy of seeds is a distinct advantage to the species. Why?

Many different factors cause dormancy in seeds. In some species, the embryo apparently must continue a part of its development under environmental conditions which are different from those in which the seeds were formed or in which they may eventually germinate. For example, some seeds may germinate well only after having been stored in a cold moist room for several months. Other seeds contain chemicals which inhibit their germination. If these are leached out, the seeds may grow immediately. Some seeds have hard coats which may prevent the entrance of water or of oxygen. They also may physically prevent growth until the coat is weakened or broken either by cracking or by the action of bacteria or fungi.

There are many other mechanisms which control dormancy in seeds. We will study only one of these in any depth. Our problem is introduced by the next Pattern of Inquiry.

PATTERN OF INQUIRY 7

Factors Affecting Seed Germination

A new home owner in Iowa was faced with the problem of establishing a lawn. His lot was on the side of a hill, and erosion was a problem, especially in the front of the house. He carefully prepared the ground and seeded it with Kentucky bluegrass, which is a very successful lawn grass in that region. Preparation of the ground and seeding of the front and back lawns were done in a similar manner, except that after scattering the seed the owner thoroughly raked the surface of the front lawn in order to cover the seed. He did not find time to do this in the back yard before a period of wet weather set in, and this prevented further working of the soil.

In a week he noticed that many seeds in the back yard had germinated. In two weeks it was green with a good stand of seedlings, but in the front yard, he found that only a small percentage of the seeds had grown. After six weeks there was still a very poor stand of grass there. What was responsible for the difference in growth of the grass in the two areas?

Parallel Reading: Some Concepts of Light Energy

The germination of the seeds of some varieties of lettuce, like that of bluegrass seeds, has been observed to be quite erratic. Light has been shown to be an important factor in the germination of these seeds. In order to explore the role of light in germination, the investigator must have a working knowledge of the nature of light. In preparation for the investigations which follow, a brief discussion of this subject is appropriate. It takes the place of the literature search and specialized study which the researcher in science properly makes before beginning work on a problem.

Present-day study of the nature of light is based largely on a combination of two theories, each of which explains some of the complex phenomena. According to one theory, light travels in waves somewhat similar in nature to water or sound waves; therefore, we speak of the frequency and amplitude of light waves. (Frequency measures the number of wave crests which pass a given point in a given time; amplitude measures the height of the waves.) We recognize differences in frequencies of light waves as colors, and differences in amplitudes as light intensities.

The corpuscular theory considers light to be composed of small particles traveling at extremely high speeds. Each particle, or *photon,* possesses a definite amount of energy, a *quantum.* According to this theory, light intensity depends on the amount of energy delivered to a given area in a given amount of time by all of the photons striking it. Light quality (color) is determined by the energy of the individual photons.

Attempts to unify these two theories have led to useful mathematical descriptions of the energy relationships of light, although a completely unified theory of light has not yet been formulated. However, the blending of the two theories permits us to deal with different aspects of radiation. The properties of reflection and refraction are best explained by the wave theory. Photochemical effects, however, are most easily explained by the corpuscular (quantum) theory.

Light, considered as a form of wave motion, is only one part of a wide span of electromagnetic radiation consisting of waves ranging in length from extremely short distances to thousands of miles. The waves that cause visible light are not the shortest of these waves, but they are too short to measure using ordinary units of length. To deal with them, the millimicron (mμ) and the Angstrom unit (Å) are used. A millimicron is 1/1,000,000,000 of a meter (1 $\times$ 10^{-9} meter). An Angstrom unit is 1/10,000,000,000 of a meter (1 $\times$ 10^{-10} meter). Thus we speak of certain radiant energy as having a wavelength of 5000 Å, or 500 mμ. As a matter of fact, 445 mμ is one way of describing a particular shade of blue, and we can describe a particular shade of red as being 6540 Å (654.0 mμ).

Figure 49, a diagram of the spectrum of the electromagnetic radiations known to man, gives an idea of the position occupied by visible light.

The visible part of the spectrum is the range of wavelengths of energy which our eyes can sense. It is bounded on the one side by violet, the shortest visible wavelength, and on the other side by red, the longest visible wavelength. These two limits encompass the series of colors familiar to us in the rainbow, because water droplets in the path of light rays separate the light into its several component wavelengths. Certain prisms will also divide white light into its various parts.

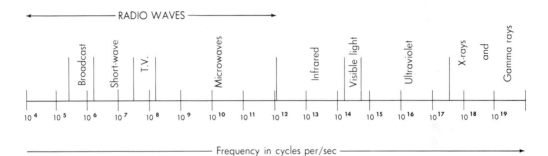

Figure 49   Spectrum of wavelengths.

Radiation of wavelengths too short to be seen is called ultraviolet, and that of wavelengths too long to be seen is called infrared. A considerable range of wavelengths still shorter than those ordinarily referred to as ultraviolet may be produced by X-ray machines or by events within the nuclei of atoms. These are called X rays and gamma rays respectively. The distinction between these two is based on the sources and not on the wavelength.

It should be noted that the frequency varies inversely with the wavelength. Radiation of short wavelength has high frequency. The quantum (the energy possessed by a single photon), is proportional to the frequency. Thus, a quantum at 350 Å has twice as much energy as one at 700 Å.

When an object in sunlight reflects all the visible wavelengths, we say that the object is white. If the object reflects none of the visible wavelengths, our eyes receive no radiation, and we say the color is black. Those wavelengths which are not reflected are either absorbed by the object or transmitted. A piece of clear glass transmits most of the light falling on it, and a piece of colored glass transmits some, absorbs some, and reflects some. We say that an object is green if it transmits or reflects green and absorbs a high percentage of the other colors present in the white light.

Light energy which is absorbed may be converted to heat, which is another form of energy; however, the energy of a photon may be transferred to an electron, causing the electron to leave its original place. An example is the photoelectric effect, the basis for such instruments as the photoelectric light meter. Again, the energy of photons may be absorbed by certain molecules in such a way that an electron in a compound is raised to a higher energy level. The structure of the molecule may be changed by this, or the molecule may react more readily. The chemical change which results is called a photochemical reaction. The conversion of ergosterol to vitamin D, and the light reaction in photosynthesis are examples of photochemical reactions.

In order to study the effects of light on plants in the laboratory, a source of light is necessary. If our results are to be compared with those of other workers, we must know the intensity and quality of the radiation. (Remember that intensity refers to the amount of energy, and quality refers to the wavelength.)

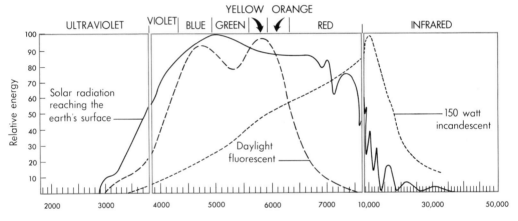

Figure 50   Distribution of wavelengths in Angstrom units.

Figure 50 shows the distribution of wavelengths given as percentages of the total light emitted by different sources. Notice that the frequencies present in sunlight are represented by the solid line. Of the many types of artificial lamps, the common incandescent and fluorescent lamps come closest to producing light similar in quality to that of the sun. Notice that incandescent lamps have relatively less energy in the lower wavelengths (below 5500 Å), and fluorescent lamps relatively less energy in the higher wavelengths (above 6500 Å). In attempting to reproduce sunlight, it is best to use a combination of incandescent and fluorescent light.

On the basis of this brief summary of the nature of light, we can now proceed to design a series of experiments on the effects of light on germination. The following Investigation is designed to explore the question, "What is the effect of light on germination?"

INVESTIGATION 22	**Effects of Light on Germination of Seeds**

There are three possible answers to the question.

1. Light promotes germination.
2. Light inhibits germination.
3. Light has no effect on germination.

First, we may ask, "Does light promote, inhibit, or have no effect on the germination of two varieties of lettuce?" To find the answer, we can set up germination test conditions with,

1. Grand Rapids lettuce seeds in light and in darkness
2. Great Lakes lettuce seeds in light and in darkness

Procedure

Develop your own procedures after class discussion of the problem. Your teacher may wish to suggest some modifications. When you have completed the experiment, combine the data obtained by your team with that obtained by other teams using the same procedure, and evaluate the results.

QUESTIONS FOR DISCUSSION

1. Is it easy to make a decision about the effect of light on the germination of the two varieties of lettuce?

2. On the basis of the data obtained by all the teams in your class, use an appropriate test of significance to determine whether the difference between the treatments in each variety is significant. Do the results for each variety represent a normal distribution within one population, or do they represent two populations?

If we can determine that light has affected the germination of one of the varieties of lettuce, the next question might be, "Do all light bands (wavelengths) equally affect germination of the seeds?" If, on the basis of the work just completed, no decision can be made as to the difference in this respect between the two varieties, then both varieties should be tested.

To answer our question, an experiment can be designed in which the wavelengths reaching the seeds are controlled. This can be done by producing the desired wavelengths with a special lamp, or by removing with filters the wavelengths not desired in natural or artificial light. An example of a lamp producing a narrow wave band is the germicidal bulb found in many clothes driers and refrigerators (2300–2800 Å).

By proper selection of filters and light sources, we can obtain fairly narrow wave bands of light which will be satisfactory for our purposes. The relative energy emitted in the different wavelengths by a daylight fluorescent lamp and by a 150-watt incandescent lamp is shown in Figure 50, page 180. Dark blue cellophane transmits little light between 5575 Å and 6575 Å. It does, however, transmit a high percentage of light which is beyond 7000 Å. Green cellophane transmits relatively little light below 5800 Å. By combining these filters with the fluorescent or the incandescent lamps, it is possible to provide four different bands of light to which the seeds can be exposed. The following table shows some of the approximate light bands which may be obtained in this way.

TABLE 15. **Light Bands Obtained Using Different Filters**

Light source		Filter		Approximate light bands
Daylight Fluorescent	+	Blue filter	=	3900–5500 Å
Daylight Fluorescent	+	Green filter	=	4700–5800 Å
Daylight Fluorescent	+	Red filter	=	5800–6800 Å
150-Watt Incandescent	+	Red and blue filter	=	7000 Å up

The design of the following experiment may be stated according to the "If . . . , then . . ." logic as follows: if the various wavelengths of light directly affect germination, then a difference in the percent of germination should be observable in seeds exposed to varying wavelengths.

INVESTIGATION 23	**The Effects of Different Wavelengths of Light on Germination of Seeds**

Procedure

After discussion with the class and with your teacher, work out procedures which may be expected to test the above hypothesis.

QUESTIONS FOR DISCUSSION

1. What conclusions can you draw from this experiment?

2. Can you think of any other factor in this experiment which might have influenced your results?

INVESTIGATIONS FOR FURTHER STUDY

1. What would be the result if you were to alternate exposures to the different light bands which influenced the germination of lettuce seeds?

2. The modern botanist is still seeking answers to the exact mechanism that "triggers" growth in seeds which show dormancy. The seeds of many plants in your area have their own unique triggering mechanisms. It would be exceedingly difficult to give specific examples, since plants vary in different areas; however, several types of plants are listed below, one or more of which probably grow in your locality. Remember that any scientific research begins with a careful perusal of all library material that is available. If a college library is near, it may be possible to locate papers that have been published about dormancy of plants in your area. Don't overlook the texts and reference materials in your school or local library. *Scientific American* reprints that will give you a great deal of assistance are "Germination" by Dov Koller (April, 1959), and "Light and Plant Development" by Butler and Downs (December, 1960).

   Collect as many different types of seeds as you can. You can then design your own investigation of germination using the materials you have available. You will need several seeds of each type so that you can vary the types of treatments used. You might try various methods of scarification; differing concentrations of gases, salts, or acids; alternate freezing and thawing of moist seeds; alternation of wet and dry periods; or combinations of these treatments.

   You may find it useful to experiment with the seeds of one or more of the following species: hawthorn, cocklebur, maple, tobacco, wild sunflower (*Helianthus annuus*), cactus (these must be taken directly from the fruit), any other desert plant, or any members of the genera *Pinus, Betula, Fraxinus, Nasturtium, Bidens,* or *Trifolium.* The seeds of many of these will exhibit some kind of dormancy.

These investigations with germinating seeds may illustrate how some research develops. The tests for germination are rather simple, but the explanation for some types of dormancy may be very difficult to obtain. The effect of light on the germination of lettuce seeds is probably a result of the effects of light on the pigment phytochrome which is also involved in the response of plants to different day lengths (photoperiodism). There is, however, still a great deal to be learned about many of these phenomena. Most certainly it will require extended work by both botanists (plant physiologists) and biochemists before complete understanding of such reactions is possible.

The same can be said for nearly all aspects of plant growth and development. You may be familiar with Van Helmont's experiments from which he inferred that a plant takes everything which it needs for growth from air and water. He neglected the few ounces of weight which were lost from the soil during the growth of the plant, probably regarding them as an error of measurement. In this case, the neglect of some of the data led to an erroneous concept of the source of raw materials for plant growth.

Since Van Helmont's day many advances have been made in our understanding of mineral nutrition of plants. The following Investigation illustrates one way in which you might study the requirements of plants for certain chemical elements.

| INVESTIGATION 24 | Mineral Requirements of Sorghum Plants |

Materials (per team)

1. Eight test tubes, 22 mm × 175 mm
2. Twenty seeds of RS610 sorghum

Materials (per class)

1. A cardboard box large enough to hold the prepared test tubes of each team, and a styrofoam plastic top with holes drilled to accommodate the test tubes. (See Figure 51, page 187.)
2. Stock solutions as shown in Table 16
3. Minus N, Minus P, Minus Fe, and complete mineral solutions for culture of plants as shown in Table 17, page 186
4. Cotton for stoppering test tubes
5. A supply of distilled or deionized water

Procedure

1. The following stock solutions may be available or students may be asked to prepare them. Be sure all glassware is chemically clean, and that only analytical grade chemicals are dissolved in distilled water. The amounts specified should be ample for the class.

TABLE 16. **Preparation of Stock Solutions for Growth of Sorghum Plants**

Chemical	Amount	Amount of distilled or deionized water
1. $Ca(NO_3)_2 \cdot 4 H_2O$	23.6 grams	200 ml
2. KNO_3	10.0 grams	200 ml
3. $MgSO_4 \cdot 7 H_2O$	4.2 grams	300 ml
4. KH_2PO_4	4.2 grams	300 ml
5. $CaCl_2$	5.6 grams	100 ml
6. KCl	1.6 grams	200 ml
7. Iron chelate (iron ethylenediamine-tetra acetate)	1.0 gram	100 ml

8. Trace elements (A stock solution should be made up to contain the following salts in the concentrations shown.)

a. $MnCl_2 \cdot 4 H_2O$	1.8 grams
b. H_3BO_3	2.8 grams
c. $ZnSO_4 \cdot 7 H_2O$	0.22 grams*
d. $CuSO_4 \cdot 5 H_2O$	0.08 grams*
e. $Na_2MoO_4 \cdot 2 H_2O$	0.025 grams*

   f. Distilled or deionized water to make 1,000 ml.

* The difficulty in weighing these small amounts of material directly can be avoided by using aliquots of more concentrated solutions of each. For example,

Weigh out:	Dissolve in:	Use:
2.2 grams of $ZnSO_4 \cdot 7 H_2O$	100 ml of water	10 ml per liter
0.8 grams of $CuSO_4 \cdot 5 H_2O$	100 ml of water	10 ml per liter
2.5 grams of $Na_2MoO_4 \cdot 2 H_2O$	100 ml of water	1 ml per liter

2. Prepare the four mineral culture solutions in which you will grow the plants. To do this, add each of the indicated stock solutions to about 500 ml of distilled or deionized water and then add enough water to make a total of one liter. (See Table 17.) If you mix the stock solutions without diluting them precipitates are likely to form, and these may be difficult to redissolve.

3. Each team should place about 20 seeds of RS 610 sorghum in a roll of moist paper towel and leave for 3 to 4 days. After the seeds are planted, stand the roll on end so that the roots will grow straight down, and the shoots straight up.

4. Each team should prepare 8 test tubes as follows: wash with a detergent; rinse thoroughly with tap water; then rinse thoroughly with deionized water. It is most important that the test tubes used in the experiment be chemically clean.

TABLE 17. **Preparation of Growth Solutions for Mineral Nutrition Investigation**

Stock solution	Number of milliliters to be added for 1 liter of culture solution			
	Complete	Minus N	Minus P	Minus Fe
$Ca(NO_3)_2 \cdot 4 H_2O$	10	—	10	10
KNO_3	10	—	10	10
$MgSO_4 \cdot 7 H_2O$	10	10	10	10
KH_2PO_4	10	10	—	10
$CaCl_2$	—	10	—	—
KCl	—	10	10	—
Iron chelate	10	10	10	—
Trace element stock	10	10	10	10
Water (distilled or deionized) enough to make:	1 liter	1 liter	1 liter	1 liter

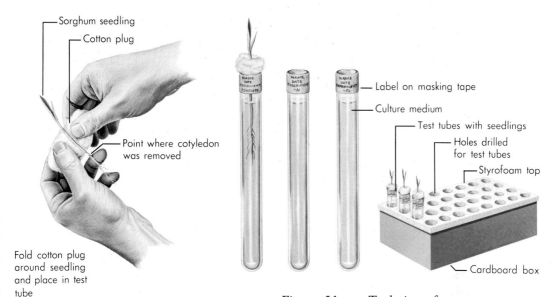

Sorghum seedling
Cotton plug
Point where cotyledon was removed
Fold cotton plug around seedling and place in test tube

Label on masking tape
Culture medium
Test tubes with seedlings
Holes drilled for test tubes
Styrofoam top
Cardboard box

Figure 51   Technique for setting up materials to study mineral nutrition.

5. Label each test tube by team, class, experiment, and date. Also label two of the tubes "complete," two "minus N," two "minus P," and two "minus Fe."

6. If you did not make them up, carefully study the formulas and procedures for making up the stock solutions and the culture solutions. Place enough of the culture solutions in the test tubes to fill them to within about 5 or 6 centimeters from the top. Each team should have two test tubes each of "minus N," "minus P," "minus Fe," and "complete" solutions.

7. Select eight uniform sorghum seedlings from the germination roll. Using a razor blade, carefully remove the cotyledon of each. Handle the seedlings with care, and keep the roots moist at all times.

8. Select pieces of cotton large enough to serve as stoppers for the test tubes. Fold the cotton around the seedling as shown in Figure 51, and insert the roots of the seedling into the culture solution. The point where the cotyledon was attached should be near the bottom of the cotton. Be careful to prevent the cotton from coming into contact with the solution. If the cotton gets wet, molds are likely to develop in it. Also be sure that the roots of each seedling dip into the solution. It is not necessary, however, that all of the root system be submerged. If the plug does not fit snugly, pack some additional cotton around it.

9. Place each labeled test tube containing a seedling in the cardboard box as illustrated in Figure 51, page 187. Then place the box in the best light available.

10. Observe the plants three times a week for at least two weeks. Keep the level of the solution high enough so that the roots always reach into it. If necessary, add distilled or deionized water, or better, discard the remaining solution and refill the tube with fresh culture medium. Study the plants carefully at each observation time. Record any changes either in the character of the root system or in color or appearance of the leaves.

QUESTIONS FOR DISCUSSION

1. Why were the cotyledons removed at the beginning of the investigation?

2. Why must the glassware be chemically clean for this investigation?

3. If you found a plant that exhibited chlorosis, how would you decide whether the deficiency was due to an inadequate supply of iron or of nitrogen?

4. On the basis of this investigation and any other information you may find, what conclusions can you draw as to the role of various elements—especially nitrogen, phosphorus, and iron—in plant growth and development?

SECTION THIRTEEN

GROWTH AND DEVELOPMENT IN ANIMALS

Since there is no characteristic or group of characteristics which enable us to draw a definite distinction between simple plants and simple animals, we cannot say that there are essential differences in the growth and development of these forms. In the higher animals, however, we find that there is more differentiation of cells into specialized tissues. The embryological development of higher animals is, therefore, more complex than that of higher plants. The formation of sperms and eggs may also involve more specialization than was described for the flowering plants.

Gametogenesis. As we have noted before, meiosis is essentially the same in both plants and animals. In the higher animals, meiosis leads almost directly to the formation of sperms and eggs, there being no intervening stages comparable to microgametophytes and megagametophytes, which are found in plants. Following meiosis, certain changes occur in the formation of sperms which result in a long-tailed, motile spermatozoan, or sperm cell. In the development of the egg, meiotic divisions of the nucleus are accompanied by unequal divisions of the cytoplasm, leading to the formation of one ovum (or egg) and three polar bodies which do not function.

Figure 52   A comparison of spermatogenesis and oögenesis in higher animals.

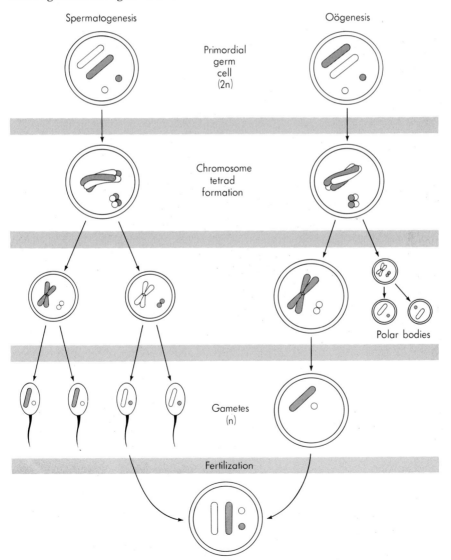

Development of sperms and eggs in higher animals is shown schematically in Figure 52.

Various sperms may look very different, but they all contain three basic parts. One part is the head, which consists of a nucleus of tightly packed chromosomes. Another basic part is the middlepiece with its centrosome, which will function in fertilization, and its mitochondria, in which presumably the processes which provide the energy for movement occur. The third part is the tail, which consists mainly of a central fiber and which is the locomotor organelle.

An egg is a giant cell compared to a sperm. In addition to a nucleus, which contains the genetic material and is similar in size to that of the sperm, the egg contains the usual constituents of the cytoplasm and the yolk or food supply for the developing embryo. The egg also has a protective covering of some sort, depending on the species of animal. There are great differences among eggs of animal species with respect to size, which depends on the amount of yolk present.

All eggs perform three functions: (1) they supply half the genetic material of the future embryo; (2) they supply all the cytoplasm of the fertilized egg; and (3) they supply food reserves that will enable the embryo to develop. The sex cells of animals are remarkably adapted to their respective roles in the reproductive process.

The Beginning of an Individual: Fusion of Gametes. If fertilization in most species of animals is to be successful, it cannot be delayed, because the eggs may die within a few hours if they are not fertilized. The egg, of course, has a good food reserve, but this is used for nourishment of the developing embryo, not for maintenance of the unfertilized egg.

Fertilization is accomplished when the sperm nucleus fuses with the egg nucleus. The first correct observation and description of the animal sperm was given in 1677 by the Dutch microscopist, Antony van Leeuwenhoek. At a later time, Leeuwenhoek postulated that the sperm penetrated the egg. He believed that the embryo developed from the sperm, and that the egg served only as a food supply.

One hundred seventy years later, sperm entry was positively demonstrated. George Newport is generally given credit for the first observation of a sperm penetrating an egg. The following is a footnote to the paper[1] in which he reported his observations of sperm penetration:

> Since this paper was communicated to the society, I have succeeded, through the adoption of a different mode of examination, in detecting spermatozoa within the vitelline cavity in direct communication with, and penetrating into the yelk [yolk]. They were first seen by myself, in company with a friend, on

[1] Newport, George. "On the impregnation of the ovum in the Amphibia and on the direct agency of the spermatozoan." *Philosophical Transactions of the Royal Society of London* for the year 1853—pp. 233–290.

the 25th of March of the present year [1853] within the clear chamber above the yelk, at about forty minutes after fecundation, when the chamber begins to be formed. I have since repeatedly observed them within the chamber, and in some instances still in motion, in which state I have had opportunities of showing them to my friend Professor Ellis of University College, and to two other medical friends, so that the presence of active spermatozoa within the vitelline cavity in the fecundated egg of the Frog may now be regarded as indisputable. The details of my investigation I reserve for a future communication, and will merely now add, that the spermatozoa do not reach the yelk of the Frog's egg by any special orifice or canal in the envelopes, but actually pierce the substance of the envelopes at any part with which they may happen to come into contact; as I have constantly observed while watching their entrance: sometime after they have entered the yelk chamber they become disintegrated and are resolved into elementary granules.

For purposes of discussion, it is convenient to consider fertilization as a sequence of phases. The first phase, or release of gametes, must occur at about the same time in both male and female because the gametes are short-lived cells. Once the gametes are released, the sperm must approach the egg. Contact between the sperm and egg is usually the result of random movement; however, some chemical attraction may occur. Although the sperms may be unguided missiles, a hit should be fairly easy when we consider the size of the egg in relation to the number of sperms. When the sperm contacts the egg, it must then enter into it; this entry is called *penetration*. The sperm head, or nucleus, may fuse with the egg nucleus. As a result of penetration followed by nuclear fusion, the egg is activated and embryo development begins. The activation of the egg by the sperm cannot as yet be completely explained. We can, however, observe these early events of development in the laboratory by using the frog as our experimental animal.

PREPARATORY TECHNIQUE 1	**Obtaining Frog Pituitaries**

To obtain frog eggs for observation and experimentation, the experimenter can induce ovulation in female frogs by injecting pituitary glands into their abdominal cavities. The number of pituitaries needed varies with the season of the year as follows:

October:	8 to 10
November and December:	5 to 6
January and February:	3 to 5
March and April:	1 to 3

To obtain the pituitaries, anesthetize as many frogs as will be required by placing them in a large container containing a wad of cotton saturated with ether or chloroform. Seal the container securely. Make certain that the frogs are under deep anesthesia before removing them from the jar.

Procedure

1. The top of the frog's head must be removed by three cuts, to avoid cutting through the pituitary. Remove the top of the head by a cut extending from the angle of the jaw past the tympanic membrane on each side of the head. Then make a transverse cut as indicated by the dotted line in A of Figure 53. Lay the top of the head mouthside upward and remove the skin from the roof of the mouth to expose the cross-shaped bone.
2. Locate the foramen magnum and carefully insert the tip of the scissors to one side. Cut through the brain case on each side as shown by the dashed lines in B of Figure 53.

Figure 53   Removal of the pituitary of a frog.

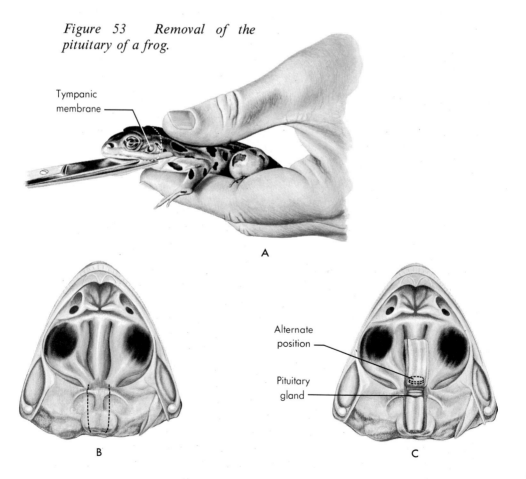

Tympanic membrane

A

Alternate position

Pituitary gland

B   C

3. Lift the flap of bone with forceps and locate the pituitary gland, a pinkish oval body. (It will be found either on the anterior end of the brain or on the flap of bone. See C of Figure 53.)

4. Remove the pituitary with forceps and strip off any adhering white tissue. Cut up the glands into small pieces and place them in a dish containing 10% Holtfreter's solution.

PREPARATORY TECHNIQUE 2	**Injecting Pituitaries**

Procedure

1. Draw the pieces of the required number of pituitary glands, along with about 1 ml of Holtfreter's solution, into the barrel of a hypodermic syringe before attaching the needle. Place a size 18 needle on the syringe and remove all the air from the syringe.

2. Hold a female frog on its back and insert the needle through the belly skin and muscle, being careful not to injure the ventral blood vessels and the intestines. Inject the pituitaries; then pinch the skin around the needle as you remove it. Continue holding the puncture closed for a few seconds to prevent the possible loss of pituitary material.

3. Draw additional solution into the syringe to check whether or not any pituitary fragments lodged in the needle. If they did, remove most of the solution from the syringe; then inject these glands as before.

4. Place the injected frog in about one-half inch of water in a covered container, and place it in a cool place (12 to 21°C).

5. Check the frog for ovulation after 48 hours by gently squeezing the abdomen toward the cloaca. Ovulation will usually occur after a period of between 48 and 72 hours. You can expect about 1000 eggs from each successful injection. When you are sure the female is gravid, keep it in the refrigerator until the eggs are needed.

CAUTION: *To be relatively sure of success, you should inject two females at a time, since there is a chance of death, or failure to ovulate. The hypodermic syringe and needle must be sterilized before and after the injection. (70% alcohol may be used for this.)*

PREPARATORY TECHNIQUE 3	**Fertilization *in Vitro***

Before removing the testes from the males and preparing the sperm suspension, the females should be test stripped to determine whether or not ovulation has been accomplished. The eggs which are removed in the test stripping should be discarded.

CAUTION: *The eggs must be stripped directly into the suspension of active sperms.* Immediately after ovulation the jelly surrounding the egg begins to swell, and those eggs not fertilized in a matter of minutes after they are stripped will not be fertilized.

Best results are usually obtained with the sperm from freshly removed testes. The testes may be dissected out a day or two before they are used, and the sperm within such testes will remain viable provided the testes are kept refrigerated.

Note: The testes must not be put in water. If they are to be stored, place them between layers of slightly moist cotton in a covered petri dish in the refrigerator.

Materials

1. A mature male frog

2. A mature female frog which has been previously injected with pituitary glands

3. Sharp, pointed scissors

4. Sharp forceps

5. Cotton

6. Covered glass dishes

7. Medicine dropper

8. 10% Holtfreter's solution

Procedure

1. To remove the testes, use a male frog that has been double pithed (that is, the central nervous system has been destroyed so that it can no longer feel anything). Open the body cavity of the frog and move the digestive organs aside to expose the testes which are whitish-yellow, ovoid bodies. Use scissors and forceps to remove the testes from the body cavity. Rinse the testes by dipping them in saline solution; then blot them gently on paper toweling.

2. To prepare the sperm suspension, place the pair of testes in a petri dish moistened with a thin film of 10% Holtfreter's solution. Use scissors and forceps to cut and tear the testes into the tiniest pieces possible. If any sizeable pieces persist, mash them with the end of a solid glass rod. Then add 20 ml of 10% Holtfreter's solution to the dish, and allow 10 minutes for the sperm to begin swimming actively.

3. To strip and to fertilize the eggs, hold the injected female frog back downward in the palm of one hand. (Do not squeeze the frog until you are ready for the eggs.) Grasp the hind legs with the other hand; then squeeze gently over paper toweling until several eggs have been stripped. Wipe the cloaca dry; then proceed to strip 100 or more eggs into the sperm suspension. When stripping the eggs, squeeze gently and move the female around over the dish so that the eggs form a ribbon and do not pile up. Draw some of the sperm suspension into a medicine dropper and use it to bathe the eggs. Allow the eggs to remain in the sperm suspension for 10 to 15 minutes. During this time, examine the orientation of the eggs and compare the number of eggs that show the black area up with the number that show the white area up. If any eggs that were fertilized earlier in the day are available, examine them to see if their orientation has changed. After 15 minutes, pour the sperm suspension out of the petri dish and replace it with pond water. Let the eggs stand until near the end of the class period, while the jelly that surrounds the eggs swells slowly.

Once the eggs have been fertilized, allow as much time as possible for the jelly to swell before transferring them. If the eggs are moved too soon, damage may result. When the newly fertilized eggs are lifted from the glass, they must be handled with great care; they should not be sucked into a pipette or medicine dropper, or subjected to any other stress that would distort them and thus destroy their organization.

PREPARATORY TECHNIQUE 4	**Establishing and Maintaining Frog Embryo Cultures**

There should be enough eggs fertilized to provide for both establishment of cultures at room temperature and development in the temperature-gradient box. In addition, enough embryos might be permitted to develop at room temperature to provide tadpoles for future investigations.

As soon as the eggs have been fertilized and the jelly has swelled to the extent that it can be recognized as a separate mass surrounding each egg, the large mass of eggs should be divided, with the aid of scissors, into smaller masses of from 5 to 10 eggs. These smaller masses can then be transferred to the appropriate dishes. Either 100 ml of pond water or 10% Holtfreter's solution in each dish is adequate for 50 eggs to develop through Stage 25. (See Figure 55, page 198.) As soon as the majority of eggs in each dish hatch, it is advisable to place either a small mass of growing filamentous algae or a sprig of *Elodea* in the dish. This will provide both food and oxygen for the embryos as they develop.

Frog embryos have the ability to develop over a wide range of temperatures, although the rate of development varies. By maintaining small batches of embryos at different temperatures and examining them every day, you will see more stages of development than if you maintained the embryos at only one temperature. Using different temperatures will also enable you to make several important observations about the influence of temperature on the rate of development. To provide conditions of varying temperature, the temperature-gradient box is used. As shown in the diagram, this is a specially constructed box to be used inside a refrigerator. Note the following points:

(a) The temperature adjustment: determine which way you must turn the screw to raise (or lower) the temperature.

(b) The light bulb: a new, long-life, 100-watt incandescent bulb is used.

(c) The 110-volt, plug-in cord: this must be plugged into an outlet or extension cord outside the refrigerator. (When the door of a refrigerator is shut, the power supply to the outlet inside the refrigerator is automatically disconnected.)

(d) The box itself: when the door is closed, the box should be as nearly airtight as possible above the air space at the bottom. This measure prevents convection currents inside the box which will destroy the gradient of temperatures.

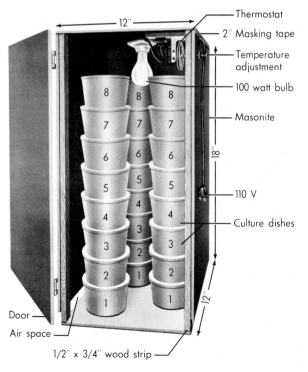

Figure 54   A temperature gradient box.

(e) The stacks of numbered dishes in the box: these are 8-ounce, polyethylene, refrigerator dishes with snap-on tops. They are numbered for identification so that the progression of numbers agrees with the progression of temperatures.

The box should be placed in the refrigerator with each of the dishes containing, as mentioned before, about 100 ml of either natural pond water or 10% Holtfreter's solution. The thermostat should be adjusted to obtain the desired temperatures; the temperature of the water should be checked and recorded daily for at least a week before the frog eggs are placed in the dishes. If the box is placed in a refrigerator that will maintain a temperature of 6°C, and the thermostat on the gradient box is adjusted so that the temperature of the eighth dish is 28°C, you should be able to maintain a fairly even gradient of temperatures from approximately 8°C to 28°C. The space at the bottom of the box aids in temperature regulation. Partial closure of this space can be used to increase the gradient of temperature inside the box.

If the refrigerator will not maintain temperatures as low as 8°C, you can still achieve satisfactory results. Some of the earlier stages in development may be missed (see page 198), but in general, at any temperature between 6°C and 14°C there should be no more than one stage of development each 24 hours.

INVESTIGATION 25   Development of the Frog Embryo

Dishes containing fertilized eggs should be placed in the temperature gradient box and in suitable locations at room temperature. They should be allowed to remain until the following day, when observation of development may begin. Observations should be compared with the stages shown on Shumway's Chart, Figure 55, page 198.

Procedure

1. First examine the eggs that have been left at room temperature. Have they changed since the previous day? Grasp an egg mass with forceps and flip it over, so that you can see the side which had faced downward. Place some of the eggs under a hand lens or dissecting microscope, illuminate them brightly, and determine as fully as you can what has happened to them in the past 24 hours. Refer to Shumway's Chart. Can you tell what stage they are in?

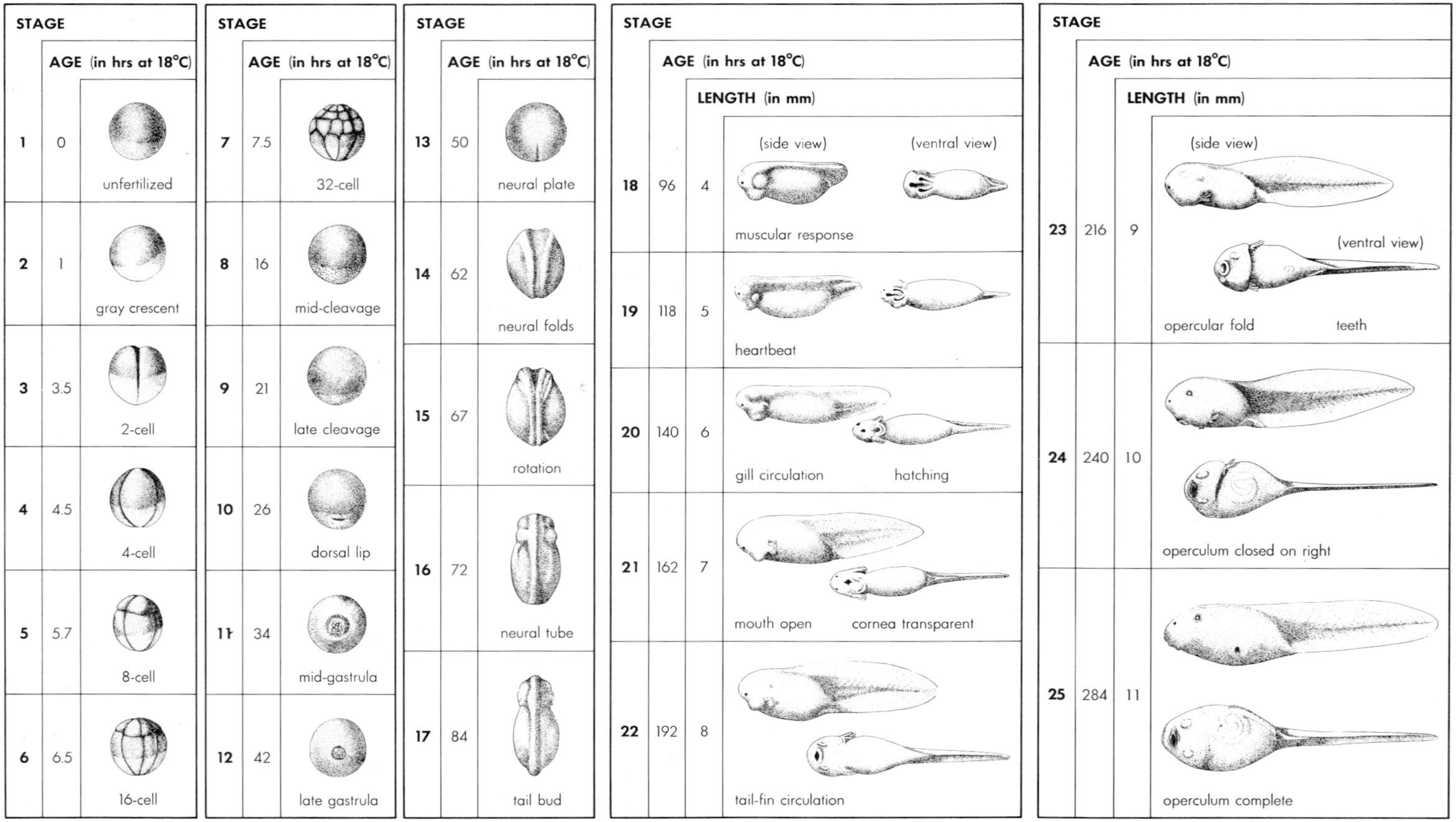

Figure 55   Shumway's Chart and drawings of the stages of development of Rana pipiens. (Courtesy of The Anatomical Record, vol. 78, no. 2, Oct., 1940.)

2. In observing the dishes from the temperature gradient box in the refrigerator, notice that the dishes in each stack are numbered consecutively with No. 1 on the bottom and the largest number at the top. Every dish must be returned to the same place in the box after each class has observed it. Each stack of dishes will serve two teams, one team observing the odd-numbered dishes, the other observing the even-numbered ones. One member from each of the two teams using a stack should remove the dishes for his team and distribute them. As soon as you get the dishes, carefully check and record the temperature of the water.

3. Examine the developing embryos, using bright illumination and a hand lens or dissecting microscope. Refer to Shumway's Chart. Can you count the cells in any of the younger embryos (i.e., those developing at lower temperatures)? Are the cells of the light yolk area the same size as those in the dark pigmented area? Is the yolk completely covered in any of the eggs?

4. Record the stage of the embryos in each dish, and note any special features that you see. All embryos in a single dish (i.e., at the same temperature) will be in approximately the same stage; any that appear to be in a different stage are probably dead or damaged, and should be removed. How much do the embryos developing at different temperatures differ from each other? Does this experiment determine the highest and lowest temperature at which frog embryos of this species will develop?

Between Stages 17 and 18, the nervous and muscular systems have developed sufficiently for some movement to be possible. As embryos reach Stage 17, notice that some do not move of their own accord. Using a fine bristle mounted on a handle, poke the embryos. Carefully note and record the extent and type of movement of embryos at various stages until you have determined the sequence of movements leading to the ability to swim.

QUESTIONS FOR DISCUSSION

1. What changes did you observe during the first 20 to 30 minutes after the eggs were fertilized?

2. Why were the egg masses cut into small groups?

3. What questions that you have answered in this section can be answered best by using statistical tests?

4. Why do you think that the zygote undergoes cleavages before developing further?

5. At what stage of development does the embryo begin to resemble an animal form? What features lend "animal form" to the embryo?

6. Do larvae raised at lower temperatures look the same as those raised at higher temperatures? Do they swim as well?

7. What does the answer which you have found to Question 6 tell you about the natural development of frog embryos out-of-doors?

Summary of Development of the Frog Embryo. Your observations of frogs have prepared you for the following summary of the various stages of embryonic development. When the amphibian egg cleaves, the actual cleavage plane can be seen to cross the surface of the pigmented animal hemisphere and slowly make its way downward into the yolky area until the entire egg is divided into two equal halves. (See Figure 56.) Before the first cleavage plane has completely extended to the light vegetal hemisphere, a second cleavage plane begins at right angles to the first and slightly above the equator. Subsequently, the egg splits into smaller and smaller cells, even though the cells of the animal region are, for a long time, smaller than those of the vegetal region. When the cells have become quite small, they all tend to move close to the surface. As a result of this movement, a fluid-filled space is formed inside the embryo. This stage of the embryo is called a blastula. (See Figure 56.)

Since you have examined most stages of development in the laboratory, only points of special interest will be described here. At the end of the blastula stage, the embryo undergoes gastrulation to become a gastrula. In this process, some of the dark surface material folds inward and forms a new inner layer of tissue. The first sign of this event is the appearance of a short, faint, black line just below the edge of the pigmented area. Experimental embryologists have shown that this point marks the mid-line of the future animal's back. Later the line becomes a definite curve, and finally a complete circle is formed. The line represents the area where material from the surface is being folded under to form the new layer inside the embryo. As it folds under, the surface material also stretches downward. You may see some embryos in which the yolk region is completely, or almost completely, enveloped by the pigmented material, leaving only a little "polka-dot" blastopore on the under surface.

The surface material actually stretches down over the yolk and then moves inside. Its movements can be traced by placing marks on the outside of the blastula and watching the movement of the marked areas. An embryo of a species having light-colored pigment is used for such a study.

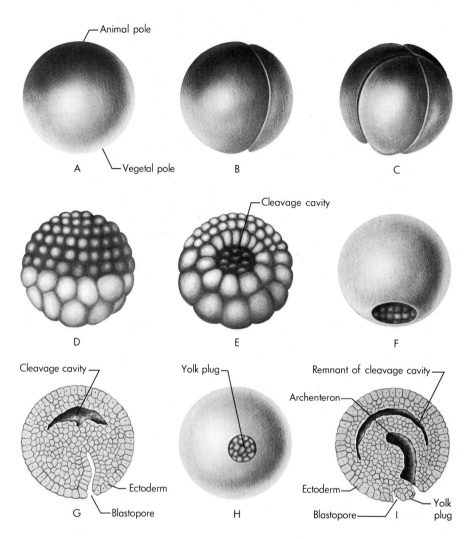

Figure 56   *Stages in the early development of an amphibian: A, single-cell stage; B and C, early cleavage stages; D, blastula, external view; E, blastula with cells removed to show cleavage cavity; F, early gastrula, external view; G, section through early gastrula; H, late gastrula, external view; I, section through late gastrula just prior to organ formation.*

Bits of agar are soaked in a vital dye (a colored substance that can stain living tissue without injuring it), and are then pressed against the embryo's surface so that small blue or red marks are printed on it. As gastrulation proceeds, the small, round marks may be seen to grow longer, move toward the region of infolding, and then turn and disappear inside. If the outer layer of the embryo is peeled away, the marks can actually be seen in the inner layer.

Once gastrulation has been completed, the embryo begins to form itself into something that can be recognized as an animal. The processes by which it does this are remarkably similar to the processes of development of the blastoderm of any vertebrate embryo and serve as a good illustration of the fact that young embryos tend to carry out their early developmental stages in a similar way. After gastrulation, the frog embryo develops a flattened neural plate. Folds rise up along the edges of this plate, then grow together until they meet in the mid-line. (See Figure 55.) The tube formed becomes the central nervous system—the spinal cord and the brain, which is very much like the embryo brain of any other vertebrate and which is formed in just the same way. As in other vertebrates, the future eyes bulge out of the brain at its anterior end.

Soon a series of block-shaped somites appear along the sides of the spinal cord; these will produce the backbone, muscles, and part of the skin. Later, a heart forms and begins to beat. The basic pattern of the circulatory system, at the time when the blood begins to flow, is identical in bird and frog embryos.

There is a brief period of time when the body plan of all vertebrate embryos is basically the same. Later, each embryo progresses toward the precise form it is to attain. The developing frog changes gradually from the short, compact larva to the active, swimming tadpole. Several months or more pass before the tadpole undergoes metamorphosis and becomes a mature frog.

Amphibians are very much limited by the fact that they must reproduce in water. The vertebrates took a big step forward in evolution when some of the ancient reptiles began to produce eggs that could be laid on land. Such eggs were necessarily large, because they had to contain sufficient water to supply the young animal through its developmental period. This step was important because it enabled the reptiles, and subsequently their bird and mammalian descendents, to move away from the edges of ponds and streams to populate the continents.

Frogs and salamanders, like all amphibians, are often called "cold-blooded" animals. This term is really a misnomer, since the body temperature of these animals is variable rather than cold. It rises and falls with the temperature of the environment. Animals which cannot maintain their own body temperatures at a constant level cannot provide heat for incubating their developing young, as birds and mammals do. The development of the frog embryo is not limited to a certain definite temperature, but rather it slows down at low temperatures and speeds up at high temperatures, just as plants grow faster in warm weather than they do in cold.

Parallel Reading: The Genetic Control of Differentiation

As outlined above, a single fertilized egg undergoes a series of mitotic divisions, and, in the process of dividing and multiplying, assumes a shape and gradually differentiates into cells of markedly different appearance, size, and function. We have previously learned to associate differences between organisms with differences in genetic makeup. How is it possible for genetically identical cells to become divergent?

One answer was suggested in 1893 by the well-known German biologist, August Weissmann, who suggested that not all daughter cells received identical sets of genetic determinants. Instead, cells in different parts of the embryo would receive different sets of "instructions," corresponding to the specializations in tissues and cells that are found in the developed organism. In modern terms this could correspond to an unlike distribution of chromosomes in cleavage.

The experiments of Hans Spemann, in the early 1900's, lent scant support to Weissmann's notion. Spemann separated the blastomeres of developing amphibian eggs at the 8-cell stage and found that he could produce two similar embryos. Evidently, at this stage, the amphibian blastomeres are still genetically identical, and this nuclear equivalence of early blastomeres has been demonstrated for the sea urchin and chick as well. In plants, F. C. Steward, of Cornell University, has isolated a single adult carrot root cell and from this cell a complete plant developed.

If we cannot look to differences in gene composition between cells of a developing embryo to account for cell differentiation, what other possibilities arise? An early experiment of Spemann again points a direction. Spemann demonstrated that a portion of the cytoplasm of the fertilized amphibian egg, the grey crescent, played a vital part in determining the location of the blastopore in the early embryo. When Spemann transplanted a portion of grey crescent to the dorsal side of a blastula, the blastopore formed there instead of at the usual site.

Spemann's experiment suggests that conditions in the cytoplasm of the cell, are capable of influencing the pattern of development. Clearly, differences in the environment of different cells of the embryo must arise as gradients of oxygen concentration, CO_2 tension, and concentrations of chemical substances are established. That environmental conditions can, in fact, influence cellular activity is shown in the following examples.

Euglena, a single celled, free swimming Protist, contains about 10 chloroplasts per cell, and these chloroplasts function in photosynthesis. When grown in the dark, the chloroplasts disappear and another mode of nutrition is used. When exposed to light, *Euglena* again makes chloroplasts. Lymphoid cells capable of antibody production will form antibodies only in the presence of an antigen, e.g., a bacterial toxin, without exposure, the cell's potentiality is not expressed.

Precisely how changes in the cellular environment, in the cytoplasm, affect differentiation is not yet clear. Evidence is accumulating which points to cytoplasmic characteristics influencing the chromosomes in the nucleus, which, in turn, determine how the cell will behave. In flies swellings have been found at particular sites along the chromosomes. These swellings, called Balbiani rings, or puffs, are sites of strong synthesis of RNA. The position of the chromosomal puff is characteristic for the age (larvae or adult) and type of cell, as salivary gland or kidney, in which they are found. When nuclei of salivary glands of advanced fly larvae are transplanted into a preparation containing cytoplasm of developing eggs, the pattern of chromosomal puffs changes to that characteristic of earlier stages. Other lines of evidence, which will not be presented, also testify to the ability of the cytoplasm to influence chromosomal activity.

The manner in which chromosomes affect cell differentiation follows. Biochemists have found that chromosomes contain a large amount of deoxyribonucleic acid (DNA). It is quite probable that the characteristic and determining part of the gene is a DNA molecule. The "instructions" for the development of the organism are provided within the molecular structure. The DNA molecule can be visualized as a long spiral structure having a pattern resulting from the repetition of 4 sets of chemical building blocks, adenine (A), guanine (G), thymine (T), or cytosine (C) attached to threads made of ribose sugar and phosphate on either side. (See Figure 57.)

Figure 57   *A diagram of a portion of the DNA molecule spiral structure.*

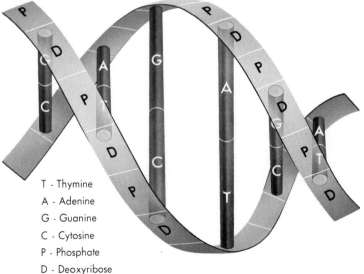

T - Thymine
A - Adenine
G - Guanine
C - Cytosine
P - Phosphate
D - Deoxyribose

Adenine and thymine always pair, as do quanine and cytosine, in the formation of the cross-pieces of the ladderlike molecule. These A-T and C-G units may be repeated or alternated in any order; thus, the possible kinds of DNA molecules are practically unlimited. We can imagine the many arrangements of parts within the DNA molecule as a kind of code, carrying the information from one cell generation to the next. The sequence in the arrangement of the four basic units is thought to constitute the message. Determining the exact nature of this code is currently one of the most exciting areas in research.

How is the message employed in the making of the rest of the cellular constituents? Biologists have obtained excellent evidence that the DNA within the nucleus, together with the proper enzymes, brings about the synthesis of another type of compound, ribonucleic acid (RNA), and that the sequences of the basic code units of the DNA are duplicated as mirror images in the RNA. The RNA moves out of the nucleus and its codes determine the order of arrangement of amino acids as they are used in the synthesis of proteins. Most of the protein in a cell is enzymes. Perhaps each gene can code the synthesis of a different enzyme. Ultimately, the remainder of the constituents and products of a cell arise through the action of these enzymes.

The problem of how genetic instructions, coded identically in each cell of the early embryo, are gradually changed as cells differentiate, remains one of the active frontiers of modern biology.

The central question now becomes how do chromosomes, cytoplasm, and environment regulate genetic expression differently in genetically identical cells? Furthermore, development seems to require a programmed regulation of cellular differentiation programmed in time as well as space. To put the question another way, how is a certain gene turned on to produce one type of RNA in some cells while the same gene in genetically identical cells at another point in space or time is not turned on? Much research is being directed currently toward answering this most fundamental question of development.

Regeneration　　Embryologists have long been interested in the process of regeneration because it apparently represents a return to embryonic conditions in a fully developed animal. The phenomenon of regeneration was first discovered in 1740 by Abraham Trembley, a tutor at the French royal court, while he was attempting to answer the question, "Are polyps plants or animals?" Trembley published the results of a remarkable series of experiments on the little animal, *Hydra,* in a paper entitled *Memoirs Concerning the Natural History of Polyps.*[1] The paper is a good example of an event that occurs frequently in

[1] Translated and reprinted from Trembley's *Histoire des Polypes;* Verbeek, Leiden, Holland; 1744.

science: an experiment answers a question quite different from the one which it was originally designed to answer. The following excerpt from this paper may give direction to our next study:

> But I would not have been satisfied if, at the time I began this work, I had only been able to establish the truth of these remarkable facts of Natural History by my own observations. For these to be believed, more than one direct witness is needed. This is what I felt as soon as I saw these animals. From the first, I could scarcely believe my eyes, and I must, with good reason, think that others would have trouble believing me. I have not neglected to show all the things I have seen. In this I have been most fortunate. The persons who have carefully followed my own observations, and those who have repeated them on their own, are, without a doubt among the best of judges. . . .

Instead of depending on Trembley's description of what he saw, we will examine the results of a similar experiment.

Regeneration of the Tadpole's Tail. The adult frog, like most higher vertebrates, has no capacity for replacing parts of its body that have been lost. Interestingly enough, however, in its tadpole stage the frog does show the capacity for regeneration which its salamander cousins retain into adult life. When its tail is cut off, the tadpole will frequently grow a new one. Because the development of the new tail really represents the return to embryonic conditions, embryologists have often studied tail regeneration in an effort to learn more about the factors which cause a mass of undifferentiated cells to develop into a perfect organ neatly fitted to its place in the whole animal.

INVESTIGATION 26   Observation of Regenerating Tissues

In the following experiment we shall clip the tails of some anesthetized tadpoles, and then wait to see whether the tails grow back again. If they do, we shall be able to determine how long the regeneration process takes and whether the new tail is a size and shape which will be in proportion with the tadpole's body.

Materials (per team)

1. One pair of fine forceps
2. One pair of fine scissors
3. Two finger bowls
4. Five or six tadpoles
5. Six petri plates

Materials (per class)

Anesthetic, either MS-222 (tricaine methane sulfonate) or Chloretone

Procedure

1. Prepare the anesthetic, MS-222 (tricaine methane sulfonate), by dissolving enough of the compound in 10% Holtfreter's solution to make a concentration of 1:12,000, or make a 1:3000 dilution of Chloretone in water.
2. Place tadpoles in a petri dish of anesthetic until they become immobilized (about 5 to 10 minutes).
3. Remove tadpoles immediately and rinse in a second container of 10% Holtfreter's solution.
4. With a pair of fine scissors amputate portions of the tail. Cuts may be made in several ways: perpendicular to the vertical axial plane of the notochord; at angles to the vertical axial plane; or at angles to the horizontal axial plane of the notochord. Place the tadpoles in pond water immediately after the tails have been excised.
5. Feed animals daily. (Use water plants, such as *Elodea,* or boiled lettuce.)
6. Observe wound-healing and daily progress of regeneration, the appearance of the blastema (the mass of undifferentiated cells which form at the cut surface), and so on.

QUESTIONS FOR DISCUSSION

1. Define regeneration.

2. In what way do the regenerations you have studied resemble embryonic development?

3. When a part of the tadpole's tail is cut off and discarded, the rest of the body contributes the raw material from which a new tail is built. Does it contribute anything besides the raw material, that is, does it influence the form, size, or orientation of the new tail? On what observations are your answers based?

4. Referring to any experimental design that you have previously applied to embryos, do you think any of these techniques would help you learn more about regeneration? Which techniques would be worthwhile applying?

Parallel Reading: Regeneration in Other Multicellular Organisms

By "regeneration" we mean the ability of an organism to repair or replace parts of its body that have been lost or damaged. Fortunately, all organisms have some capacity for regeneration. In the course of your childhood you probably suffered numerous cuts and abrasions that were smoothed over by the regenerative powers of your skin. Most parts of the body can repair wounds; broken bones will knit together, and even a cut or torn nerve may regenerate if the severed ends are brought together. Actually, the skin and the lining of the intestine are continuously regenerating, for the surfaces of both organs are steadily being worn away and replaced by new cells that move out to the surface.

However, while a man cannot replace an eye or a tooth or even a finger tip that has been lost, a few vertebrates are able to regenerate large and complex structures. Perhaps you have heard that certain lizards, when caught by the tail, quickly snap it off and subsequently grow a new one. As you have seen, frog tadpoles can regenerate a tail that has been cut off; so can adult salamanders. The salamander, in addition, has the surprising ability to replace an entire limb that has been amputated. If a salamander's leg is cut off, even at the shoulder, a mass of undifferentiated cells appear at the wound surface. Over the course of several months, these cells gradually build up a perfect limb, with all the bones, muscles, nerves, and blood vessels correctly formed and in their normal positions.

One problem that has attracted a great deal of attention is the origin of the mass of cells (the blastema) from which the new limb or tail is formed. Does new bone come only from old, cut bone, and new muscle only from old muscle? Or is damaged bone able to give rise to muscle, and skin to bone? Or does the animal contain some kind of "reserve cells" that swarm to the amputation site and organize a new limb or tail? This problem is of great theoretical significance, because an understanding of these aspects of regeneration would lead to an understanding of what happens as embryonic cells are converted into mature tissue.

It is of practical importance, too, because it might help us learn whether it will ever be possible to induce regeneration of lost body parts in man. During the Second World War, one biologist succeeded in bringing about limb regeneration in adult frogs, which ordinarily do not replace lost structures. The technique used was to keep the wound open for a long time by interfering with the healing process. But no one has ever been able to bring about regeneration of a limb in a mammal.

There is practical interest in the possibility that human beings might some day be able to regrow all tissues and organs, but apart from this possibility, regeneration holds interest for the biologist because it demonstrates developmental processes in an adult organism. Experiments with frogs and salamanders indicate the possibility that every organ has the power of regrowth, needing only the appropriate environmental situation to bring it about. The proper environmental situation may include the presence of certain substances such as enzymes and hormones.

SECTION FOURTEEN

HORMONAL REGULATION

The coordination of the cells and groups of cells which make up any multicellular organism is another problem in biology which is not yet completely understood. Our incomplete knowledge of the causes of cell differentiation has been pointed out. It is also true that while much is known, much remains to be learned about the mechanisms by which the differentiated cells and tissues are controlled so that they act in harmony with others in the organism.

In animals, much of the coordination is controlled by the nervous system. Plants have no structures which correspond to the nervous system of animals. And even in higher animals, it is probable that the regulation of growth, development, and behavior is controlled as much by chemical regulators called hormones as by the nervous system.

Hormones are substances which are produced in one part of an organism but have their effect in some other part. Hormones were first recognized in animals, but several substances which fit this definition have since been found in plants.

Hormonal Regulation in Animals. Most of the hormones which have been identified in animals are produced in *endocrine* glands. The endocrines are glands which have no ducts. The names of some of these glands, such as the thyroid, the pituitary, the pancreas, the adrenals, and the gonads should be familiar to you.

Each endocrine gland produces either one or several specific hormones. These are released from the gland into the blood stream and thus circulate through the body. Taken up by various tissues, they control many kinds of chemical processes. Insulin, a hormone produced by the pancreas, is essential for the release of energy from carbohydrates in food. Thyroxin, a product of the thyroid gland, allows the body to get the maximum amount of energy and body heat from food. Testosterone, produced by the testes, brings about the biochemical changes that cause secondary sex characteristics in the male, such as growth of a beard or change of voice. In fact, almost everything that goes on in our bodies is influenced by hormones.

To remain in vigorous health, an animal must have normally functioning endocrine glands. Hormones are not only essential for the general day-to-day welfare of the body; they are also needed for many special functions. The production of eggs and sperm, and, in some organisms, the processes of courtship, mating, and care of the young are all controlled by hormones from the sex glands and the pituitary gland.

Hormones in Frogs. The influence of hormones on the function of reproduction in animals is strikingly illustrated in frogs, in which reproductive activity occurs only once a year. In the summertime, frogs spend their time hunting food; meanwhile, sperm develop in the testes of the males, and large masses of eggs are formed in the ovaries of the females. During the winter, the animals hibernate in sheltered spots under stones and logs. When spring comes, the frogs emerge and make their way to the nearest pond. There the males and females pair in a long-continued embrace called *amplexus.* After this embrace has lasted several days, the eggs from the female and sperms from the male are released simultaneously. The sperms fertilize the eggs just at the moment that the eggs are emerging from the female's body.

The fact that both males and females move to the water at the same time and are then able to release viable gametes that have been stored for several months poses some important problems. Evidently the frogs are responding to the change of season. Through the senses, the nervous system is informed of changes in light, temperature, and moisture, but how is this information relayed to the gonads? We now know that influences coming from the nervous system stimulate the pituitary gland, which is attached to the brain. The pituitary then releases the hormones called *gonadotrophins,* the hormones that tend to nourish and stimulate the gonads. When the time for egg-laying approaches in the spring, gonadotrophins are poured into the blood stream. Upon reaching the ovaries, these gonadotrophic hormones cause the eggs to be liberated into the oviducts. In the males, the testes are stimulated by the same hormones. The stimulated gonads in turn secrete hormones of their own, and these sex hormones, in some way not yet well understood, influence the nervous system, causing the frogs to leave their winter hiding places to migrate to the edges of the ponds.

Since frogs that lay their eggs in the spring build up a new crop of eggs in the summer when food is abundant, the eggs are fully formed when the females go into hibernation at the approach of cold weather. The ovaries need only the stimulus of gonadotrophins to release these eggs. As shown in Preparatory Technique 3, page 193, ripe eggs can be obtained out of season (in the fall or winter) by injecting gonadotrophic hormone into the mature female. Since the gonadotrophin content rises during the year, a large number of pituitaries are needed in the fall, but only one or two just before the normal laying season.

Hormonal Control in the Frog Embryo. The tadpole contains millions of cells, all derived from the single fertilized egg. As long as these cells remain a part of the developing animal they are marvelously coordinated, each committed to a precise role in the adult organism. It is obvious that during the period of development each cell comes under influences that restrict its growth and multiplication; if it did not, the final result would not be a tadpole.

The influences at work in an embryo, whatever they are, regulate the growth of the cells and assign to each a specific role in the total organism. These regulations are at work in all organisms and must have been perfected early in the evolution of living things. Thus we can study such organisms as oat seedlings, tadpoles, or chicks and learn about the basic problems of growth and differentiation in all organisms, including the human species.

The cycle of development in individual organisms involves a number of simultaneous changes. A process involving a number of simultaneous changes is called a *synchrony*. The problem is, what causes a synchrony?

In the laboratory, it is possible to remove or to injure the thyroid gland in young or even unborn animals, and to study the consequent effects on growth and development. Or, conversely, one can administer thyroxin to young animals and study the effects produced. Experiments like these have provided a great deal of information about the part which the thyroid gland plays in normal development.

In 1912, Frederick Gudernatsch tried feeding various dried glands (purified hormones were not available in those days) to frog tadpoles. In our laboratory experiments, we could try to repeat Gudernatsch's original experiment by feeding dried thyroid to some tadpoles. Since pure thyroxin is now available, however, we shall try to do the experiment with this thyroid hormone itself.

Thyroxin has been referred to as "the" hormone produced by the thyroid gland. Actually, thyroxin was one of the first hormones to be understood chemically. Its structural formula was determined in 1926, and in England the following year, Sir Charles Harrington succeeded in making the hormone in the laboratory. For the next quarter of a century, it was believed that the problem of the chemical nature of thyroxin was solved.

In 1952, two British physiologists examined mammalian blood plasma by the then new technique of chromatography. In the plasma they found a previously unknown substance that chromatographed differently from thyroxin. They showed that the new substance could be found in extracts of the thyroid gland. Chemical analysis of the new substance showed that it differed from thyroxin in one respect; it contained three iodine atoms per molecule, whereas thyroxin contains four. Thus, the new substance was named triiodothyronine. (Thyroxin can be properly called "tetraiodothyronine.")

The big surprise came when triiodothyronine was tested and compared with thyroxin. Quite unexpectedly, the new substance turned out to be four or five times more effective than thyroxin itself. When we say that triiodothyronine was more effective than was thyroxin, we are referring to tests of thyroid activity made in *mammals*. One might ask whether this triiodothyronine is also more effective in other animals. This question can be investigated by placing tadpoles in triiodothyronine solutions, one-half or one-quarter as concentrated as our thyroxin solutions. If triiodothyronine proves to be more effective in amphibians, we should expect that a given amount of it should affect metamorphosis to the same degree as does a larger amount of thyroxin.

There is also the possibility that triiodothyronine will have effects quite different from those produced by thyroxin. In biological research, it is essential to realize that results obtained with one species cannot be applied to another without first being tested. Even animals as much alike as the mouse and rat sometimes differ strikingly in their response to a certain drug or hormone. The fact that triiodothyronine is more effective than thyroxin in certain animals does not necessarily apply to relative effectiveness of the two substances in other animals. For example, in chickens it has been shown that triiodothyronine is *not* more effective than thyroxin.

Both thyroxin and triiodothyronine contain iodine. Actually, the essential function of the thyroid gland is the collection of iodine from the blood stream (we take it in with our food and drinking water) and the synthesis of thyroid hormones. Iodine is apparently indispensable if the body is to carry on its normal chemical processes. If there is not enough iodine in the diet, the thyroid may become very much enlarged and thus may trap more effectively the small amount of the element that is available; such greatly enlarged thyroids are called goiters and may grow to 50 times the normal size of the gland. If the thyroid fails to get sufficient iodine, the supply of thyroid hormones diminishes, and the affected individual becomes dull and sluggish.

One might ask what chemical is really responsible for the effects of the thyroid gland on bodily function. Is it the iodine, the thyroxin, or the triiodothyronine? Perhaps we can answer this question by comparing the effects of each of these substances on test animals.

INVESTIGATION 27	Hormonal Control of the Development of Frog Embryos

Materials (per team)

1. Seven large, flat, culture dishes or pans. (Each dish should be able to hold 1 liter of culture solution.)

2. Seven stones or bricks (large enough to extend above the 1-liter water level, yet not so large as to prevent the free movement of tadpoles)
3. One 1-liter graduate cylinder
4. Thirty-five tadpoles just preceding, or in, the hindlimb bud stage
5. Stock solutions of thyroxin (1 mg per liter), triiodothyronine (1 mg per liter), and iodine (1 mg per liter)
6. Three 10 ml graduated pipettes

Procedure

1. Label each of the culture dishes (team, solution).
2. Add to each dish the proper solution as follows:

   a. Twenty-five micrograms of thyroxin per liter. (Prepare by adding 25 ml of the thyroxin stock solution to 975 ml of pond water.)
   b. Ten micrograms of thyroxin per liter. (Prepare by adding 10 ml of the thyroxin stock solution to 990 ml of pond water.)
   c. Ten micrograms of triiodothyronine per liter. (Prepare by adding 10 ml of the triiodothyronine stock solution to 990 ml of pond water.)
   d. Two and one-half micrograms of triiodothyronine per liter. (Add 2.5 ml of stock solution to 997.5 ml of pond water.)
   e. Two micrograms of iodine per liter. (Add 2 ml of iodine stock solution to 998 ml of pond water.)
   f. One microgram of iodine per liter. (Add 1 ml of stock solution to 999 ml of pond water.)
   g. One liter of pond water for pond water control.

3. Divide the 35 tadpoles into 7 groups of 5 each, selecting them so that each group will include the same range of developmental stages. Place one group in each of the seven containers. Keep the containers at room temperature.
4. Observe and record your observations every second or third day. At the same time, feed the tadpoles, and replace the culture solutions with fresh ones. If any tadpoles die, remove them promptly (do not replace them).
5. As the tadpole hindlimbs become well developed, place a rock in each container for the tadpoles to crawl onto. Without this precaution, the tadpoles will drown.

   In concluding this work, carefully compare the results obtained in each of the solutions. Then write a summary of the evidence which you have obtained in this experiment.

Metamorphosis involves a complete remaking of the body of the tadpole so that it becomes quite a different organism. Some of the changes that occur are internal and will not be visible. For example, the intestine becomes much shorter, and the gills are replaced by lungs. Other changes, however, are plainly visible.

Record the time at which each of the following external changes are observed in the individual animals cultured in the various solutions. The times at which these visible changes occur in the various culture solutions, should provide you with data which you may use to evaluate the effectiveness of each solution in causing these changes. Note carefully when:

1. The tail shortens and finally disappears.
2. The hindlimbs, which begin as tiny buds, grow and develop joints and feet.
3. Eardrums appear on the surface of the head.
4. The forelimbs erupt through a window of skin onto the surface of the body. Note whether both of the forelimbs break through the skin at the same time.
5. The small mouth, which is toothless but has a horny beak, is replaced by a wide gaping mouth which extends from the tip of the head back past the level of the eyes.
6. The body loses its ovoid shape and begins to resemble that of an adult frog.

QUESTIONS FOR DISCUSSION

1. What is the purpose of matching the development of controls with that of the thyroxin-treated tadpoles at the beginning of the experiment?

2. When a tadpole dies, why should it not be replaced with another from the stock?

3. Was the first developmental event to occur in one group also the first to occur in all the others?

4. Did some concentrations of thyroxin appear to overstimulate development? Why?

5. Did metamorphic changes occur at different rates in the various concentrations of thyroxin? If so, how much difference was there?

6. Did the untreated controls undergo any metamorphic change during the period of observations? Why were controls included in this experiment?

7. Does triiodothyronine increase or decrease the rate of meta-morphosis more than thyroxin? On what evidence is your answer based?

8. Do your results suggest what may regulate the changes which occur in normal tadpoles when metamorphosis takes place spontaneously? What experiments could be used to test the correctness of your hypothesis?

9. If a very young larva were deprived of its thyroid gland, do you think it could undergo metamorphosis in response to thyroxin? How could this point be tested?

INVESTIGATION 28   Control of Development in Chicks

The influence of sex hormones on sex differentiation is a subject that has been extensively studied in laboratory animals. Under controlled con-ditions, one can inject male or female sex hormones into immature animals and learn something about the factors that control the animals' ability to respond to the hormones. To set up a simple study of this sort, it is a good idea to use animals in which there are clear-cut differences in the appear-ance of the two sexes, since such differences make it easy to detect what the hormone is doing. External differences are not always easily discern-ible; a human observer can, for example, distinguish between male and female flickers only by their behavior, since their outward appearances are nearly identical. Male and female chickens, on the other hand, differ strikingly from one another in appearance as well as in behavior.

To investigate the control of development in laboratory animals, we shall inject newly hatched cockerels and pullets with the sex hormone testosterone propionate, and the trophic hormone, chorionic gonadotro-phin. Because these hormones are soluble in different carriers, it will be necessary to inject two sets of control birds, each with a separate, pure solvent. Uninjected chicks should also be used as a third control group against the action of the solvents.

Materials (per team)

Five 1-day-old male and five 1-day-old female chicks

Materials (per class)

1. Brooder for chicks
2. Four hypodermic syringes, graduated to 0.1 ml, and equipped with No. 21 or 22 needles

3. Testosterone propionate
4. Sesame oil
5. Gonadotrophin
6. Saline solution
7. A beaker of 70% ethyl alcohol
8. Chick food

Unless otherwise directed by the teacher, the class will work as five teams. Four of the teams will each use a different hormone, or solvent for a hormone. The fifth team will maintain the noninjected control group of chicks.

A system of color codes may be used to prevent a mix-up in the five lots of chicks. The sex of the chicks may be readily distinguished by placing loops made of pipe cleaners around one of their legs. Two loops can be used to designate males and one loop to designate females. The pipe cleaners can be dyed with ink or food coloring. Since chicks are likely to peck at anything red, it would be well to avoid using that color.

For example the color code for the pipe cleaners might be: Testosterone, blue; sesame oil carrier, yellow; gonadotrophin, green; saline carrier, white; untreated controls, black.

Procedure

1. Carefully twist a loop of pipe cleaner of the proper color around the leg of each female chick. Do not make it too tight, but be sure it is tight enough so that it will not fall off. Place two loops on a leg of each male. It will add some interest and some value if you can number the individuals and keep separate records for each.

2. Determine each chick's weight and "comb factor" (see Figure 58) and record these in your notes. The comb-factor is calculated from the following equation:

$$CF = \frac{CL \times CH}{2}$$

where CF = comb factor
CL = comb length
and CH = comb height

Comb length is measured as the distance between the points indicated as A and B in Figure 58. Comb height is measured perpendicular to the skull at the point where the comb is tallest.

3. Prepare to inject your chicks as follows. Keep your sterile hypodermic syringe, with needle attached, partly submerged in a beaker of 70%

Newly hatched chick showing comb

Normal cockerel about 3 weeks old, showing comb

Figure 58   Comb development in chicks.

ethyl alcohol. When you are ready to inject, take the vial containing the solution you are to use, and swab off the rubber cap with cotton soaked in alcohol. Insert the needle into the rubber top of the vial, and draw some of the solution into the barrel of the syringe. Holding the syringe with the point of the needle up and the vial above, push back all but 0.1 ml of the solution, along with any air that may have entered the syringe. Withdraw the needle, and inject the chick as described in

Step 4. Chicks should receive a daily dose of 0.1 ml of either the hormone solution or carrier every day of the first week unless this includes
a weekend. Then a single double dose should be administered Friday.
After the first week, the dosage should be doubled to 0.2 ml daily.

4. The cockerels and pullets should be less than three days old when you
   start injecting them. Because it is difficult for one individual to inject
   a young chick, two people should cooperate in the operation. One
   person grasps the chick, belly up, so that its back is in the palm of the
   hand and its head is held between the thumb and forefinger. The other
   then pinches up the loose skin under the chick's wing or leg and barely
   inserts the needle through it. The needle, attached to the syringe with
   the proper volume of solution, should be held parallel to the chick
   during insertion. A No. 21 or 22 needle should be used because the
   sesame oil carrier is fairly viscous.

5. Place the chick back in the brooder, making sure food and water are
   available. Rinse out the syringe in a beaker of alcohol by drawing it
   full of alcohol and then emptying it several times. Clean your equipment and return it to its proper place.

During the course of the experiment, watch for and record any change
in the color, shape, and turgidity (swollen appearance) of the combs.
Weigh the chicks every other day, and keep a record of their weights. Plot
the weights and "comb factors" on appropriate graphs. Graphing the
results of the experiment will bring out most clearly any differences that
might be produced by the various treatments. Indicate individual points
on the graph; you do not properly represent your data by showing a
plotted line with no points to indicate the values from which it was derived.

As you observe the chicks which have been injected with the various
solutions, you should note the behavioral changes resulting from sex-
hormone treatment. These observations will be of as much value as the
comb factor and weight in determining the effectiveness of the treatments.
To make these observations you must approach the chicks quietly, without
disturbing them. What you want to see is how the chicks behave among
themselves when they are not frightened. Therefore, you should make
these observations each day *before* you pick up the chicks to examine or
inject them.

Keep an accurate record of the time at which various behavioral
changes are first observed in each chick. Watch for the following behavior
traits in each set of chicks and record their presence or absence and the
time of their onset.

1. Scratching, with and without food
2. Pecking, with and without food
3. Preening

4. Vocalizations, which begin as peeps and trills, and later become crowing in some groups
5. Huddling together, and the reaction to being isolated at increasing ages. (Huddling may be a response to being too cold.)
6. Strutting, posturing, and "neck-stretching"
7. Fighting

QUESTIONS FOR DISCUSSION

1. Do your data indicate that the hormones affect the rate at which the chicks gain weight? If so, what are the effects?

2. Do the data indicate that the injected hormones affect the rate of development of the combs on the males? on the females? If so, what are the effects?

3. Are the changes in weight and comb growth correlated with any behavioral effects you have observed?

4. In what ways does testosterone propionate influence the development of young chicks?

5. What aspect of experimental design enables you to feel sure that the effects of testosterone which you have observed are due to testosterone specifically?

6. Would you conclude that testosterone (which is called "the" male sex hormone) affects only sexual characteristics? Does it seem to have any other function?

7. If you were to dissect out and weigh the testes of the control and testosterone-injected cockerels, what might you find? Why?

8. How can you explain the observed effects of gonadotrophin?

9. If you were to determine the size of the gonads of the chicks used in this experiment, what differences would you expect?

INVESTIGATION 29	The Gonads of Hormone-Treated Chicks

What influences the differentiations between male and female chicks? We showed that hormones can influence development, and that the sex glands produce hormones, at least in mature animals. Is it possible that in the very young cockerel the testes begin to produce the male sex hormone, and that this in turn causes the growing chick to develop the characteristics of size, structure, and behavior that soon distinguish it from the young hen?

The time at which each of the structural and behavioral sex traits appear is the index to the influence of the solutions injected. Removal and examination of the gonads of these chicks after they have been injected for two weeks should help you understand the action of the treatments used.

Materials

1. Apparatus for killing chicks
2. Medium-sized scissors
3. Sharp pointed forceps
4. Small glass dishes and paper toweling or filter paper
5. Balance which will weigh to centigrams
6. Hormone-treated chicks from Investigation 28

Procedure

1. The chicks may be killed either by placing them in a covered vessel together with a wad of cotton soaked in ether or chloroform, or by cutting off their heads with a single stroke of a heavy knife or scissors. Rapid decapitation is probably the swiftest and most humane. If you decide to decapitate the chicks, do so over a tray or at the sink, since the neck will bleed for a short time. Do not be disturbed at the fact that the body moves after the head has been cut off; once the connection to the brain is severed, the trunk cannot feel pain.

2. To remove the gonads of a cockerel, lay the chick on its back, and cut open the belly surface from the posterior end to the breastbone. Extend the cut to each side, so that you expose the contents of the abdominal cavity. You can now identify the intestine and the two stomachs, the heavy muscular gizzard which grinds the food which is eaten (remember that birds have no teeth), and the thinner walled *proventriculus,* which produces the digestive enzymes. Push the intestinal tract aside and find the testes resting against the body wall. The two testes are somewhat flattened, long, whitish bodies of about equal size. Reach under them and lift them out. If much blood or fluid clings to a testis, blot it lightly on filter paper or toweling. Next place the testes in a *covered* dish (to prevent drying) until you have a chance to weigh them. Be sure to record the number of each chick you autopsy, so that you can compare its gonad weight with the data collected in Investigation 28.

3. Make comparable observations on the female chickens.

QUESTIONS FOR DISCUSSION

1. Does a young chick have to be a genetic male in order to respond to testosterone?

2. Using your knowledge of hormones and genes, explain what determines whether the infant animal will mature to look and act like a male or female.

Parallel Reading: Regulation in Plants

At first thought it would seem that the problem of regulation in plants should be much better understood than is regulation in animals. There is less specialization of cells in plants than in animals. Plants exhibit little motility or motion; motility is characteristic of most animals. So far as we know plants have nothing which compares with the nervous system of higher animals as a coordinating system.

Cells of plants do differentiate as the organism develops, and the several parts of the plant operate in patterns serving the whole. Young plants mature, produce flowers and seeds and eventually die. Annual or biennial plants complete this cycle within a fairly definite time schedule.

Our understanding of the control of these processes is still quite incomplete. As with animals, we have learned much, but no doubt even more remains to be learned.

We will study but a few examples of regulation in plants.

The factors which affect the growth of plants are similar to those affecting growth in animals. Some of these are internal and may be determined chiefly by heredity. Others are environmental.

INVESTIGATION 30	The Effect of Light on the Growth of Seedlings

You know that light is necessary for the formation of foods by photosynthesis. However, what is the effect of light on the process of growth in plants? Three possibilities can be considered: (1) light accelerates the growth of the plant, (2) light inhibits the growth of the plant, or (3) light has no effect on the growth of the plant. The following investigations should yield data which will answer these questions.

Materials (per team)

1. Germination trays   2. Seeds of Alaska peas

Procedure

1. Each team should place about 40 Alaska peas in each of two germination trays containing sand or vermiculite.
2. Water the sand or vermiculite well but drain off excess water. Place one tray in the dark and leave the other tray in the room exposed to light.
3. After 7 to 9 days examine all of the plants and make detailed observations and measurements which might provide information to help you evaluate your hypothesis. Record these data in your notebook.

QUESTIONS FOR DISCUSSION

1. What effect does light have on the growth of stems?

2. What effect does light have on the expansion of leaves?

3. What effect does light have on the formation of chlorophyll?

4. Is there any need for the use of statistics to determine that the effects of the two treatments are different?

5. Do you have any information which will help explain how light affected the growth of the stems?

Parallel Reading: A Brief History of our Knowledge of Auxins

At least a part of the effects of light on the growth of plants can be explained by the action of growth hormones called auxins. Our present knowledge of these substances has developed quite slowly.

Man has long observed the effect of light on stem growth, including the bending of plants towards light. In 1880 Charles Darwin and his son Francis investigated the role of light in plant growth movements. They are given credit for laying the foundation for the modern study of plant-regulating mechanisms. A portion of their pioneering study is reprinted here.

LOCALISED SENSITIVENESS TO LIGHT, AND ITS TRANSMITTED EFFECTS[1]

by CHARLES and FRANCIS DARWIN

Phalaris canariensis. Whilst observing the accuracy with which the cotyledons of this plant became bent towards the light of a small lamp, we were impressed with the idea that the uppermost part determined the direction of the curvature of the lower part. When the cotyledons are exposed to a lateral light,

---

[1] Darwin, Charles and Francis. 1880. *The Power of Movement in Plants.* London.

the upper part bends first, and afterwards the bending gradually extends down   Darwin
to the base, and as we shall presently see, even a little beneath the ground.
This holds good with cotyledons from less than .1 inch (one was observed to
act in this manner which was only .03 inches in height) to about .5 of an inch in
height; but when they have grown to nearly an inch in height, the basal part, for
a length of .15 to .2 of an inch above the ground, ceases to bend. As with young
cotyledons the lower part goes on bending, after the upper part has become
well arched towards a lateral light; the apex would ultimately point to the
ground itstead of to the light, did not the upper part reverse its curvature and
straighten itself, as soon as the upper convex surface of the bowed-down
portion received more light than the lower concave surface. The position
ultimately assumed by young and upright cotyledons, exposed to light entering
obliquely from above through a window, is shown in the accompanying figure
and here it may be seen that the whole upper part has become very nearly
straight.

When the cotyledons were exposed before a bright lamp, standing on the
same level with them, the upper part, which was at first greatly arched towards
the light, became straight and strictly parallel with the surface of the soil in the
pots; the basal part being now rectangularly bent. All this great amount of
curvature, together with the subsequent straightening of the upper part, was
often effected in a few hours.

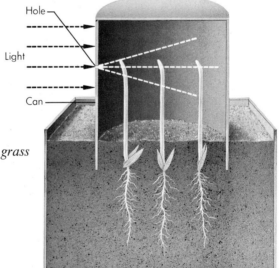

*Figure 59   Bending of grass
seedlings in unilateral light.*

After the uppermost part has become bowed a little to the light, its over-
hanging weight must tend to increase the curvature of the lower part; but any
such effect was shown in several ways to be quite insignificant. When little caps
of tinfoil (hereafter to be described) were placed on the summits of the cotyledons, though this must have added considerably to their weight, the rate or

Darwin amount of bending was not thus increased. But the best evidence was afforded by placing pots with seedlings of *Phalaris* before a lamp in such a position, that the cotyledons were horizontally extended and projected at right angles to the line of light. In the course of 5½ h. [hours] they were directed towards the light with their bases bent at right angles; and this abrupt curvature could not have been aided in the least by the weight of the upper part, which acted at right angles to the plane of curvature.

It will be shown that when the upper halves of the cotyledons of *Phalaris* and *Avena* were enclosed in little pipes of tinfoil or of blackened glass, in which case the upper part was mechanically prevented from bending, the lower and unenclosed part did not bend when exposed to a lateral light; and it occurred to us that this fact might be due, not to the exclusion of the light from the upper part, but to some necessity of the bending gradually travelling down the cotyledons, so that unless the upper part first became bent, the lower could not bend, however much it might be stimulated. It was necessary for our purpose to ascertain whether this notion was true, and it was proved false, for the lower halves of several cotyledons became bowed to the light, although the upper halves were enclosed in little glass tubes (not blackened), which prevented, as far as we could judge, their bending. Nevertheless, as the part within the tube might possibly bend a very little, fine rigid rods or flat splinters of thin glass were cemented with shellac to one side of the upper part of 15 cotyledons; and in six cases they were in addition tied on with threads. They were thus forced to remain quite straight. The result was that the lower halves of all became bowed to the light, but generally not in so great a degree as the corresponding part of the free seedlings in the same pots; this may perhaps be accounted for by some slight degree of injury having been caused by a considerable surface having been smeared with shellac. It may be added, that when the cotyledons of *Phalaris* and *Avena* are acted on by the apogeotropism, it is the upper part first which begins to bend; and when this part was rendered rigid in the manner just described, the upward curvature of the basal part was not thus prevented.

To test our belief that the upper part of the cotyledons of *Phalaris,* when exposed to the lateral light, regulated the bending of the lower part, many experiments were tried; but most of our first attempts proved useless from various causes not worth specifying. Seven cotyledons had their tips cut off for lengths varing between .1 and .16 of an inch, and these, when left exposed all day to a lateral light, remained upright. In another set of 7 cotyledons, the tips were cut off for a length of only about .05 of an inch (1.27 mm) and these became bowed towards a lateral light, but not nearly so much as the many other seedlings in the same pot.

We next tried the effects of covering the upper part of the cotyledons of *Phalaris* with little caps which were impervious to light; the whole lower part being left fully exposed before a southwest window or a bright paraffin lamp. Some of the caps were made of extremely thin tinfoil blackened within; these had the disadvantage of occasionally, though rarely, being too heavy, especially when twice folded; the basal edges could be pressed into close contact with the cotyledons; though this again required care to prevent injury. Nevertheless,

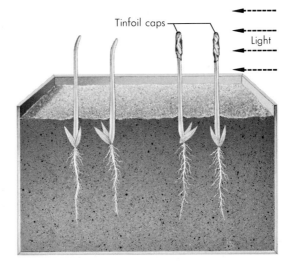

Tinfoil caps

Light

Figure 60   Light-proof caps over the coleoptile tips prevent unilateral light from bending the coleoptile, even if its lower portion is exposed to the light.

any injury thus caused could be detected by removing the caps, and trying whether the cotyledons were then sensitive to light. Other caps were then made of the thinnest glass, which when painted black served well, with the one great disadvantage that the ends could not be closed. But tubes were used which fitted the cotyledons almost closely and the black paper was placed on the soil round each, to check the upwards reflection of light from the soil. Such tubes were in one respect better than the caps of tinfoil, as it was possible at the same time to cover some cotyledons with transparent and others with opaque tubes; and thus our experiments could be controlled. It should be kept in mind that young cotyledons were selected for the trial, and that these when not interfered with bowed down to the ground towards the light. . . .

Darwin

The summits of nine cotyledons, differing somewhat in height, were enclosed for rather less than half their lengths in uncolored or transparent tubes; and these were then exposed before a southwest window on a bright day for 8 h. All of them became strongly curved towards the light, in the same degree as the many other free seedlings in the same pots; so that the glass tubes did not prevent the cotyledons from bending toward the light. Nineteen other cotyledons were, at the same time, similarly enclosed in tubes thickly painted with Indian ink. On five of them, the paint, to our surprise, contracted after exposure to the sunlight, and very narrow cracks were formed, through which a little light entered; and these five cases were rejected. Of the remaining fourteen cotyledons, the lower halves of which had been fully exposed to light for the whole time, 7 continued quite straight and upright; 1 was considerably bowed to the light, and six were slightly bowed, but with the exposed bases of most of them almost or quite straight. It is possible that some light may have been reflected upwards from the soil and entered the bases of the seven tubes as the sun shone brightly, though bits of blackened paper had been placed on the soil around them. Nevertheless, the seven cotyledons which were slightly bowed, together with the 7 upright ones, presented a most remarkable contrast in appearance with many other seedlings in the pot to which nothing had been

Darwin   done. The blackened tubes were then removed from 10 of these seedlings, and they were now exposed to the lamp for 8h; 9 of them became greatly, and 1 moderately, curved toward the light, proving that the previous absence of any curvature in the basal part, or the presence of only a slight degree of curvature there, was due to the exclusion of light from the upper part. . . .

From these several sets of experiments, including those with the tips cut off, we may infer that the exclusion of light from the upper part of the cotyledons of *Phalaris* prevents the lower part, though fully exposed to the lateral light, from becoming curved. The summit for a length of .04 or .05 of an inch, though it is itself sensitive and curves toward the light, has only a slight power of causing the lower parts to bend. Nor has the exclusion of light from the summit for a length of .1 of an inch a strong influence on the curvature of the lower part. On the other hand, an exclusion for a length of between .15 and .2 of an inch, or of the whole upper half, plainly prevents the lower and fully illuminated part from becoming curved in the manner (see figure) which invariably occurs when a free cotyledon is exposed to a lateral light. With very young seedlings, the sensitive zone seems to extend rather lower down relatively to their height than in older seedlings. We must therefore, conclude that when seedlings are freely exposed to a lateral light some influence is transmitted from the upper to the lower part, causing the latter to bend.

End of Article

Growth movements in response to stimuli from one direction are called tropisms. The work began by the Darwins was continued by others. Notable among the early workers were Boysen-Jensen, Paal, and F. W. Went. These men showed that the stimulus for the response studied by the Darwins could move downward from the tip of a cut coleoptile through a block of gelatin placed between the tip and the lower part of the coleoptile, and that the stimulus could not pass through a substance such as mica. They proved that the stimulus (now suspected to be a substance) could be trapped in a gelatin block, and if such a block were then replaced on a decapitated coleoptile it would act much as does a tip in the intact plant. They showed that placing a block which contained the growth substance on one side of a decapitated coleoptile resulted in curvature away from the side on which the block was placed. They developed methods of quantitatively estimating the amount of the growth regulating substance.

After this early research indicated the presence and action of plant hormones, specific identification of the chemical compounds involved soon followed. In 1934 the specific substance indoleacetic acid (IAA) was isolated and identified. Initially this substance was isolated from urine, but it was shown to have growth-promoting activity in plants. It has subsequently been found to be an important, naturally occurring, growth substance in plants. This, and other substances which have similar effects, have been given the name *auxin,* which means "to increase." Many naturally occurring auxins have now been identified, and many more synthetic ones have been manufactured by chemists.

The amount of auxin in plants is so small that a bioassay is used to measure the quantity in a given plant or plant part. One of the most sensitive structures for such measurement is the coleoptile of the oat seedling.

When an oat grain germinates, the first part of the plumule to emerge is the coleoptile. (The Darwins called this structure a cotyledon, but present knowledge of the structure of grass seeds is greater than in Darwins' time. The structure which we now call the cotyledon remains within the seed during germination.) The coleoptile consists of a sheath which covers the remainder of the plumule until after emergence from the soil. Soon after exposure to light, the coleoptile stops growing, and the enclosed leaves split its tip and continue their growth upward. The very young coleoptile has a region of rapidly dividing cells near its tip, but by the time of emergence almost all of its growth is the result of cell elongation, and very little cell division occurs. The elongation of the cells is strongly influenced by auxin. Under normal conditions of seedling growth, the auxin is produced in the tips and it then moves downward. If the tip is removed, then the main source of auxin is removed, and the portion of the coleoptile behind the tip will grow in proportion to the amount of auxin that is supplied externally provided the supply of food is adequate. Therefore, we can supply known quantities of auxin and determine the amount of growth (increase in length) which will result. The growth resulting from different concentrations of auxin can be used as standards to determine the amount of auxin or auxin-like substances in an unknown sample.

In the following investigation, you will determine first, the relationship between auxin concentrations and the growth in length of oat coleoptiles. Second, you will use this information to determine the concentration of auxin present in an unknown solution. These are the techniques used in one method for the bioassay of an auxin.

INVESTIGATION 31   A Biological Assay

Materials

1. Several hundred grains of oats, *Avena sativa,* variety Victory
2. Germination box equipped with red cellophane and light shield. (See Figure 61.)
3. Indoleacetic acid
4. Sucrose
5. Cutter for cutting uniform sections of coleoptiles. (See Figure 62.)
6. Six petri plates per team
7. Millimeter rulers
8. One 10 ml pipette per team

Procedure:

1. Each team should count out 50 grains of oats.

2. Divide the grains equally among the team members and remove the husks. Husking is a somewhat tedious operation, but it may be made easier if the grains are placed on a piece of paper towel and rolled with the palm of the hand. Label the grains (class, team, experiment, date) and stored at room temperature until the next class day.

3. Before placing the husked grains in the germination box, soak them for *not less than 2 hours* and *not more than 4 hours.*

4. Place the husked grains in uniform rows on several layers of moist paper towels in a germination box. Cover the box with a sheet of clear polyethylene and then cover the box with the lid with the red filter and light shield as shown in Figure 61. Be sure the lid fits snugly and that the light shield over the top allows no light to enter even through the red cellophane.

   Leave at room temperature for 24 hours.

5. After 24 hours, remove the light shield (not the box top). Allow light to pass through the red cellophane for a period of 30 minutes. Replace the light shield on the box cover.

Figure 61   *Germination box with red filter and light-proof shield.*

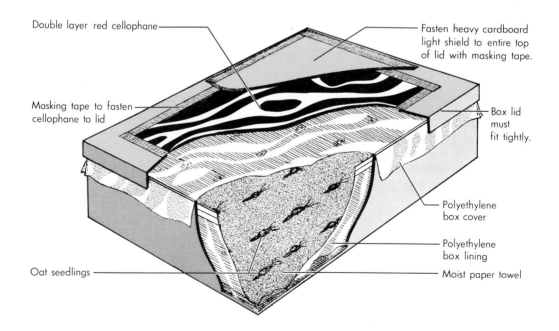

Double layer red cellophane

Fasten heavy cardboard light shield to entire top of lid with masking tape.

Masking tape to fasten cellophane to lid

Box lid must fit tightly.

Polyethylene box cover

Polyethylene box lining

Oat seedlings

Moist paper towel

6. Immediately after the 30-minute exposure, darken the room as much as possible. (Ideally you should work in a dark room with only a red light, but if you work rapidly with low light intensity the experiment should be successful.) Working quickly, remove the box cover and the polyethylene cover and carefully add previously moistened vermiculite to a depth of $\frac{1}{2}$ inch over the germinating grains in the germination box. Gently pack the vermiculite to a uniform level and immediately replace the polyethylene cover and the box cover with its light-tight shield. Leave the germination box at room temperature for 2 to 3 days without opening it.

7. Stock solutions of 4% sucrose and various concentrations of IAA should be prepared. A stock solution containing 100 mg of indoleacetic acid per liter may be prepared as follows: Dissolve 100 mg of IAA in 1 to 2 ml of alcohol and add this to about 900 ml of distilled water. Warm this mixture gently on a hot plate or steam bath to drive off the alcohol. Then make up to 1 liter with distilled water.

   Solutions containing 20.0, 2.0, 0.2, and 0.02 mg of IAA per liter can be prepared by serial diluting this stock solution.

   These dilutions should be prepared shortly before using, because IAA is not very stable. The stock solution may be kept for one or two weeks if refrigerated in a dark bottle. Prepare enough of each dilution for all teams. (Each team will use 10 ml of each.) The instructor will provide a solution of IAA the concentration of which will be unknown to you.

8. On the day that the seedlings will be ready, each team will prepare 6 clean petri plates. After labeling each dish, add solutions to each as follows:

TABLE 18. **Preparation of Petri Plates for IAA Assay**

Dish No.	Add
1	10 ml water + 10 ml 4% sucrose solution
2	10 ml 0.02 mg/l IAA stock solution + 10 ml 4% sucrose solution
3	10 ml 0.2 mg/l IAA stock solution + 10 ml 4% sucrose solution
4	10 ml 2.0 mg/l IAA stock solution + 10 ml 4% sucrose solution
5	10 ml 20.0 mg/l IAA stock solution + 10 ml 4% sucrose solution
6	10 ml unknown + 10 ml 4% sucrose solution

Calculate the final concentration of IAA and sucrose in all dishes.

9. Approximately 2 to 3 days after covering the germinating grains with vermiculite, darken the room as much as possible and remove the

germination box cover and polyethylene cover. Select 30 seedlings with straight coleoptiles from 1.5 to 2.5 cm in total length.

10. Cut off and discard the root and remaining part of the seedling and carefully line up the coleoptiles, two or three at a time, on a block of paraffin. Using the special cutter, as shown, cut from each coleoptile a 10 mm section back of a 3 mm tip and place five of the 10 mm sections in each of the petri plates previously prepared. Store them in the dark for 24 hours at a temperature as near 25°C as possible.

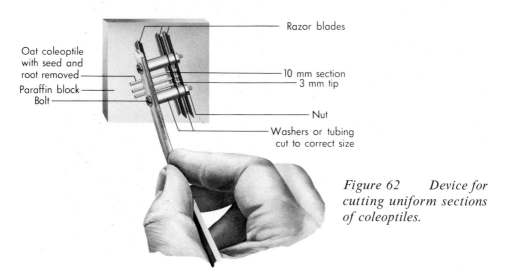

Figure 62   Device for cutting uniform sections of coleoptiles.

11. At the end of the 24 hours, remove the coleoptile sections from the dishes and measure their lengths to the nearest 0.5 mm. Record the results in a chart similar to Chart D, page 231.

QUESTIONS FOR DISCUSSION

1. Plot your data on a graph with increments of growth on the vertical axis and concentration of IAA on the horizontal axis.

2. Compare the results of your team with those of other teams in your class, and if possible with those of other classes.

3. Compute the mean increase in length of the coleoptiles in each dish. Are the data continuous or discrete?

4. Using the proper test, determine if the means in each dish with IAA are significantly different from each other and from that of the controls.

CHART D.   **Effect of IAA on Coleoptile Elongation**

Coleoptile section	*Dish No. 1 no IAA*	*Dish No. 2 0.01 mg/1 IAA*	*Dish No. 3 0.1 mg/1 IAA*	*Dish No. 4 1.0 mg/1 IAA*	*Dish No. 5 10.0 mg/1 IAA*	*Dish No. 6 unknown*
1						
2						
3						
4						
5						
Average length						
Initial length						
Average change in length						

5. What is the concentration of your unknown solution?

6. Explain the mechanism of phototropism and geotropism.

Biologists have found many compounds which have effects on plants which are similar to indoleacetic acid. Probably very few of these are synthesized by plants. But one substance which appears to be as important in the regulation of growth in plants as is IAA was discovered in the following manner. A disease of rice plants results in overly rapid growth of the seedlings, which as a result become tall and weak, and finally fall over. (This was called "foolish seedling" disease, *bakanae*, by the Japanese farmers.) A scientist on Formosa found that the disease was caused by the fungus *Gibberella fujikuroi*. Japanese scientists were able to produce symptoms of the disease with cell-free extracts of the fungus, and later isolated a substance in the extract which was the active agent. This substance was named gibberellin. Since that time, several related compounds have been found in the culture medium in which the fungus has been grown. One of these is gibberellic acid.

In the study which follows, you will investigate the effects of gibberellic acid on pea plants whose genetic constitution causes them to be dwarfs. Our problem is to determine whether genetic characteristics can be modified by the application of gibberellic acid.

Materials (per team)

1. Seeds of Alaska and Little Marvel peas
2. Four 4-inch flower pots (or similar containers)
3. Solution of gibberellic acid (100 mg per liter)
4. Germination trays

Procedure

1. Place the two varieties of pea seeds in clearly separated halves of a germination tray between layers of moist paper towel. Store in the dark or keep covered for 3 to 4 days.
2. Mix equal parts of sand and soil, then moisten lightly. Add this mixture to four 4-inch flowerpots or similar containers. Each container should be about $\frac{2}{3}$ full. Transfer the 3- or 4-day old germinated seedlings to separate pots as follows:

TABLE 19. **Preparation of Pea Plants**

Pot	Variety of Peas	No. of Seedlings
1	Alaska	5
2	Alaska	5
3	Little Marvel	5
4	Little Marvel	5

Label each pot (team, class, pot number, date). Add about $\frac{1}{4}$ to $\frac{1}{2}$ inch of the sand-soil mixture to each pot. Keep soil moist *but not wet!*

3. When the seedlings are about 10 days old, or several centimeters high, measure the height in millimeters from the soil to the tip of the shoot apex of each seedling and record the measurements for each plant separately in a chart such as Chart E. Record these figures as the initial measurement.
4. Using a hand atomizer, spray one pot of Alaska peas and one pot of Little Marvel peas with a solution containing 100 mg of gibberellic acid per liter (experimental group). With a different atomizer, spray the plants of each variety in the other pots with pure water (control). Spray the plants until the leaves and shoot apex are wet enough to form droplets which will almost run off, but do not permit *appreciable*

CHART E. **Effect of Gibberellic Acid Treatment on the Growth of Two Varieties of Pea Plants**

Pea variety	Treatment	Individual	Length (mm) initial measurement	Length (in mm) on days following initial measurement				
				1st	2nd	3rd	4th	7th
Alaska	Sprayed with gibberellic acid	1						
		2						
		3						
		4						
	(Experimental)	5						
		Average						
	Sprayed with water	1						
		2						
		3						
		4						
	(Control)	5						
		Average						
Little Marvel	Sprayed with gibberellic acid	1						
		2						
		3						
		4						
	(Experimental)	5						
		Average						
	Sprayed with water	1						
		2						
		3						
		4						
	(Control)	5						
		Average						

amounts to drip into the soil. Since some of the spray for the experimental treatments may drift, it is advisable to place control plants and experimental plants in different parts of the room. However, be sure that they are both exposed to similar and maximum light conditions. Label each group as "control" or "experimental."

5. Measure the height of each plant in both experimental and control groups on each of the four days following the initial measurement, and then on the seventh day after the initial measurements. Record the measurements on your chart. As the plants in both experimental and control groups grow tall, it may be necessary to place stakes in the pots and tie the plants loosely to them.

QUESTIONS FOR DISCUSSION

1. Plot on millimeter graph paper the average measurements of each of the four groups in the chart you have made. Plot the days along the horizontal axis and the height of the plants along the vertical axis.

2. Compare the heights of the treated and control plants of each variety. Are the differences significant?

3. Compare the heights of Little Marvel peas sprayed with gibberellic acid with the heights of Alaska peas sprayed with water.

4. What hypotheses can you make with regard to the mechanism by which the genetic trait of dwarfism may operate in Little Marvel peas?

A brief review of what we have learned up to this point about growth regulation in plants may be useful. A group of growth-regulating substances called auxins accelerate the elongation of plant cells. Unilateral stimuli such as light or gravity may result in unequal distribution of the auxin, IAA, on two sides of a stem or root and thus cause the curvatures which result in phototropism or geotropism. Light may destroy or inactivate IAA, and this probably accounts for the inhibiting effect of light on elongation of plants. Gibberellins also appear to be involved in the elongation process, at least in some plants. Research in these areas has revealed many other roles of plant growth regulating substances. Some of these will be investigated in the laboratory and others will be discussed.

One interesting problem in the behavior of plants is illustrated by the geotropic response of stems and roots. Stems tend to bend upward; roots tend to bend downward. How can gravity produce opposite responses in these two kinds of organs? Review your data from Investigation 32. Then study the relationships shown in Figure 63, and answer these questions:

1. Explain why roots grow down (positive geotropism) and shoots grow up (negative geotropism).

2. Explain how the tissues of two different types of plants might react to the same concentration of IAA.

3. Suppose research showed that narrow-leafed plants responded very weakly to a concentration of a growth regulator which had a very striking effect on broad leaf plants. Can you think of any practical way to use this information?

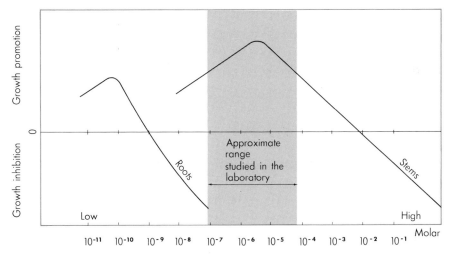

Figure 63   Approximate growth responses of roots and stems to indoleacetic acid. (Courtesy of K. V. Thimann, American Journal of Botany, *vol. 24, 1937.)*

You have now studied the way in which two compounds, indoleacetic acid and gibberellic acid may act in the regulation of certain aspects of growth and development in plants. These and other compounds may have other effects in other circumstances. Such phenomena as the development of adventitious roots, control of axillary bud growth by the terminal bud, imitation of flowering, setting of fruits, fruit fall, and leaf fall are examples of other aspects of plant development which may be controlled by plant growth regulating substances. (If such compounds are produced by the plant, we call them hormones.)

The purpose of the next investigation is to explore the effects of some well known growth substances on a common plant.

| INVESTIGATION 33 | **Effects of Growth Regulating Substances on Plants** |

We might well select different growth regulators than the ones mentioned here, and plants other than bean for this investigation. It is suggested that some teams may wish to modify their experiments. The following outline may serve as a useful guide.

Materials (per team)

1. Sixty to eighty seeds of pinto beans. (Any other variety of *Phaseolus vulgaris* might be used, or you may wish to use plants from other genera or families.)
2. One germination tray.
3. Twenty-one bottles (baby food jars work well) for holding cuttings, and if possible a holder for the bottles. (See Figure 64.)

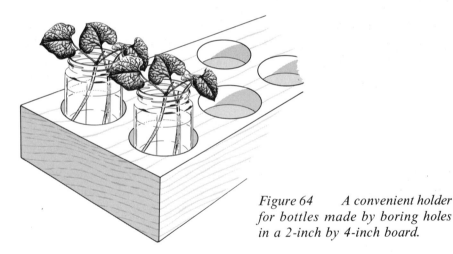

Figure 64   A convenient holder for bottles made by boring holes in a 2-inch by 4-inch board.

4. Plant growth regulators as follows:
   a. Indoleacetic acid, IAA; 100 ppm in 4% ethanol
   b. IAA, 0.1% and 1.0%, in lanolin paste
   c. Indolebutyric acid, IBA; 100 ppm in 4% ethanol
   d. IBA, 0.1% and 1.0%, in lanolin paste
   e. Gibberellic acid, G.A.; 100 ppm in 4% ethanol
   f. G. A.; in 0.1% and 1.0% in lanolin paste
5. Control carriers; 4% ethanol and lanolin
6. Dropper pipettes, toothpicks, and razor blades

Procedure

1. Each team should plant 60 to 80 bean seeds in a germination tray.
2. When the seedlings are ready for cutting (the heart-shaped leaves should be fairly well expanded; this usually takes 9 to 14 days), select the 40 most uniform plants. With a razor blade, cut them off near the soil level and immediately immerse the cut ends in water.
3. Label 21 bottles as shown in the following list. Fill the bottles with tap water. Place two cuttings in each bottle. The cuttings may remain in better health if you cut off the bottom 2 or 3 cm of each under water. This helps prevent air plugs in the xylem vessels. Cut off the stems of each plant about 1 or 2 cm above the pair of heart-shaped leaves. Then treat each pair of cuttings as indicated. Use a different toothpick or medicine dropper for each different formulation of growth regulator.

> No. 1: Lanolin Control: With a toothpick place a dab of plain lanolin on one of the remaining leaves, and another dab on the cut end of the stem of each plant as illustrated in Figure 65.
>
> No. 2: Ethanol control: With a small-tipped medicine dropper, place a drop of 4% ethanol on one leaf and another on the cut end of the stem of each plant.
>
> No. 3: Control: No treatment.

Second pair of leaves

Drop of paste

Figure 65   Cuttings of bean plants. The shoot was cut off above the first pair of leaves. Lanolin paste, with or without growth regulator, is applied to the cut end as indicated.

No. 4: IAA, 100 ppm in 4% ethanol. Apply a drop of the solution to one leaf of each plant.

No. 5: IAA, 100 ppm in 4% ethanol. Apply a drop of the solution to the cut end of the stem of each plant.

No. 6: IAA, 0.1% in lanolin. Apply a dab of lanolin containing 0.1% IAA to one leaf of each plant.

No. 7: IAA, 0.1% in lanolin. Apply a dab of lanolin containing 0.1% IAA to the cut end of the stem of each plant.

No. 8: IAA, 1.0% in lanolin; apply lanolin containing 1.0% IAA to one leaf of each plant.

No. 9: IAA, 1.0% in lanolin; apply lanolin containing 1.0% IAA to the cut end of stem of each plant.

No. 10: IBA, 100 ppm in 4% ethanol, applied to leaf; same as No. 4, but use IBA in place of IAA.

No. 11: IBA, 100 ppm in 4% ethanol, applied to cut stem; same as No. 5, but use IBA.

No. 12: IBA, 0.1% in lanolin, applied to leaf.

No. 13: IBA, 0.1% in lanolin, applied to cut stem.

No. 14: IBA, 1.0% in lanolin, applied to leaf.

No. 15: IBA, 1.0% in lanolin, applied to cut stem.

No. 16: GA, 100 ppm in 4% ethanol, applied to leaf.

No. 17: GA, 100 ppm in 4% ethanol, applied cut stem.

No. 18: GA, 0.1% in lanolin, applied to leaf.

No. 19: GA, 0.1% in lanolin, applied to cut stem.

No. 20: GA, 1.0% in lanolin, applied to leaf.

No. 21: GA, 1.0% in lanolin, applied to cut stem.

4. Place all of the cuttings in a well lighted but cool place. Avoid direct sunlight if the room is above 25°C to 28°C. Observe them daily. Note the development of lateral shoots from the buds in the axils of the two heart-shaped leaves. Record these data each day in a chart similar to Chart F.

5. Measure the length of the axillary shoots on each plant each day. Carefully remove each cutting from the water, and, being careful not to injure the plant, measure the lengths of several representative roots on each. Count the number of adventitious roots (if they are not too numerous to count). Record these data each day in your chart. Make other charts for other growth regulators.

6. After 5 or 6 days complete the experiment by making final measurements and noting any abnormalities or other effects which may have resulted from the treatment.

CHART F. Effects of Indoleacetic Acid on the Growth of Roots and Shoots of Pinto Beans

Plant number	*Average Length of Roots (r) and Shoots (s) by Days*					Number of roots	Abnormalities
	Day 2	Day 3	Day 4	Day 5	Day 6		
1 r s							
2 r s							
3 r s							
4 r s							
5 r s							
6 r s							
7 r s							
8 r s							
9 r s							
10 r s							
11 r s							
12 r s							
13 r s							
14 r s							
15 r s							
16 r s							
17 r s							
18 r s							
19 r s							
20 r s							
21 r s							

QUESTIONS FOR DISCUSSION

1. Which of the growth regulators has the greatest tendency to stimulate the formation of adventitious roots? Which has the greatest tendency to increase the growth in length of the roots?

2. Which substance had the greatest effect in stimulating elongation of stems?

3. Which method of application seemed most effective?

4. Which concentrations were most effective? Were the higher concentrations inhibitory?

Parallel Reading: Hormonal Influence on Plants—A Series of Papers

As autumn approaches, certain deciduous trees (trees that lose their leaves annually) will lose all their leaves except those which are very near a street light. These leaves near the light may remain on the tree for weeks after the rest of the tree is bare.

By checking leaf fall systematically, scientists have found that leaves fall not only in autumn, but also fall from the trees in small numbers all through the growing season. The leaves that fall are usually the older ones on a branch. Some of the more observant early biologists noticed that even young leaves would fall quickly if the blade (the flat part of the leaf) were injured or eaten away by insects. In 1916 a German scientific magazine carried a paper by a biologist, Küster, describing detailed experiments on leaf fall. Küster cut off the leaf blade and found that the remaining leafstalk fell quite soon; in fact, it fell many weeks before the intact leaf. But if only a tiny bit of the blade were left on, the fall was very much delayed. This disproportionate effect of a bit of the leaf blade suggested to Küster that the blade must be producing a chemical which, even in tiny amounts, could prevent leaf fall.

Küster's paper gives us a good example of why scientists work on a particular plant or animal. Trees are very awkward organisms to study. They are too big, grow too slowly, and take up too much space. Although their autumn leaf fall is spectacular, it is quite inconvenient to wait from one year to the next to study it. Küster made a survey of many plants, looking for a small, fast-growing plant that could be grown in the laboratory or greenhouse and which had a regular, and fairly continuous leaf fall. He found such a plant in *Coleus blumei,* a member of the mint family from the tropics. This is the common house plant whose genus name has become so familiar that we use it as a common name. As often as once a week, this plant sheds its oldest (bottom) pair of leaves and makes a new pair of young leaves at the top, in the apical bud.

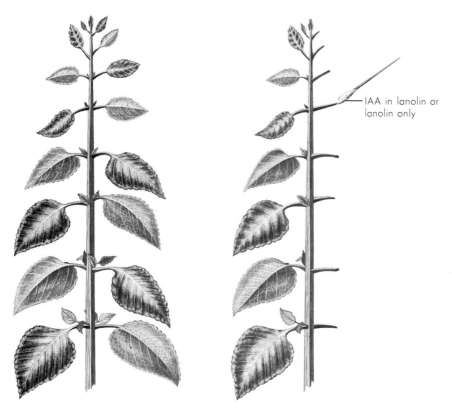

IAA in lanolin or
lanolin only

Figure 66   Structure of Coleus *shoot and arrangement of leaves for experimentation.*

Ever since Küster reported the special advantages of *Coleus*, it has been the favorite plant for use in studies of what makes leaves grow old and fall.

The general structure of *Coleus* is shown in Figure 66. In this illustration the upper leaves have been removed. Like most plants, *Coleus* has a shoot portion (above the ground) and a root portion. The shoot portion, consisting of one main shoot (the upright stem) and one or more side shoots, grows at its tip by developing new leaves and stem tissue. The cluster of primordial leaves, within which much of this development goes on is called the apical bud. In the axil of each leaf is another bud, called an axillary bud. These may give rise to axillary, or lateral branches. Toward the bottom of the main shoot, the axillary branches grow larger and the leaves of the main shoot become progressively older. By the time a leaf of the main shoot is approximately 8 or 9 leaves down from the apical bud, it falls off. (The axillary branches, as you can see from Figure 66, remain on the main shoot and continue to grow.)

Several years ago, Dr. W. P. Jacobs became interested in the problem of why leaves fall. He has published several papers on this subject.

The following exercise is designed to show the aspects of experimental design used by Jacobs and others, and for our present purposes, precise knowledge of plant hormones and growth is considered of secondary importance.

It is often possible to follow all of the steps of a previous experiment by reading about them, and thus gain a great deal of understanding. If time permits, you might try to duplicate the steps of Dr. Jacobs and his coworkers to see if you obtain similar results.

In order to reduce the number of factors involved in their experiments on *Coleus,* Wetmore and Jacobs removed all axillary branches, and during each experiment removed any new side shoots that developed. The plants which were used were all derived from a single original plant, not by collecting seeds and growing them, but by taking repeated stem cuttings. The experimental design is outlined in the following steps which you can repeat, if time permits.

1. Select six plants and arrange into three sets of two plants each. The two plants of any one set should be similar in height, color, and leaf size. Remove all side shoots. In selecting plants, match each pair by the lengths of their younger leaf blades. Use the youngest leaf pair which is from 50 to 100 mm long. Leaves on the plants of any matched pair should differ no more than 5 mm in length.
2. Cut off the leaf blades of one of the leaves at each node all the way up the stem to leaf pair 1. Leave the petioles intact.
3. Select at random one plant of each matched pair to be treated with indoleacetic acid (IAA).
4. One half of the IAA treated plants will receive 1.0% IAA in lanolin; the other half will receive 0.1% IAA in lanolin. Cover cut ends of each of the debladed leafstalks of those plants selected for treatment with a dab of lanolin containing the designated concentration of IAA.
5. Treat the debladed leafstalks of the second plant in each pair with plain lanolin, applied in exactly the same way.

QUESTIONS FOR DISCUSSION

1. Why is such extreme care in matching the plants necessary?

2. Why is the control treated with plain lanolin, instead of being left untreated?

3. What are the advantages of using repeated stem cuttings rather than growing the plants from seeds?

The foregoing was a description of the way in which Jacobs designed an experiment. Several reprinted papers now follow, as illustrations of the way in which he and others reported their results.

WHAT SUBSTANCE NORMALLY CONTROLS A GIVEN BIOLOGICAL PROCESS?[1]

by WILLIAM P. JACOBS

Probably the question asked most often by developmental physiologists is the one posed in the title. In the current stage of our branch of science, we are culturally conditioned to ask this question, and to try to answer it. But there is no uniformity in the evidence provided in our answers. A search through the literature has uncovered no explicit formulation of what constitutes worth-while evidence. Yet it is obvious that there *are* rules, at least some of which are tacitly assumed by all researchers in the field. The purpose of this paper is to formalize the rules already in use, discuss their application to some already published research, and then in the companion paper to demonstrate their application to a well-known developmental problem.

But before formulating the rules, we should explain what assumptions lie behind the question in the title. (We are using the word "controls" in the title as a conventional, shorthand way of saying "is the factor which limits the rate of.") The most obvious assumption is that the process is being controlled by only one substance. It is theoretically possible that more than one substance is controlling the process. However, applying the suggested rules to each substance in turn will elucidate any such phenomenon. And rule 6 (see below) is specifically designed to ferret out this case, if it exists.

A second assumption, scarcely less obvious, is that the process is controlled by a substance, rather than by a physical process. Although it is the current fashion to think in terms of chemical substances, we should keep in mind the possibility that any given biological process may be controlled by, for instance, a rate of diffusion.

With these qualifications in mind, then, what general types of evidence would be considered to verify the hypothesis that "the development of structure S is normally controlled in organisms by chemical C"? There are six basic types incorporated in the rules listed below. Each type of evidence confirms the hypothesis; and the more of them that are satisfied, the greater the likelihood that the hypothesis is correct.

[1] Reprinted by permission from *Developmental Biology*, Volume 1, No. 6, December, 1959. Copyright © 1959 by Academic Press Inc. Printed in U.S.A.

Jacobs

1. Demonstrate that the chemical is normally present and that the amount of the structure varies in the *intact* organism in parallel fashion with the amount of the chemical.

   a. If a quantitative relation can be demonstrated in such *normal* parallel variation, this strengthens the case.

2. Remove the source of the chemical, and demonstrate subsequent absence of formation of the structure.

   a. If a quantitative relation can be demonstrated between the amount of this *artificial* decrease of the chemical and the amount of decrease of the structure, this strengthens the case.

   b. The chemical is sometimes removed by selecting genetic mutants.

   c. A less direct—and therefore less satisfactory—method of meeting this requirement is to add other chemicals presumed to more or less specifically block chemical C, and show that the structure is blocked, too.

3. Substitute pure chemical C for the organ or tissue which had been shown to be the normal source of the chemical in the organism and demonstrate subsequent formation of the structure.

   a. Quantitative evidence, as usual, strengthens the case. In the form of *exact substitution*—i.e., adding exactly the amount of chemical which is normally produced by the excised organ—it is particularly important when considering natural inhibition effects attributed to hormones. (Adding surplus hormone will unspecifically inhibit a variety of processes.) The ideal application of this rule would be to add a number of concentrations of the chemical—with one of the number providing exact substitution—and to demonstrate quantitatively parallel variation in the amount of the structure. Exact substitution should, of course, give exactly the normal amount and type of structure.

   b. Since the isolation of a naturally occurring chemical (particularly when it is a hormone) is a task which has often thwarted developmental physiologists, they may be driven to the following progressively less direct modifications of the rule: substitute an *extract* of the organ; substitute chopped-up pieces of the organ; merely replace the excised organ with a diffusion gap between it and the region where the structure is to form.

4. Isolate as much of the reacting system as possible and demonstrate that the chemical has the same effect as in the more intact organism. This reduces the probability that the chemical is acting primarily on some other process, or part of the organism, and only secondarily on the structure in question.

   a. The part of biochemistry concerned with the *in vitro* reactions of extracted enzyme systems to added chemicals can be considered to represent the most extreme application of the isolation rule. Progressively less extreme isolations would be reactions of subcellular organelles; individual cells, tissues, pieces of organs, or whole organs (as in sterile cultures); leaf cuttings, etc.

5. Demonstrate the generality of the results by showing that the other five points hold for species from a number of different families, as well as for the development of the structure in different kinds of organs.

6. Demonstrate that naturally occurring chemicals other than *C* have no such effect on the structure.

(These six rules can be more easily remembered by using the mnemonic device "PESIGS"—representing Parallel variation, Excision, Substitution, Isolation, Generality, Specificity.)

If covering these six "rules" in their quantitative form represents a useful ideal, how many times has this ideal been realized? Very seldom, to my knowledge. Most of the thorough, quantitative work known to me does not fully follow the last two rules. Most papers in the field of plant development follow only rule 3 ("substituting the chemical") and that only qualitatively: exact substitution is very rare.

The action of auxin as the normal controlling factor for the growth of *Avena* coleoptiles is one of the few cases in plants which has been thoroughly investigated. Parallel variation in the normal plant is shown in Fig. 27 of Went and Thimann (1937). The decreased growth resulting from excision of the source of auxin is shown in their Fig. 7. Substitution of auxin for the excised natural source causes increased growth, the amount of extra growth being proportional to the amount of auxin added (their Fig. 24). By adding 50 parts per million of synthetic indoleacetic acid to decapitated coleoptiles, Went (1942) was able to bring the growth rate up to that of the intact controls (his Table II). However, I have not been able to find a case where *exact* substitution of the auxin coming from the coleoptile tip has been attempted. Isolated sections of the coleoptile were found to give increased growth with increases in added auxin (Bonner, 1933), and these isolated sections have been used for many later papers, including some elegant recent work in which kinetic treatment has been applied to the growth data (Bonner and Foster, 1955). The general applicability of the results with *Avena* coleoptiles has been checked to some degree in many plants by many different investigators (cf. Went and Thimann, 1937; Söding, 1952). The chemical specificity has also been thoroughly checked.

Similarly, auxin has been shown to be the normal limiting factor for the differentiation of xylem cells in *Coleus* shoots, in quantitative studies of normal production, of excision effects, and of exact substitution (Jacobs, 1947, 1952, 1954, 1956; Jacobs and Morrow, 1957). Isolation has not yet been applied to *Coleus,* but in two other genera the addition of synthetic auxin speeded differentiation of xylem in tissue cultures (Torrey, 1953; Wetmore and Sorokin, 1955). The generality of the results with *Coleus* has been checked even less—one can only say that there are indications in the literature that auxin controls xylem differentiation in many different plants. The specificity of auxin in this effect has not yet been checked at all.

The only other area where the PESIGS rules have been followed in quantitative detail is the role of auxin in preventing the fall (abscission) of leaves. Parallel variation and the effect of excising the sources were demonstrated in *Coleus* (Wetmore and Jacobs, 1953). Synthetic auxin could completely substitute for the normal auxin sources; however, exact substitution for the normal auxin production was not attempted. Addicott and co-workers were the first to isolate the abscission area and to demonstrate that the isolated system of bean leaves functioned qualitatively the same as the intact one (particularly well shown in Addicott and Lynch, 1951). That auxin can inhibit abscission has been shown in many plants and in a variety of organs, and the chemical specificity of auxins for this effect has been looked into more than usual.

If there are so few cases of thorough application of the PESIGS rules even in the field of auxin physiology—a field which has been under intensive investigation for thirty years—one may well ask why more researchers do not routinely use these rules. One part of the answer may be that the rules have not previously been explicitly stated in connection with developmental research. It is also immediately obvious to any practicing researcher that there are many scientists who would be antipathetic to the chore of gathering such detailed evidence. Because of basic personality traits, they would not function as well as scientists if required to follow quantitative PESIGS rules as they do by checking, say, one of the rules in a qualitative way. This difference in the investigators is to some extent aesthetic—akin to the difference between Frans Hals and van Eyck. Both Hals and the qualitative investigators probably thought that their work adequately represented the real world. But, in the case of experimental biology this is not always the case; qualitative checking of only one of the PESIGS rules has often led to erroneous conclusions. Consider the following examples.

Elegant quantitative experiments showed that auxin moved with strict basipetal polarity in sections cut from a specialized organ of oat seedlings (Went and White, 1939). Quantitative work on other organs from other seedlings also showed strict basipetal polarity. Generalizing from these results, similar results from less thorough investigations of plants which were past the seedling stage were taken as evidence that strict basipetal polarity was a general phenomenon in the plant world. Phenomena which could, with some likelihood be ascribed to the action of auxin, would be considered to be not due to auxin "because auxin cannot move upwards." In essence, this was generalizing to all organs, including trees, on the basis of work with a few organs from seedlings. When auxin transport was Jacobs quantitatively checked in stems of an independently growing plant, substantial upward transport was found. It could be demonstrated quantitatively, by parallel variation studies, that this upward transport was physiologically significant (Jacobs, 1952, 1954). One of the special virtues of quantitative work was shown in the cited work: although the experimenter, familiar by both reading and practice with the "fact" that auxin only moved down, did not believe his own results at first, their quantitatively reproducible nature finally forced him to change his preconceptions. If the work had been qualitative, he could easily have cast aside the evidence—as some of the earlier qualitative workers had done (cf. Jacobs, 1954, p. 334).

A well-publicized case in which parallel variation was, by itself, taken as sufficient evidence of a causal relation is that of dwarf corn. The type of corn called "Dwarf-1" results from a single gene mutation. Its mature height is about half that of the normal strain. Once van Overbeek (1938) showed that coleoptile tips from the dwarf seedlings produce about half as much auxin as the normal seedling, the small amount of growth hormone was taken as the cause of the decreased growth. After twenty years, this was reinvestigated by Phinney. He confirmed the parallel variation between growth and auxin production, but, in addition, tried substitution. Auxin added to the dwarf plants gave no increased growth (Phinney, 1956a), nor was there any increased growth from a variety of related compounds. However, when the more recently exploited substance, gibberellic acid, was added to the dwarf plants, their growth was brought up to that of the normal plants (Phinney, 1956b). (Normal plants were essentially unaffected by the same amount of added gibberellic acid.)

A third example, that of the role of auxin in apical dominance, we shall deal with in a subsequent paper. This is a case where exact matching, under the substitution rule, has not been tried except in the first, classic paper on the subject (Thimann and Skoog, 1934).

Summary

Six rules (the "PESIGS" rules) are stated for determining what naturally occurring substance normally controls a given biological process. The application of these rules, in quantitative form, is urged on developmental physiologists.

References

Addicott, F. T., and Lynch, R. S. (1951). Acceleration and retardation of abscission by indoleacetic acid. *Science* 114, 688–689.

Bonner, J. (1933). The action of the plant growth hormone. *J. Gen. Physiol.* 17, 63–76.

Jacobs   Bonner, J., and Foster, R. J. (1955). The growth-time relationships of the auxin-induced growth in *Avena* coleoptile sections. *J. Exptl. Botany* 6, 293–302.

Jacobs, W. P. (1947). The effect of some growth-hormones on the differentiation of xylem around a wound. *Am. J. Botany* 34, 600.

Jacobs, W. P. (1952). The role of auxin in the differentiation of xylem around a wound. *Am. J. Botany* 39, 301–309.

Jacobs, W. P. (1954). Acropetal auxin transport and xylem regeneration—a quantitative study. *Am. Naturalist* 88, 327–337.

Jacobs, W. P. (1956). Internal factors, controlling cell differentiation in the flowering plants. *Am. Naturalist* 90, 163–169.

Jacobs, W. P., and Morrow, I. B. (1957). A quantitative study of xylem development in the vegetative shoot apex of *Coleus. Am. J. Botany* 44, 823–842.

Phinney, B. O. (1956a). Biochemical mutants in maize: dwarfism and its reversal with gibberellins. *Plant Physiol.* 31, (Suppl.), XX.

Phinney, B. O. (1956b). Growth response of single-gene dwarf mutants in maize to gibberellic acid. *Proc. Natl. Acad. Sci. U. S.* 42, 185–189.

Söding, H. (1952). "Die Wuchsstofflehre." Georg Thieme, Stuttgart.

Thimann, K. V., and Skoog, F. (1934). On the inhibition of bud development and other functions of growth substance in *Vicia faba. Proc. Roy. Soc.* B114, 317–339.

Torrey, J. G. (1953). The effect of certain metabolic inhibitors on vascular tissue differentiation in isolated pea roots. *Am. J. Botany* 40, 525–533.

Van Overbeek, J. (1938). Auxin production in seedlings of dwarf maize. *Plant Physiol.* 13, 587–598.

Went, F. W. (1942). Growth, auxin, and tropisms in decapitated *Avena* coleoptiles. *Plant Physiol.* 17, 236–249.

Went, F. W., and Thimann, K. V. (1937). "Phytohormones." Macmillan, New York.

Went, F. W., and White, R. (1939). Experiments on the transport of auxin. *Botan. Gaz.* 100, 465–484.

Wetmore, R. H., and Jacobs, W. P. (1953). Studies on abscission: the inhibiting effect of auxin. *Am. J. Botany* 40, 272–276.

Wetmore, R. H., and Sorokin, S. (1955). On the differentiation of xylem. *J. Arnold Arboretum (Harvard Univ.)* 36, 305–317.

End of Article

SUMMARY

We have employed the basic processes of science as we explored some of the ways in which different parts of an organism are coordinated. We have seen that coordination is effected by means of nervous systems and by hormones. In plants, nervous tissue is not known. In most animals, regulation is maintained by interlocking reactions of the nervous system with the endocrine system, although elements of either system may be predominant in the control of many individual sets of reactions.

Control of the reactions of most animals is very complex, and as yet it is not well understood. The next section will consider in some detail a few examples of animal behavior.

QUESTIONS FOR DISCUSSION:

1. What does PESIGS stand for?

2. How could a scientist determine if his results were reasonably valid without using all six steps?

3. What two obvious assumptions does the author list as underlying the question in his title?

STUDIES ON ABSCISSION:
THE INHIBITING EFFECT OF AUXIN[1]

by R. H. WETMORE and WM. P. JACOBS

The first indication that abscission of leaves is controlled by auxin was given by the work of Laibach (1933). He showed that pollinia of orchids, applied to the distal cut end of a petiole, inhibited abscission of the petiole. Orchid pollinia were known to contain auxin, and a few years later La Rue (1936) reported an experiment showing that synthetic auxin in the form of indoleacetic acid (IAA) was also very effective in delaying abscission, if it were applied in the dark or in shade. The first thorough investigation as to whether auxin was the factor which typically in nature controlled petiolar abscission was the work of Myers (1940a). Using *Coleus* as his experimental material, he showed that those leaves which normally stayed longest on the plant were also those which gave the greatest amount of diffusible auxin; that removing the leaf blade greatly accelerated petiolar abscission; and that the presence of IAA on the debladed petiole inhibited abscission as well as did the presence of the leaf blade.

The experiments cited above give a picture of abscission in which the speed with which any given petiole abscises is directly controlled by the amount of diffusible auxin coming down from the leaf blade. That is, so far as abscission is concerned, each leaf seems to act as a physiological entity.

The experiments to be described below confirm and extend these earlier experiments, while the experiments in the second paper of this series (Rossetter and Jacobs, 1953) show that we must discard as being too simple the view that "with respect to abscission, each leaf is a physiological entity."

METHODS.—A clonal stock of *Coleus blumei* Benth. was grown in the greenhouse. The variety was the same as that used by Jacobs (1952), Rossetter and Jacobs (1953), and Jacobs and Bullwinkel (1953). Supplementary lighting was used during winter months to obtain faster growth.

[1] Reprinted by permission from the *American Journal of Botany*, Vol. 40, No. 4, 272–276, April, 1953. Printed in U.S.A.

Wetmore
and Jacobs

The plants were trained to a two-branched form by excising the main stem and allowing only two of the axillary branches to develop. All other axillary branches were removed. The terminology used in referring to parts of each shoot is the same as that used in Jacobs (1952) and is shown diagrammatically in Figure 1.

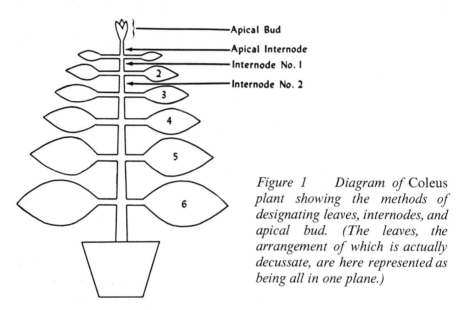

Apical Bud

Apical Internode

Internode No. I

Internode No. 2

Figure 1   Diagram of Coleus *plant showing the methods of designating leaves, internodes, and apical bud. (The leaves, the arrangement of which is actually decussate, are here represented as being all in one plane.)*

A "spiral" pattern of deblading was used: that is, the leaf blade of one member of each leaf pair below the apical bud was excised, and the debladed petioles were arranged in a spiral on the stem (see Figure 1 of Rossetter and Jacobs, 1953). The intact leaf of each pair is listed as the control; the debladed petiole as the treated petiole.

IAA and naphthaleneacetic acid (NAA) were applied at 1 per cent concentrations in lanolin; 8 shoots were used for each treatment. Determinations of diffusible auxin were run as described in Jacobs (1952).

The plants were checked every day for abscission by tapping each main stem rather vigorously before counting leaf fall.

Material for histological study was embedded in paraffin, sectioned at 10μ, and stained with haematoxylin and safranin.

Statistical methods and terminology follow Snedecor (1946).

RESULTS.—1. *Normal development of abscission layer.*—Figures 2–5 show the abscission region in leaves 2, 3, 5 and 6. A readily detectable abscission layer is first visible in leaf 3; the fully differentiated layer being visible is leaf 6. The normal order of abscission with the characteristic time intervals can be seen from the control leaves of Figure 7. The younger the leaf (i.e., the nearer the apical bud it is), the longer it stays on the plant. Another way of saying this is that *Coleus* leaves usually abscise when they are in leaf position 6–8.

Wetmore and Jacobs

Figures 2–5   *Photomicrographs of the prospective abscission zone in petioles 2, 3, 4, and 5 respectively.*

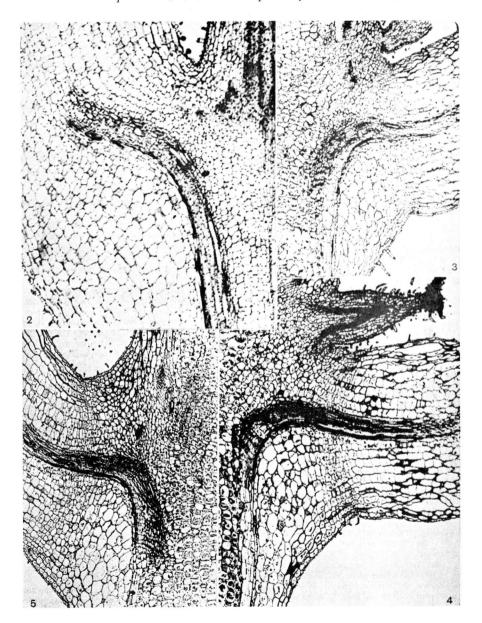

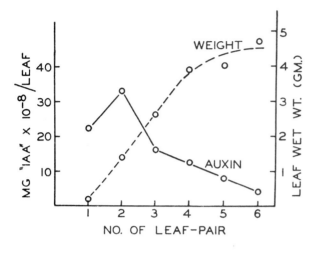

Figure 6   Amounts of diffusible auxin obtained from Coleus leaves from various positions on the stem.

Wetmore
and Jacobs

2. *Diffusible auxin from the leaf blades shows a high correlation with the length of time petioles are normally retained.*—Figure 6 shows typical results of a diffusion experiment on *Coleus* leaves. In general agreement with the findings of predecessors, successively greater absolute amounts of auxin were obtained from successively younger leaves, but with leaf 1 showing a decrease relative to leaf 2. Calculation of the correlation coefficient for amount of diffusible auxin and length of petiolar retention, omitting the values for leaf 1, gave r = 0.9525, a value which is statistically significant.

3. *Removing leaf blades speeds abscission.*—Excising the leaf blade of one member of each leaf pair, and placing plain lanolin on the petiolar stump gave results as shown to the left in Figure 7. The controls show the expected

Figure 7   *Pre-abscission intervals for intact leaves (shaded) and debladed petioles, in* Coleus *plants with "spiral" deblading, when the debladed petioles are treated with plain lanolin, NAA-lanolin, and IAA-lanolin, respectively.*

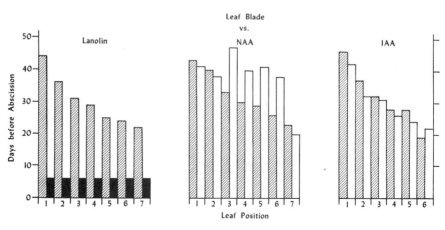

gradient of petiolar abscission. The debladed petioles, on the other hand,
abscise very much faster and show no gradient along the axis with respect
to the time of abscission. (The lack of a gradient in the debladed petioles
does not agree with Myers' (1940a) results.)

4. *Auxin replaces the leaf blade in slowing abscission of the proximal petiole.*—When plants are treated as above except that synthetic auxin is applied in lanolin to the petiolar stump, the treated petioles stay on as long or longer than do those which have the leaf blade still attached. Results with IAA are shown to the right of Figure 7. One per cent IAA almost exactly replaces the leaf blade in causing petiolar retention. NAA in lanolin acts even more effectively to prevent petiolar abscission (center of Figure 7).

DISCUSSION.—Study of histological developments in the abscission zone of *Coleus* shows that this plant resembles cotton, pepper and poinsettia studied by Gawadi and Avery (1950) in that a distinct abscission layer is differentiated prior to abscission. In agreement with Myers' (1940a) report for *Coleus,* the layer is first recognizable in leaf pair 3 and is fully differentiated in leaf pair 6. As our Figures 2–5 show, the abscission layer is remarkably well developed even in leaf pair 3, leaves which are only two-thirds of their full size and which will not actually abscise for about 30 days (Figures 6, 7). These observations support the contention of Gawadi and Avery that the so-called abscission layer has no *causal* relationship to the actual abscission of leaves.

These experiments confirm those of Myers in showing the importance of diffusible auxin in controlling the normal pattern of leaf abscission. In agreement with the results of Myers (1940a), excision of the leaf blade speeds up markedly abscission of the debladed petiole. Myers found that debladed petioles showed a gradient like the intact leaves, in that petiole 1 abscised later than petiole 2, etc. No such gradient was detectable in our plants (cf. also Rossetter and Jacobs, 1953, Figure 2 and 3). IAA added to the cut surface of the debladed petiole was found, in agreement with Myers (1940a), to replace very closely the effect of the leaf blade in delaying abscission. NAA was for most of the petioles *more* effective than the intact leaf blade. Finally, the general agreement noted by Myers between the amount of diffusible auxin produced by the leaves and the length of time they would normally stay on the plants was confirmed, and it was further shown that there was a high and statistically significant correlation between the amount of diffusible auxin from leaves 2–6 and the pre-abscission period of those leaves.

On the basis of these experiments we conclude that the diffusible auxin from the leaf blade is the factor which normally controls the pattern of leaf abscission. Once the petiole reaches a certain stage of development (e.g., as in leaf 2), its pre-abscission interval is correlated with the amount of auxin which is being released into the petiole from the distal leaf blade.

That this correlation is causal is indicated by the experiments in which auxin was substituted for the leaf blade.

It is important to note two uncertainties which have not yet been resolved. First, we have no indication as to *where* in the petiole the auxin exerts its effect. The most obvious guess is directly on the abscission layer. But, since auxin seems necessary for growth of the petiole (Mai, 1934; Myers, 1940a, b) and since the petioles normally continue to elongate after the blades have ceased growing (Myers, 1940a; and our observations), it may be that auxin prevents abscission only indirectly (i.e., through its effect on growth of the petiole). This possibility was apparently first suggested by Myers (1940b). Support for this interpretation comes from a detailed comparison of the growth of debladed petioles treated with IAA-lanolin and of normal petioles with distal intact leaves. In Figure 7 it can be seen that IAA-lanolin does not quite "replace" the leaf blade in inhibiting abscission of petioles 1 and 2, but "*more* than replaces" the leaf blade for petiole 6. The same result is shown in Figure 4 of Myers' paper (1940a), where data for petioles 7 and 8 show even longer retention when IAA is added. If one now inspects Figure 1 of Myers' other paper (1940b), where the effect of IAA-lanolin versus the leaf blade is shown for the *elongation* of petioles, one can see that there is an exact parallel with the abscission effects. This hypothesis, that auxin inhibits abscission indirectly through its stimulating effect on petiole growth, has two advantages. First, in contrast to the hypothesis that auxin inhibits abscission by a direct effect on the abscission layer, this hypothesis explains the apparently contradictory findings that A) the amount of auxin from the various leaf blades shows such a high correlation with the pre-abscission interval of the leaves, although B) auxin added to debladed petiole 6 gives relatively fast abscission even though the *same* concentration of auxin keeps debladed petiole 3 on for the same time as does the intact leaf blade. Secondly, the hypothesis of the "indirect effect" has the advantage of explaining the action on abscission of the growth-substance, auxin, by a growth effect instead of necessitating the assumption of still another type of effect to the already bewildering multiplicity of auxin effects.

The second uncertainty which has not been discussed is that although the experiments reported above seem unequivocal in showing the primary role of auxin from its own leaf blade in preventing abscission of a given petiole, no study has yet been reported which investigates the influence of the *rest* of the organism on the abscission of a leaf petiole. Such a study will be reported in Rossetter and Jacobs (1953).

SUMMARY

The anatomy and physiology of the development of the abscission layer in *Coleus* leaves has been investigated. The abscission layer is first apparent, and is almost fully differentiated anatomically, in leaf pair 3. The pre-abscission interval of leaves at various positions along the stem (and thus of varying ages) shows a significant correlation with the amount of diffusible auxin produced by the leaves. Removing the leaf blades (and thus the auxin-sources) speeds up abscission very markedly. The leaf blades can be replaced in their inhibiting effect on abscission by the application of synthetic auxin. The experiments are interpreted as showing the dominant role of diffusible auxin from the leaf blades in controlling the normal order and intervals of leaf abscission.

Biology Department,
  Harvard University,
    Cambridge, Massachusetts

Biology Department,
  Princeton University,
    Princeton, New Jersey

LITERATURE CITED

Gawadi, A. G., and G. S. Avery, Jr. 1950. Leaf abscission and the so-called "abscission layer." Amer. Jour. Bot. 37: 172–180.

Jacobs, W. P. 1952. The role of auxin in differentiation of xylem around a wound. Amer. Jour. Bot. 39: 301ff.

———, and B. Bullwinkel. 1953. Compensatory growth in *Coleus* shoots. Amer. Jour. Bot. In press.

Laibach, F. 1933. Versuche mit Wuchsstoffpaste. Ber. Deutsch. Bot. Ges. 51: 386–392.

La Rue, C. D. 1936. The effect of auxin on the abscission of petioles. Proc. National Acad. Sci. (U.S.) 22: 254–259.

End of Article

QUESTIONS FOR DISCUSSION

1. Compare this paper by Wetmore and Jacobs to the paper by Darwin (page 222). Note the difference in style. Was the experimental design as obvious in both papers?

2. Which of the PESIGS rules do the authors follow?

3. While the author's use of the statistic called the correlation coefficient may be unfamiliar to you, his statement that "$r = 0.9525$, a value which is statistically significant," does have meaning. Tell briefly what this means, in relation to the rest of the paper.

STUDIES ON ABSCISSION:
THE STIMULATING ROLE OF NEARBY LEAVES[1]

by F. N. ROSSETTER and WM. P. JACOBS

Current interpretations of the physiological basis of petiole abscission, as described in Wetmore and Jacobs (1953), are slightly unsettling to a researcher accustomed to interpreting plant behaviour in terms of the organismic concept. The view that each leaf is a physiological entity as far as abscission is concerned is quite unexpected if one stops to think of the great mass of evidence indicating dependencies and interdependencies among various organs of higher plants.

Scepticism as to the completeness of the view that auxin from its own leaf blade was the controlling factor in preventing abscission of a given petiole, led one of us (WPJ) to begin some of the investigations reported in this paper. It will be seen that as far as abscission is concerned, leaves do not act like independent "colonies" fastened to a common stem, but are influenced by the rest of the organism.

MATERIALS AND METHODS.—A variety of *Coleus blumei* Benth. was used for these experiments. The plants were grown as described in Jacobs (1952) and belong to the same clone as the plants used by Jacobs (1952), Wetmore and Jacobs (1953), and Jacobs and Bullwinkel (1953). The method of designating leaf numbers, etc. is the same as that used by Jacobs (1952) and is illustrated in Figure 1 of Wetmore and Jacobs (1953). Only single stemmed upright plants were used. Axillary buds and branches were removed. In their experiments Wetmore and Jacobs (1953) used a "spiral" arrangement of debladed leaves. That is, one blade of each leaf pair was excised, and the debladed petioles were in a spiral arrangement on the stem (Figure 1). Although it is not stated explicitly, Myers (1940) apparently used a spiral arrangement, too. Such a spiral arrangement means that each debladed petiole has an intact leaf just above, just below, and immediately opposite it. The main patterns of leaf deblading used in our experiments were as follows:

1) Spiral deblading with plain lanolin on the petiolar stumps (Figure 1).

2) "Two-sided" deblading with plain lanolin on the petiolar stumps (Figure 1).

3) "Four-sided" deblading with plain lanolin on the petiolar stumps. That is, *all* leaf blades below the apical bud were excised.

[1] Received for publication on August 7, 1952.

Report of work supported in part by an American Cancer Society Grant recommended by the Committee on Growth of the National Research Council and in part by funds of the Eugene Higgins Trust allocated to Princeton University.

Reprinted by permission from the *American Journal of Botany,* Vol. 40, No. 4, 276–280, April, 1953. Printed in U.S.A.

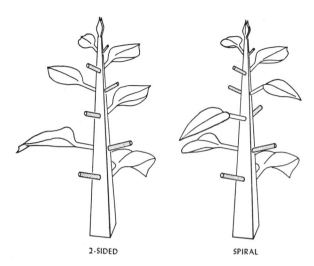

2-SIDED   SPIRAL

Figure 1   Diagrams to show the "spiral" and "two-sided" deblading patterns. One petiole of each leaf pair has been debladed. The debladed petioles are designated by stippling. The top debladed petiole (i.e., the one nearest to the apical bud) is Petiole No. 1, the bottom one (in these diagrams) is Petiole No. 6.

4) "Four-sided" deblading with indoleacetic acid in lanolin on the petiolar stumps.

Rossetter and Jacobs

In each pattern of leaf deblading the leaves of the apical bud, which had not yet unfolded, were left untreated and untouched. Indoleacetic acid (IAA) was used in 1 per cent concentration in lanolin. The lanolin or IAA-lanolin was applied to the distal cut surface of the debladed petioles. The plants were checked every day for abscised petioles. A seemingly more uniform method than that used in Wetmore and Jacobs (1953) for testing leaves about to abscise was employed by applying a slight but relatively constant pressure to each petiole daily to ensure that the petiole was not being retained by only a few intact strands of vascular tissue, the cells of the abscission layer having already separated. The pressure was applied with a few strands of fine soft wire in a transfer-needle handle.

Except where noted under "Results," there were at least three replications of each experiment, with statistically significant results within each replication. Results were essentially the same in each replication, the variability in terms of absolute numbers being apparent from Figures 2–4. Five to fifteen plants were used for each treatment.

The "t" test was used as a measure of statistical significance. Statistical methods and terminology follow Snedecor (1946).

RESULTS.—To test the effect of nearby leaves on the abscission of debladed petioles, the four treatments described under "Materials and

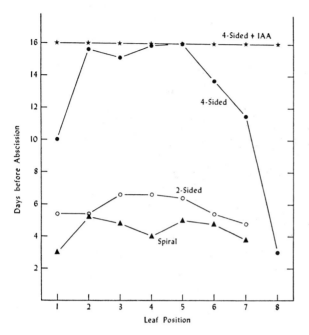

Figure 2   Influence of deblading pattern and of IAA-lanolin versus plain lanolin on the retention of debladed Coleus *petioles at different positions along the stem. The horizontal line at 16 days for IAA-treated petioles shows that these petioles had not abscissed when the experiment was ended after 16 days. Casual observation indicated that they were retained for periods approximating those in figure 6 of Wetmore and Jacobs (1953).*

methods" were used. Results of a typical replication are shown in Figure 2 and Table 1.

In confirmation of earlier work, spiral deblading resulted in very fast shedding of the debladed petioles, no matter what their position on the stem.

TABLE 1. **Influence of Deblading Pattern and IAA on Retention of** *Coleus* **Petioles.**

Petiole position	*Spiral*	*Two-sided*	*Four-sided*	*Four-sided plus IAA*[b]
1	3.0 ± 0.3 (5)	5.4 ± 1.9 (5)	10.0[a] (10)	16+ (10)
2	5.2 ± 0.6 (5)	5.4 ± 0.4 (5)	15.6[a] (10)	16+ (10)
3	4.8 ± 0.6 (5)	6.6 ± 0.2 (5)	15.1[a] (10)	16+ (10)
4	4.0 ± 0.3 (5)	6.6 ± 0.6 (5)	15.9[a] (10)	16+ (10)
5	5.0 ± 0.4 (5)	6.4 ± 0.2 (5)	16+ (10)	16+ (10)
6	4.8 ± 0.9 (4)	5.4 ± 0.2 (5)	13.7[a] (10)	16+ (8)
7	3.8 ± 0.5 (4)	4.8 ± 0.2 (5)	11.5[a] (8)	16+ (4)

[a] Denotes averages which include petioles which stayed on for 16 days or longer (records ceased after 16 days). These are minimum averages, since 16 days was taken as the true value in such cases.

[b] Every petiole treated with IAA stayed on for 16 days or longer.

The data in the table are expressed as "Average number of days before abscission ± standard error." The numbers in parentheses represent the number of petioles included in the averages.

The "two-sided" deblading, however, resulted in significantly longer retention of the debladed petioles. In the particular replication shown in Figure 2, there was a significant difference between the overall averages for petioles 1–7 in each treatment; but when differences between petioles at any *one* position were considered, both in the cited replication and in the other replications, significant differences were found only at positions 3, 4 and 5.

Rossetter
and Jacobs

As might be expected from previous reports, "four-sided" deblading coupled with treatment of the petiolar stumps with auxin gave retention of all petioles, no matter what their position, for 16 days or longer.

Quite unexpected were the results obtained from "four-sided" deblading when plain lanolin was added to the cut surface. All petioles were retained much longer than with plain lanolin treatment of any other deblading pattern used. Even those petioles which already have abscission layers fully differentiated (i.e., No. 6 and 7) are retained longer than in the "spiral" or "two-sided" groups. This result was obtained with each of 5 replications.

These results demonstrate that the presence of other leaf blades speeds up the abscission of debladed petioles. The presence of an intact leaf just above, just below, and just opposite each debladed petiole (as in "spiral" deblading) gives faster abscission than having no intact expanded leaves above or below the debladed petiole in the same orthostichy, even though intact leaves are opposite as well as above and below at right angles (as in "two-sided" deblading). Slowest abscission of all results from having no intact leaves above, below *or* opposite the debladed petioles (e.g., "four-sided" deblading).

In both the "two-sided" and "spiral" groups, intact leaves were opposite each debladed petiole as well as above and below it at the next nodes (i.e., on the adjacent orthostichies). In an attempt to separate effects of opposite

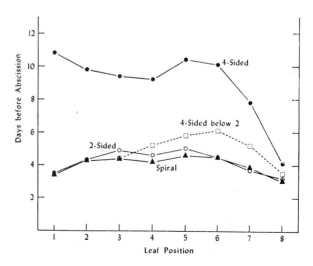

Figure 3   Influence of deblading pattern on the retention of debladed petioles which had been treated with plain lanolin on their distal cut surface.

TABLE 2.

Petiole position	Four-sided deblading	Four-sided below Leaf 2	Two-sided deblading
3	9.4 ± 0.4 (20)	4.4 ± 0.2 (20)	4.9 ± 0.2 (15)
4	9.2 ± 0.4 (20)	5.2 ± 0.2 (20)	4.6 ± 0.2 (15)
5	10.4 ± 0.4 (20)	5.8 ± 0.2 (20)	5.0 ± 0.3 (15)
6	10.1 ± 0.5 (20)	6.1 ± 0.2 (20)	4.5 ± 0.3 (15)
7	7.8 ± 0.7 (20)	5.2 ± 0.3 (20)	3.7 ± 0.2 (15)
8	4.1 ± 0.2 (18)	3.5 ± 0.3 (18)	3.2 ± 0.2 (12)

Rossetter and Jacobs

leaves from leaves above and below, there was added to the three plain lanolin treatments used above a new treatment in which all leaves below the No. 2 position were debladed ("four-sided below 2"). Results are shown in Figure 3 and Table 2. It can be seen that the presence above the debladed petioles of intact leaf pairs 1 and 2, in addition to the intact leaf pairs of the apical bud, markedly speeds up abscission of the subjacent petioles, although the petioles are retained longer than with "spiral" or "two-sided" deblading. Results from a similar experiment, but with all leaves debladed below leaf pair 3 in one of the treatments is shown in Figure 4. It can be seen that the presence of all leaves at and above the leaf 3 position speeds up abscission in petioles 4–8 to the same degree as does the presence of one member of each leaf pair all the way down the stem.

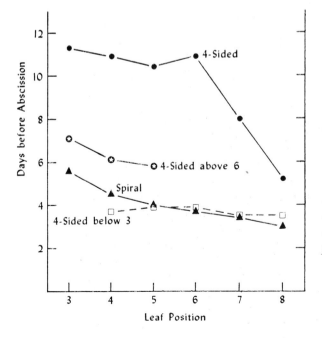

Figure 4   Influence of distal leaves versus proximal leaves on the retention of debladed Coleus petioles treated with plain lanolin.

To determine the effect, if any, of older proximal leaves, an experiment was tried with "four-sided" deblading below the apical bud as far down as leaf pair 6 (Figure 4, Table 3). With leaf pairs 6, 7, and 8 left intact, debladed petioles 1–5 abscised faster than their counterparts in the "four-sided" debladed controls. The difference was statistically highly significant for each petiole position.

Rossetter
and Jacobs

TABLE 3.

Petiole position	Four-sided deblading	Four-sided above Leaf 6	Spiral deblading
3	11.3 ± 0.3 (10)	7.1 ± 0.2 (10)	5.6 ± 0.3 (10)
4	10.9 ± 0.3 (10)	6.1 ± 0.3 (10)	4.5 ± 0.3 (10)
5	10.4 ± 0.4 (10)	5.8 ± 0.5 (8)	4.0 ± 0.2 (9)

(The special treatments described in the above two paragraphs were each tested only once.)

DISCUSSION.—The experiments described above show that, contrary to the impression left by the experiments of Myers (1940), abscission of a petiole is not independent of nearby leaves and thus dependent solely on amounts of diffusible auxin coming from the leaf blade of that petiole. When the pre-abscission period of debladed petioles was determined, it was found that the more leaves there were around the debladed petiole and the closer they were, the faster the petiole abscised. Maximum retention of petioles treated with plain lanolin was obtained when all the leaf blades below the apical bud were excised.

The abscission-stimulating effect of intact leaves is not strictly polar in its movement, judging by the treatment in which leaves 6–8 were left intact (Figure 4). This treatment resulted in petioles 4 and 5 (just above the intact leaves) abscising significantly faster than in the "four-sided" controls, although they abscised significantly slower than did corresponding petioles which were just below intact leaves 1–3.

We have no evidence so far as to whether this difference is due to a polar difference in *movement* of the abscission-stimulating effect or to a difference in the *strength* of the effect as produced by old versus young leaves.

The general conclusions are confirmed by a more thorough investigation of the individual petioles. For instance, if the opposite and distal leaves are more important than the proximal (and older) ones in determining the speed of abscission, we could predict that debladed petioles 1 and 2 of the "spiral" and "two-sided" groups would fall off at nearly the same time, since a glance at Figure 1 shows that these petioles have exactly the same pattern of intact leaves opposite and distal to them. Corresponding to

Rossetter
and Jacobs

expectation, the pre-abscission period of "spiral" petiole 1 was not signifi-cantly different from that of "two-sided" petiole 1 in any of the three replications in which such data were recorded. The same was true of petiole 2 in the two treatments.

It is only in relation to debladed petioles 3, 4, etc., that there are differ-ences between "spiral" and "two-sided" plants in the position and number of distal intact leaves; and it is between these petioles that significant differences in pre-abscission times first appear.

What is the physiological basis of this abscission stimulating effect? The two most obvious hypotheses are: 1) that intact leaves produce some sub-stance which speeds abscission of nearby petioles, 2) that removing leaf blades induces compensatory growth of the remaining debladed petioles, with a consequent inhibition of their abscission. Such compensatory growth in the petioles would scarcely be surprising in view of the complex compensatory relations described by Jacobs and Bullwinkel (1953) for this same clone of *Coleus*. However, experiments bearing, perhaps, on the first suggestion are already in the literature. In view of the interesting find-ing of Addicott and Lynch (1951), who studied the abscission zone between a bean leaflet and its petiole, that IAA applied *proximally* to this abscission zone *speeded* abscission one might suspect that the intact leaves of *Coleus* speeded abscission of nearby debladed petioles by acting as sources of proximal auxin. Even the abscission-stimulating effect of leaves *below* the debladed petioles would not be unexpected, according to this auxin hypothesis, since it has been shown by direct transport tests that auxin can move acropetally in *Coleus* stems as well as basipetally (Jacobs, 1952; confirmed by Leopold, private communication). However, evidence that the leaves are *not* speeding abscission by means of their production of auxin can be deduced from Figure 5[2] and Figure 6 of Myers' (1940) paper. After "four-sided" deblading, one member of each petiole pair was treated with IAA-lanolin, the other member with plain lanolin. When results are compared with "four-sided" deblading in which all the petioles were treated with plain lanolin, one finds that treating half the petioles with auxin has no effect on the speed of abscission of the petioles treated with plain lanolin. We have obtained the same result with our clone of *Coleus* in a recent experiment. Thus, although IAA can substitute for the leaf blade in retarding the abscission of that leaf blade's petiole (Wetmore and Jacobs, 1953), it apparently can not substitute for a leaf blade in speeding the abscission of nearby petioles in *Coleus*.

First results from a series of experiments now in progress indicate that the active agent is a gas. Ethylene, a gas long known to speed abscission, is suspected to be the active agent. Results of these experiments will be reported in a later paper.

[2] The legends for fig. 4 and fig. 5 (Myers, 1940) should be exchanged.

Rossetter
and Jacobs

The following interpretation of the normal abscission pattern seems indicated by our experiments. Each leaf has acting on it an abscission-stimulating effect from the nearby leaves. Whether due to polar movement, or to a gradient among the leaves in the strength of this effect, the younger expanded leaves (leaf pairs 1–3) have a greater influence than the older leaves. This abscission stimulating effect is opposed, for any one petiole, by the diffusible auxin moving into it from its attached leaf blade. The younger leaves normally stay on longest both because they are the greatest producers of diffusible auxin and also because they have a smaller number of abscission-stimulating leaves above them. The older leaves normally fall off very quickly both because they have a much larger number of abscission stimulating leaves above them and because they produce the smallest amounts of diffusible auxin. The high correlation found by Wetmore and Jacobs (1953) between the production of diffusible auxin and the pre-abscission period of various leaves indicates that normally the auxin effect over-rides the other effect.

This physiological mechanism (elucidated here for the control of abscission) whereby a stimulator is balanced by an inhibitor, is probably of widespread occurrence in regulatory mechanisms for biological organisms. Such a "balancing" mechanism would be expected to have marked selective value. It ensures that the younger leaves not only stay on longer under normal conditions but that they also hasten the shedding of the older, less actively metabolizing leaves. Furthermore, it ensures that accidental loss of some of the leaves will be compensated for by the longer retention of the remaining leaves—a result which will be made possible by the very loss of the other leaves (and of their abscission-inducing effect).

SUMMARY

Evidence that intact leaves speed up abscission of nearby debladed petioles has been obtained by deblading in various patterns a clonal stock of *Coleus* plants. The younger, still growing leaves have a greater abscission-stimulating effect than the older, fully-grown leaves, but whether this is due to polar movement of the effect or to stronger stimulus from the younger leaves has not yet been established. Reasons for thinking that the abscission stimulator is not auxin but may be ethylene are briefly discussed.

Department of Biology,
    Princeton University,
        Princeton, New Jersey

LITERATURE CITED

Addicott, F. T., and R. S. Lynch. 1951. Acceleration and retardation of abscission by indoleacetic acid. Science 114: 688–689.

Jacobs, W. P. 1952. The role of auxin in differentiation of xylem around a wound. Amer. Jour. Bot. 39: 301–309.

————, and B. Bullwinkel. 1953. Compensatory growth in *Coleus* shoots. Amer. Jour. Bot. In press.

Myers, R. M. 1940. Effect of growth substances on the absciss layer in leaves of *Coleus*. Bot. Gaz. 102: 323–338.

Snedecor, G. W. 1946. Statistical methods. Iowa State College Press. Ames, Iowa.

Wetmore, R. H., and W. P. Jacobs. 1953. Studies on abscission: the inhibiting effect of auxin. Amer. Jour. Bot. 40: 272–276.

End of Article

QUESTIONS FOR DISCUSSION

1. Why was the study reported in this article undertaken?

2. This paper reports some experimental refinements over the techniques used in the last report. What were they?

3. The authors report they used the t test in this study. Can you use the *t* test on the data reported in Table 1, or in Table 2?

At the present time, much research is being done in attempts to further explain regulation in plant growth and development. Although there is very good evidence that flowering is controlled in at least some plants by hormones, no one has been able to isolate the hormone. Many plants will flower only when exposed to proper periods of light and darkness. The hormone in this case appears to be produced in leaves and is then translocated to buds where it causes the imitation of flower parts.

We know that some substance which is produced in apical buds of many plants inhibits the growth of axillary buds. If the apical bud is damaged or removed, the axillary buds develop. The hormone in this case appears to be auxin (IAA).

Some of the effects of auxins are shown in Figure 67.

SECTION FIFTEEN

ANIMAL BEHAVIOR

At dawn of the last day of the third quarter of the moon and the first day of the fourth quarter, during October and November, the Palolo worm, *Palolo viridis,* swarms in the ocean near Samoa. At that time only, the elongated posterior segments break away from the body of the worm and spawn near the surface in an eerie luminescent display in which sperm and egg unite in fertilization. In Africa, the migratory locusts periodically

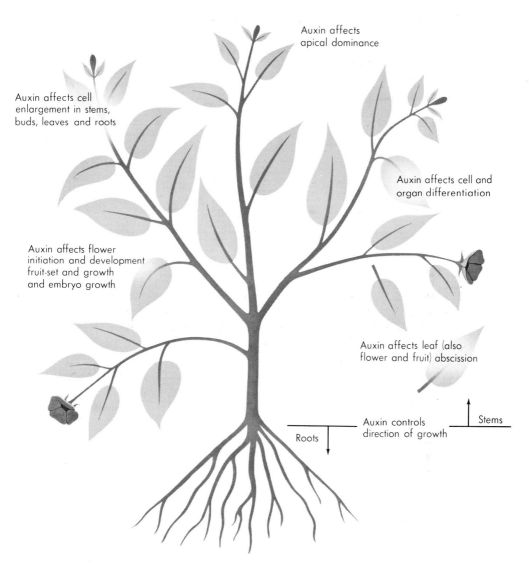

Auxin affects
apical dominance

Auxin affects cell
enlargement in stems,
buds, leaves and roots

Auxin affects cell and
organ differentiation

Auxin affects flower
initiation and development
fruit-set and growth
and embryo growth

Auxin affects leaf (also
flower and fruit) abscission

Auxin controls
direction of growth

Roots

Stems

*Figure 67   Effects of auxins on
plant growth and regulation.*

transform from a scattered population of harmless, solitary individuals to
a dense population of gregarious forms which assemble in vast numbers.
These huge swarms of locusts travel over the continent of Africa, eating
vegetation in their path, and destroying in excess of 90 million dollars
worth of vegetation per year during locust outbreaks. The western newt
Taricha breeds in streams of northern California, but spends most of the
year in the wooded hillsides above the streams. Each year the newts return

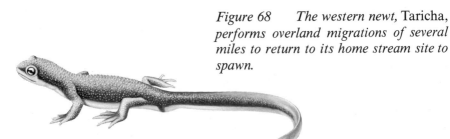

Figure 68   The western newt, Taricha, *performs overland migrations of several miles to return to its home stream site to spawn.*

to the same part of their home stream in order to breed. Newts will return to their stream site after being displaced as much as five miles from it. In Mexico and Central America, the orange-fronted parakeet builds its nests and rears its young in active nests of a species of tree-dwelling termite. The bird hollows out a cavity in the termite nest and the termites then seal off the inner exposed portions of the nest, separating the termites from the intruders.

How do the Palolo worms time their annual display so precisely? What causes the transformation of locust populations from solitary to gregarious phases, and what stimulates these insects to aggregate and migrate in such large numbers? By what means does the western newt locate the same spawning site each year? How does the orange-fronted parakeet recognize the termite's species in whose nest it builds? Is there some advantage to the parakeet in nesting in termite nests? How did this behavior evolve?

Answers to many of these questions are not yet available, and some of these behavior patterns, such as those of the migratory locusts, are currently under investigation. However, these are the kinds of phenomena, together with the questions which they raise, that form the basis for our study of animal behavior. The behavior of an animal cannot be defined precisely, but it includes activities carried on by the entire animal such as movement, sleeping, feeding, reproducing, and finding its way.

In trying to understand behavior, biologists want to know:

a. What patterns of behavior does a particular species possess?
b. How do the behavior patterns of an animal contribute to the survival of its species?

In attempting to understand specific behavior patterns, biologists ask:

a. Under what conditions does the behavior appear?
b. What anatomical, physiological and biochemical features of the animal are involved in the expression of the behavior?
c. How does the expression of the behavior change with time, and with the experiences of the animal?
d. How, if at all, is the pattern inherited?
e. How did the behavior pattern evolve?

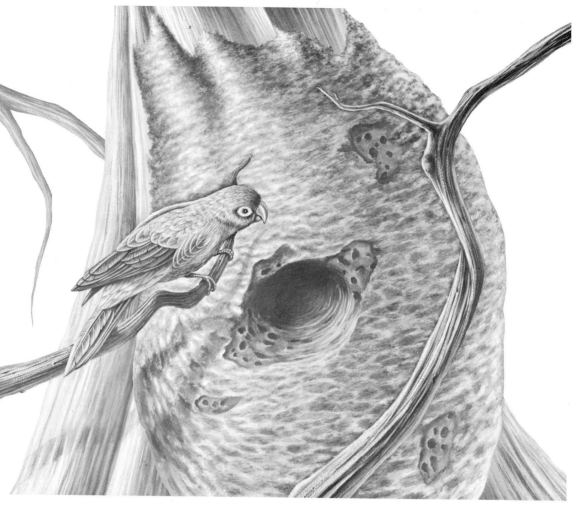

Figure 69   In Central America, the orange-fronted parakeet hollows its nest out of active termite nests built on the branches of trees.

Satisfactory answers to these kinds of questions permit biologists to make generalizations about the nature of behavior in animals, and to provide meaningful hypotheses for the investigation of human behavior.

Extensive studies of the behavior of a wide range of animal types among the invertebrates and vertebrates have already led to important generalizations. It is now clear, for instance, that the behavior exhibited by an animal at a specific time depends on the animal's developmental history, on its anatomical, physiological, and biochemical characteristics, and on the environment in which the animal finds itself. Biologists have gathered evidence which demonstrates that a specific animal's perception of its environment differs from our own or from that of other kinds of animals. This difference can be explained in the light of the organization of the nervous system and in the limitations and special capabilities of sense organs. Bees, for example, can detect infrared light; male gypsy moths can detect the female moth's scent in concentrations below that of the most sensitive instruments; rattlesnakes can detect temperature changes of 0.001°C; Mormyrid fish can detect alterations in a surrounding electric field; and bats can hear ultrasonic sounds.

Furthermore, it is characteristic of many behaviors that the stimuli which elicit one particular behavior are highly specific. For example, during the breeding season, male yellow-shafted flickers will attack other males within their territories, but not females. The specific stimulus by which a male flicker recognizes another flicker as a male is the presence of a black patch at the corner of the mouth, the so-called moustache. When a female flicker is captured and painted with a black patch at the corner of the mouth, she is attacked by her mate. When the patch is removed she is again accepted. Evidently, among all of the characteristics by which male flickers differ from females, only the black patch is significant in eliciting attack.

Figure 70   The black patch at the base of the bill (left) serves as a signal for the recognition of male flickers. Females (right) lack this patch.

Young ducklings show escape responses to a short-necked, long-tailed model moving overhead. This model resembles the outline of a predator, such as a hawk. When the same model is moved in the opposite direction, now resembling the outline of a duck or goose, the ducklings show no response. We see that from the total environment, the animal detects certain specific features which are then capable of acting upon it as stimuli, eliciting responses.

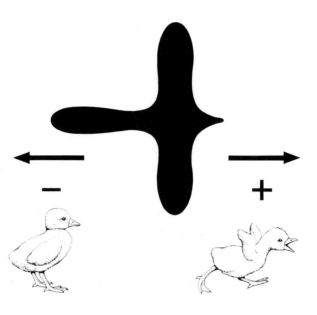

Figure 71   When the silhouette in the illustration is moved to the left over a group of ducklings, the birds show no response. When moved to the right, the birds attempt to escape.

Leopard frogs feed exclusively on moving prey, especially insects, but they do not perceive insects as we do. Microelectrodes implanted into single fibers within the optic nerve indicate that impulses are sent to the brain by any small form with a convex edge moving toward the center of the field of vision for that fiber. In this way, the frog recognizes an abstract of features common to a majority of insects and responds by leaping to catch its prey.

Figure 72   Frog vision differs greatly from that of man. A small form, with convex edges, moving toward the center of the frog's vision is recognized as an insect.

Kinds of Behavior

An important task of the biologist is to recognize and describe entities which exist in biological systems. Once the gene was identified as a biological unit whose duplication and transmission determined the pattern of inheritance of traits, rapid progress was made in our understanding of the mechanisms of genetics.

In similar fashion, it is desirable to recognize as an entity, or unit of behavior, the single behavioral action and to group as a category similar-appearing patterns or sequences of behavioral actions. Unfortunately, the internal mechanisms underlying a behavior pattern are usually not known. This places the grouping of similar-appearing behaviors on uncertain footing. Nevertheless, it appears desirable to classify behaviors in order to generalize about them, and several approaches have been developed.

Studies of the relationships of animal groups demonstrate that major groups (phyla) of animals differ in a graded fashion in the complexity of their nervous system. Correspondingly these groups differ in their ability to carry out elaborate and difficult tasks, to solve complicated kinds of problems, and to cope with changes in the environment in a flexible and reasoned way.

The following classification of behavior patterns appears to be based upon an increasing complexity of the underlying neural mechanisms. The study of the neurological bases underlying behavior is still so new that a more definite statement cannot be made. However, the broad distribution of these behaviors among animal groups reflects this assumption, since the more complex behaviors are found among those groups with the most highly developed and elaborate nervous systems, such as those found in birds and mammals.

Kinesis (plural, *kineses*) is an unlearned and undirected response of an animal to a stimulus. The response may be an increase or a decrease in the rate of turning, of movement, or of locomotion. For example, planarian worms are usually found in wet, dark habitats, such as the underside of stones, leaves, or twigs. When brought into the laboratory and placed in uniform conditions under dim, diffuse light, the planarian, *Dendrocoelum lacteum,* turns occasionally; the number of degrees turned, right or left, in one minute can be measured. When the light intensity is increased, the rate of turning increases. In this manner, the chances of the planarian's finding a darkened habitat are increased. (See Figure 73.)

Woodlice, sometimes called sowbugs or pillbugs, are land isopods (Crustacea) which occur commonly in rotten logs, under stones, and in moist leaf litter. The ability of most species to resist desiccation is poor. In the laboratory, *Porcellio scaber* and *Oniscus asellus* (two species of woodlice) are active in dry air and show a marked increase both in movement and in the rate of turning. In a saturated atmosphere they are almost motionless. Without any directional movement, this kinetic response

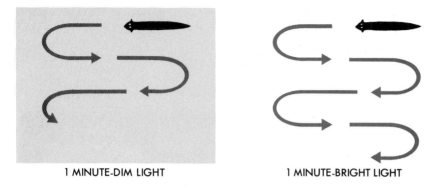

1 MINUTE-DIM LIGHT   1 MINUTE-BRIGHT LIGHT

Figure 73   Kinesis. *The rate of turning of the planarian worm increases in response to an increase in light intensity. This increase in locomotion will continue until the worm accommodates to the new conditions. In nature, this behavior will often bring the worm into contact with leaves or stones, where it finds shelter.*

enables woodlice to encounter and remain in moist habitats in their vicinity.

Taxis (plural, *taxes*) is an unlearned, oriented response of an animal with respect to a stimulus such as light, heat, gravity, chemicals, or surfaces. The response may simply be a moving toward or away from the source of the stimulus, as a moth responds by moving toward light, or the response may maintain some constant relationship to the stimulus, such as an ant's holding a 45° angle to the sun when returning to its nest. Taxes function to help the animal avoid unfavorable environmental situations, find more optimal conditions (such as warmer or drier locations), locate places in which food is more likely to be found, and maintain its position while flying, walking, or swimming.

For example, the brine shrimp *Artemia*, which lives in the Great Salt Lake and other inland saline waters, normally swims with its ventral side up. If a light is placed underneath it, *Artemia* swims dorsal side up. Thus *Artemia*, as well as many fairy shrimp such as *Branchinecta*, use the direction of light, normally the sun's rays, as a stimulus for maintaining their swimming position. (See Figure 74, page 272.)

When placed in an aquarium at room temperature in which there is a tube warmed from 33°C to 35°C by circulating water through it, the medicinal leech *Hirudo medicinalis* moves directly toward the tube. By this means, this parasite can locate its host and move to its vicinity. The clam mite *Unionicola ypsilophorus* is a parasite of the freshwater, bottom-dwelling clam, *Anodonta*, in which it lives and feeds in the mantle cavity and on the gills. In an aquarium, lighted from above and containing only clam mites, the mites are photopositive and move to the top of the aquarium. When an extract of *Anodonta* tissue is added to the water, the mites become photonegative and move to the bottom where they would have a greater chance of encountering their host.

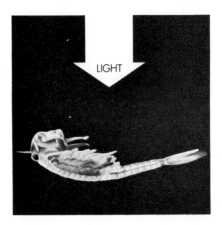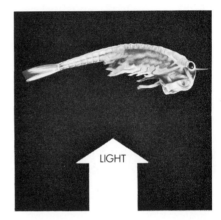

Figure 74   Taxis. *Swimming position of fairy shrimp is maintained by reference to the direction of light. As the direction of light changes, the swimming position changes accordingly. Under usual conditions, light comes from above and the shrimp swim upside down.*

Several different patterns of orientation to a directional stimulus are now known to occur, enabling taxes to be further subdivided on the basis of the mode of orientation used. It is important to remember that an animal is capable of responding to more than one stimulus at a time, and that variations in the internal state of the animal, such as those which occur with hunger, alter responses to stimuli.

Reflexes involve simple, stereotyped movements, usually only by part of an organism in response to a stimulus. The stimulus in a reflex is generally localized, the response following shortly after the stimulus. Reflexes invariably involve the central nervous system. The underlying neural mechanism may be relatively simple, as in the *stretch reflex* affecting flexion and extension of muscles in vertebrates, or it may be complex, involving portions of the brain as in *righting reflexes*. Reflexes can be either innate or learned, as in the conditioned reflex. In man, for example, both the pupil reflex in response to increasing light intensity and the knee-jerk reflex are well known. In the frog and in the cockroach, a drop of dilute acetic acid placed on the dorsal region will elicit scratching movements by a hind leg, even in animals which have been decapitated.

Instincts form the basis of another behavioral classification. The concept of instinctive behavior is very old, and its meaning has undergone modification over the years as a result of healthy criticism. As currently used by animal behaviorists, instincts refer to those stereotyped, sequentially patterned acts the expression of which is typically not influenced by the past experiences of the animal. Because of the emphasis on the *unlearned* nature of instinctive behavior, classifying a behavior as instinctive is essentially a statement about the development of that pattern. The best studied examples of instinctive behavior are to be found among the birds, fishes, and insects.

Because of their tendency to be specific for each species, instincts are ideal taxonomic characteristics and highly useful in the study of the evolution of behavior. The inflexibility of some instinctive patterns is nicely shown in the following example from the work of Dr. T. C. Schneirla.

The army ant of the American tropics conducts above-ground foraging raids. These raids are conducted by the workers and soldiers which form tight columns reaching over 900 feet in length and containing thousands of ants. In studying the organization of these columns, it has been found that the continuity of the column is maintained by a strong tendency of the ants to follow a chemical trail established by the ants ahead of them in the column.

One day, quite by chance, the leading end of a column under observation began to circle a large wooden post which had once served as a building support. The rest of the column automatically followed producing a complete ring of ants which continually circled the post for an entire day

Figure 75   When army ants are maneuvered into forming a circular trail, they continue to circle, each ant following the worker preceding it, until the assemblage dies of exhaustion. This lack of flexibility in behavior is a characteristic of many instinctive patterns in lower animals.

and terminated only after the exhaustion and death of the foragers. Under natural conditions, the substrate surrounding trees is so disrupted by roots and other irregularities that this circular column of milling behavior, or "suicide mill," seldom occurs.

The usefulness of instinctual behavior studies to taxonomy has become evident in the study of similar, closely related species. While studying the digger wasp, *Ammophila campestris,* Reverend Adriaanse of the Netherlands noticed some individuals in the population with strikingly different behavior traits involving care of the young. In typical *A. campestris* individuals, the female digs a hole, deposits an egg, collects paralyzed insects which it places with the egg, and then closes the hole. Careful study of the behavior of the aberrant individuals in the population led to the discovery of a new species of wasp, now called *Ammophila pubescens.*

TABLE 20.   **Behavioral Differences Between the Two Species**

Behavior	*Ammophila campestris*	*Ammophila pubescens*
Nest hole filled with material from	nearby digging	flown in
Choice of food for developing young	sawflies	caterpillars
Sequence of egg-laying and provisioning of nest	first egg, then sawflies	first caterpillars, then egg

The way in which instinctive patterns of behavior are used to shed light on the evolution of behavior is shown by the work of Dr. Howard Evans of Harvard University on the prey-carrying of wasps. In a solitary wasp such as the digger wasp *Ammophila,* discussed earlier, the female digs a shallow nest in sand or soil, closes the nest, and then proceeds to capture insects. These prey are paralyzed by stinging and then are carried to the nest. After the nest is reopened, the prey is inserted and an egg is laid on the side of the abdomen. The prey serves as food for the developing larva.

Primitive wasps such as spider wasps, Pompilidae, capture only spiders, which are seized in the mandibles and dragged backwards into the nest. Some spider wasps have evolved the ability to straddle the spider and therefore can move forward by walking or by a series of short hops, but the prey-carrying behavior of spider wasps has certain disadvantages. Before the female can reopen her nest to deposit her prey she must release it and free her mandibles which are required in nest digging. While the female is thus occupied, foraging ants may carry off the prey, or parasitic wasps or flies may deposit their eggs on it. Either possibility can be disastrous for the young larva.

Digger wasps, Sphecidae, and vespid wasps have evolved the ability to hunt smaller insect prey which are transported in flight, held by the mandibles and legs. These insects can therefore be gathered from greater distances than large spiders which must be dragged over the surface, and nest

Figure 76   The evolution of wasps.

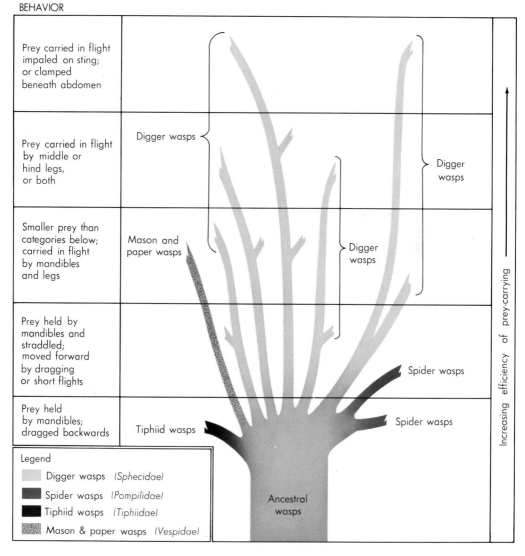

BEHAVIOR

Prey carried in flight impaled on sting; or clamped beneath abdomen

Prey carried in flight by middle or hind legs, or both

Digger wasps

Digger wasps

Smaller prey than categories below; carried in flight by mandibles and legs

Mason and paper wasps

Digger wasps

Prey held by mandibles and straddled; moved forward by dragging or short flights

Spider wasps

Prey held by mandibles; dragged backwards

Tiphiid wasps

Spider wasps

Increasing efficiency of prey-carrying

Legend
- Digger wasps (Sphecidae)
- Spider wasps (Pompilidae)
- Tiphiid wasps (Tiphiidae)
- Mason & paper wasps (Vespidae)

Ancestral wasps

provisioning can be accomplished more rapidly. In four groups of digger wasp species the prey is carried slung under the body and held by either the middle or the hind legs, sometimes both. In two groups of digger wasp species, the prey is held by the end of the abdomen, either impaled on the sting or grasped by a kind of clamping, freeing the legs completely. Now the female need not release her prey while she reopens her nest, permitting fewer opportunities for predators or parasites to attack.

The phylogeny of the major groups of wasps has been investigated on the basis of the structural characteristics of the larvae and adults. Accompanying this evolution of structure has been the evolution of more efficient means of transporting prey to the nest, described above, of nest-building behavior, and of the selection of different kinds of prey.

Learning is a physiological process which results in changes in behavior as a result of experience. These changes are usually adaptive and of sufficient duration so that we exclude the effects of fatigue, sensory accomodation or injury, as well as maturational change. Because of the importance of learned behavior to man, the learning process has been intensively investigated, principally by psychologists, who recognize several types of learning: trial and error learning, habituation, conditioning, insight learning, reasoning, and so on.

In the 1930's Dr. Konrad Lorenz of Germany, an eminent student of animal behavior, divided an egg clutch of a Greylag goose into 2 groups. One group was incubated by the goose; the other was placed in an incubator. Upon hatching, the first group followed the mother; the second group, upon seeing Lorenz, followed him. When the two batches of

Figure 77   The imprinted ducklings are following the first object which they saw after hatching. Instead of their mother, they are following Dr. Konrad Lorenz, a well-known student of animal behavior.

goslings were marked and placed together, they each followed the first moving object they had seen upon hatching. This phenomenon, called imprinting, is a type of learning which falls close to the margin of the continuum between instinctive behavior and learned behavior.

Further work has verified and extended Lorenz's results. Laboratory investigations with mallard ducks indicate that there is a critical age, a matter of hours after hatching, during which ducklings can be imprinted. While mallard ducklings respond to the size, form and color of the object, ducklings of wood ducks, which nest in trees, are imprinted to the parent bird in response to sounds made by the parents. Imprinting appears greatest in those species in which the young can move about and follow the parents shortly after birth or hatching.

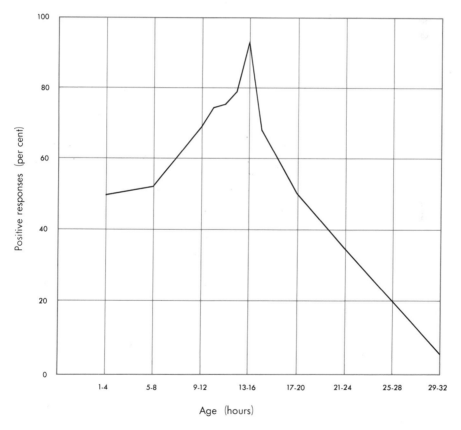

Figure 78   *Between 13 and 16 hours after hatching, the critical period, ducklings are most susceptible to imprinting. After that time, imprintability declines rapidly.*

The classification of behavior into categories such as kineses, taxes, instincts and learned behaviors, and the intensive analysis of a large number of each kind of behavior, will eventually permit further generalizations about these kinds of behavior.

The question, "How does behavior contribute to the survival of the species?" provides another way of examining animal behavior. Here, we group behaviors that appear to be serving similar *functions,* such as orientation, communication, habitat selection, feeding, elimination, sanitation, defense, reproduction, care of young, etc. As examples of this approach to the study of behavior, we shall consider the questions "How do animals orient in space?" or, more simply, "How do animals find their way?" and "How do animals communicate?"

Orientation in Animals

In 1793, the Italian biologist, Spallanzani, blinded several night-flying bats and found that they not only flew as well as before, but could also catch food, for the stomachs of blinded and recaptured bats were packed with flying insects. However, when Spallanzani plugged their ears, these bats collided with buildings, trees, and other obstacles. Evidently bats orient in space and locate objects using their ears, but how?

The problem remained unsolved until the 1940's when G. W. Pierce, at Harvard, using instruments sensitive to high frequency sound, found that night-flying bats emit loud noises in the form of short, frequent bursts in the high frequency range of 10,000 to 150,000 cps (cycles per second). (By contrast children can detect sounds up to approximately 20,000 cps although many adults cannot detect frequencies higher than 10,000 cps.) When their mouths were covered, the bats tested could not orient. Evidently bats orient by some technique requiring emission and reception of high frequency sounds.

Figure 79   Many bats possess the remarkable ability to fly at night, avoiding obstacles and catching tiny flying insects.

Professor Donald Griffin of Harvard, has demonstrated that the detection of echoes, or *echolocation,* is the simplest, and therefore the preferred explanation of the way bats employ these sounds in orientation. As a bat flies along at night, it emits pulses of high frequency sound which strike objects at a distance in front of the bat. The time required for the echo to return to the bat's ear is proportional to the distance of the object from the bat at the time the sound was emitted. By detecting these echoes bats are continually informed not only of the presence of large obstacles but also of tiny objects such as flying insects.

This ability to detect objects at a distance is very highly developed in bats. When released into a completely darkened room with wires strung in several directions, bats could fly about and avoid collision with walls, ceiling, or wires. When the wire diameter was reduced, Professor Griffin

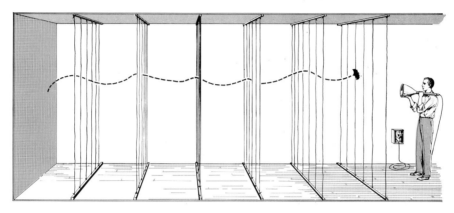

Figure 80   When a bat is released into a darkened room across which wires are strung, the bat is able to fly back and forth without touching the wires. The man at right holds a microphone to detect high frequency cries which the bat emits as it flies.

found that bats could avoid wire as thin as 0.12 mm in diameter! This extraordinary behavior is only possible because of specializations in the structure of certain organs: the bat's sound-producing organ, the larynx, and the ear. (See Figure 81, page 280.) Examination of the bat's brain shows great development and relative enlargement in those areas concerned with perception of sound and a high development of the neuro-motor system related to hearing. There is a corresponding reduction of the sensory and motor systems not related to sound perception.

Since this discovery, biologists have found evidence of orientation by echolocation in porpoises, in cave-dwelling birds, and in the shrew, a rodent that lives underground. Surprisingly, certain night-flying moths, typical prey of bats, are capable of detecting the high frequency cries of

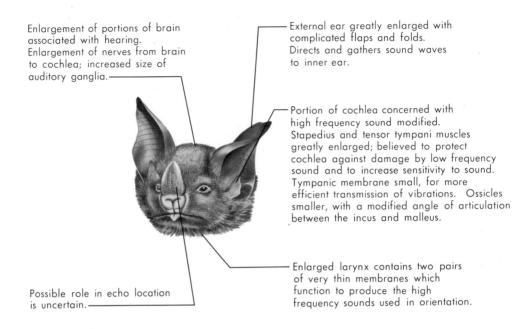

Enlargement of portions of brain associated with hearing. Enlargement of nerves from brain to cochlea; increased size of auditory ganglia.

External ear greatly enlarged with complicated flaps and folds. Directs and gathers sound waves to inner ear.

Portion of cochlea concerned with high frequency sound modified. Stapedius and tensor tympani muscles greatly enlarged; believed to protect cochlea against damage by low frequency sound and to increase sensitivity to sound. Tympanic membrane small, for more efficient transmission of vibrations. Ossicles smaller, with a modified angle of articulation between the incus and malleus.

Enlarged larynx contains two pairs of very thin membranes which function to produce the high frequency sounds used in orientation.

Possible role in echo location is uncertain.

Figure 81   The echolocation ability of bats is only possible because of anatomical and physiological specializations which accompany the behavior.

bats. They respond to these cries by performing power dives, passive dives, or a series of loops and turns which gradually carry them to the ground. (See Figure 82, page 281.) These maneuvers aid moths in escaping from insect-hunting bats. Mites which attack the hearing organs of these moths are never found on more than one hearing organ.

Worker fire ants are recruited and guided to a source of food by means of an *odor trail*. The trail-marking substance is laid by the workers that first discover the food. It consists of a volatile chemical secreted by a small abdominal gland, Dufour's gland. The trail substance is released in minute amounts when the sting is touched to the ground. Ants encountering this attractant simply follow the trail until the food source is reached. An extract of Dufour's gland can be used to create artificial trails, and worker fire ants will follow these artificial trails in circles, loops or other patterns.

The western newt, mentioned earlier, probably recognizes its breeding site by means of the specific odor of the stream. When the newt's olfactory receptors are destroyed, the newt cannot home correctly.

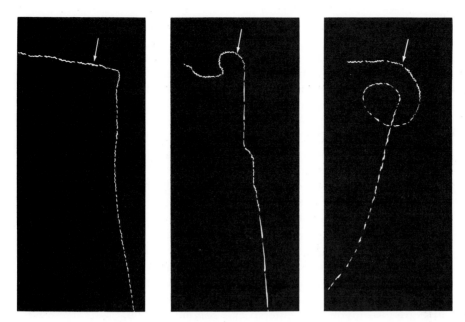

Figure 82   In response to high frequency sounds, such as the cries of bats, certain nocturnal moths drop to the ground. In the diagrams above, ultrasonic sound was emitted at the arrow, and the downward course followed by three moths is shown. Moth flights include a passive dive (left), power dive (center), and double roll and dive (right). (Modified from photos of K. D. Roeder.)

Many animals including migratory birds, bees, sea turtles, and some fish are able to orient by means of the direction of the sun. Certain fish, such as the African river fish, *Gymnarchus,* can orient in muddy waters by detecting distortions in an electrical field which the fish generates about itself. These distortions are caused by the presence of fish or other obstacles.

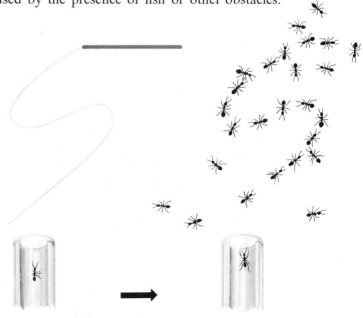

Figure 83   Ants respond to an odor track marked by an extract of Dufour's gland, by movement along the marked trail.

Communication Among Animals The complex social organization of groups of animals such as bees, monkeys, and many kinds of birds, demands from these animals an ability to transmit information among members of their group. This information may concern food sources, presence of enemies, boundary of territories, readiness to mate, and so forth; however, even animals whose relationships with other members of their species are very limited, oysters and barnacles for example, need to communicate essential information such as that which signals the release of gametes. Therefore, ability of animals to communicate with other members of the species occurs very widely. This inter-animal communication, however, is not limited to members of the same species. A parent killdeer feigning a broken wing to lure a predator away from its nest and the walkingstick, an insect whose structure and posture, when disturbed, resembles a twig, are attempting to communicate with their predators. Duck hunters with their decoys, fishermen using lures or flies, and flowers, scented to attract pollinating insects and birds, are also involved in interspecies communication.

Animals communicate when one animal produces a signal, measurable in the language of physics or chemistry, which affects the behavior of

Figure 84   Examples of interspecies communication among animals. In the case of the Viceroy butterfly and the hog-nosed snake, the message is an untruthful one, while the walkingstick is attempting not to communicate with potential predators.

another animal. Some animals can also communicate with themselves, as do dogs when they encounter their own scent on a post or tree. We may classify the kinds of animal communication on the basis of the receptor involved: chemical or olfactory, visual, acoustical, tactile or mechanical, and electrical. There is some overlap between acoustical and mechanical types of communication. Signals can also be classified as transient, exemplified by the bark of a dog, or persistent, such as the black "moustache" of a male yellow-shafted flicker.

As an example of the ways in which animals communicate, we shall examine the behavior of a honeybee scout returning to the hive, with information about the distance, direction and scent of a source of food. More than 20 years ago, Dr. Karl von Frisch of Germany, using glass-sided observation hives, noticed that returning scout bees performed a kind of dance on the vertical honeycomb within the hive. Worker bees eagerly followed the scout, touching its body with their antennae. From information received during the dance, the other bees are able to locate the food source, but precisely what are the signals by which this information is communicated?

By training scout bees to feed at food dishes containing scented sugars at increasing distances from their hive, von Frisch noticed that for food sources up to approximately 80 meters scout bees perform a "round dance." After perceiving this dance and the scent of the food clinging to

Figure 85   Scout bees perform food dances on the vertical honeycomb of the hive. The round dance (right) is performed when a food source is within 80 meters. This dance contains no information concerning direction. The waggle dance (left) conveys information as to both distance and direction of food sources from the hive.

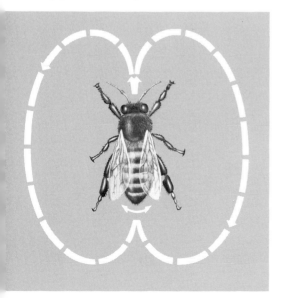
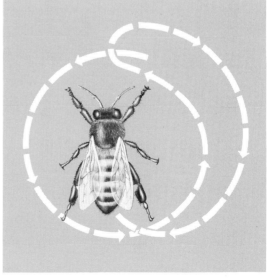

the scout bee's hairs, nest bees are able to locate the food source after searching in all directions close to the hive. Evidently, the round dance contains the information, "There is a source of food close to the hive." The vigor and duration of the dance denotes the quality of the food.

For food sources beyond 80 meters, von Frisch noticed that the dance suddenly switched to a figure-eight pattern, or "tail waggling dance." By placing food not only at varying distances from the hive, but also in different directions, von Frisch was able to determine that the tail waggling dance instructed nest bees not simply how far to fly for food, but in what direction. Since the tail waggling dance is performed on the vertical honeycomb of the darkened hive, the scout bee obviously cannot "point" toward the food. Instead, the dancing bee indicates the angle at the nest which is identical to the angle between the food source and the sun. In describing this angle, bees use a simple transposition. The direction toward the sun is indicated by the top of the vertical honeycomb; the direction away from the sun by the bottom. Thus, toward the sun is up, or away from gravity; away from the sun is down, or toward gravity. The transposition is therefore from a phototactic to a geotactic orientation. To indicate a food source 45° to the right of the sun's position, the scout bee orients the tail waggling dance by moving in an angle 45° to the right of the vertical.

Figure 86   The waggle dance informs hive bees about the direction of food sources by indicating on the vertical honeycomb the angle between the sun, hive, and food. Toward the sun is indicated by dancing upward, away from the sun by dancing downward.

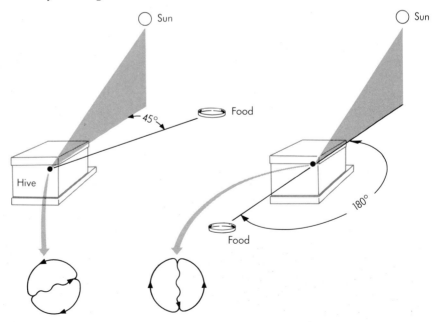

Scout bees can perform a correctly oriented tail waggling dance even when the sun is obscured by clouds. If a patch of clear sky is visible, the direction of polarized light vibration indicates the sun's direction. If the sky is completely overcast, bees can, nevertheless, perceive the sun's position by the slight increase in the amount of ultraviolet light which penetrates the clouds.

The rhythm of the dance changes with increasing distance of the food source from the hive. By measuring the frequency of tail waggling runs during each dance, von Frisch has determined that the number of runs per 15 seconds decreases as the food source is placed farther and farther away. More recently, biologists have found that during the tail waggling dance, scout bees emit bursts of low frequency sounds, each burst composed of approximately 32 pulses of sound per second. With increasing distance of

Figure 87   With increasing distance of food from the hive, the speed of the waggle dance decreases, left, and the duration of sound bursts made by scout bees increases, right.

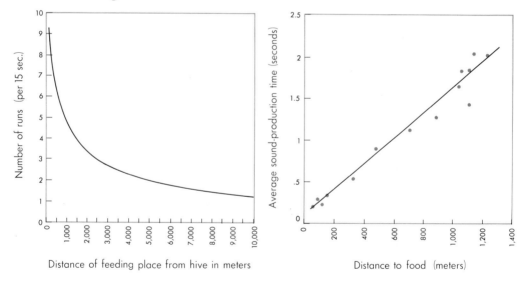

food from the hive, both the length of the burst and the number of pulses per burst increase. Thus, nest bees are furnished with both auditory and tactile signals which are correlated with food distance.

Variations in the pattern of food dancing exist among the races of honey bees. The Italian race, for example, indicates direction of food sources even for short distances from the hive by a distinct "sickle dance." For each of the races investigated, both the distance indicated by the round dance and the relationship between tail waggling frequency and distance varies.

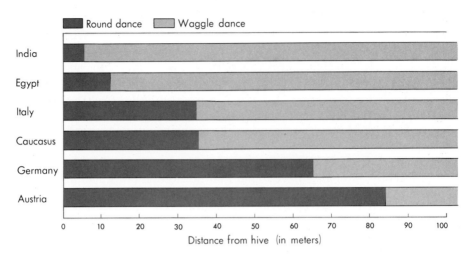

Figure 88   The distance of food from the hive at which round dancing ceases and waggle dancing begins, differs among the separate races of honeybees. This difference suggests a genetic basis for the determination of the pattern of bee dances.

How could such a remarkable and precise behavior pattern have evolved? When von Frisch first announced his discoveries—the ability of bees to communicate distance and direction by means of food dances, to detect and orient by means of polarized light, and to transpose a light orientation to a gravity orientation—were not known in other animals, even closely related forms. The pattern is essentially an elementary form of map-making and map-reading. In stingless bees, for example, the scout bee is capable of alerting and recruiting nest bees for foraging, as is the honeybee, but a pilot bee must guide the recruits to the food source over a scent trail which the scout bee has established.

Recent investigations, however, have shown that certain flies have a simple, light-oriented food dance, that ants and a species of dung beetle show a transposition from a phototactic orientation to a gravity orientation, and that several arthropods can detect and orient to polarized light. Therefore, we can surmise that the evolution of communication in bees has involved the selection and gradual refinement of behavior traits and sensory capabilities already present among the arthropods.

The use of chemical substances to transmit information is widespread among animals, including most mammals. Mammals employ scent in a number of ways: as sex attractants in rats; as repellents in skunks; to mark territories as in dogs; for recognition, as in elk which can thus identify their own young. Chemical substances used in animal communication are called *pheromones,* and a number of these pheromones have been isolated and chemically identified. The pheromone of the female gypsy moth, *gyplure,* is used as an attractant to enable males to locate females. It has been synthesized and is effective in gypsy moth control.

While most pheromones act as stimuli eliciting behavioral responses, some alter physiological mechanisms which in turn alter behavior. In the migratory locust, mentioned earlier, adult male, gregarious-phase locusts secrete a volatile substance which accelerates maturation in young locusts. Termite and honeybee queens secrete a pheromone which inhibits production of additional queens.

The use of pheromones for communication presents special difficulties not present in acoustical or visual communication. Olfactory signals tend to persist; they have a long fade-out time, and are therefore unsuitable for conveying information about position, change, or mood. Yet, their very persistence makes pheromones ideal for trail-marking, and they are so used by ants and certain bees. Furthermore, olfactory signals are capable of only limited modulation, so that a multiplicity of signals, as in bird calls, is not possible for animals with only one or two pheromones.

The outstanding advantage to their use lies in the fact that some pheromones are capable of stimulating receptors at exceedingly low concentrations, approaching a few hundred molecules, and acting at considerable distances from their point of origin. Thus, males of certain moth species have been lured to females from distances of two and one-half miles. German police dogs can distinguish between two trails left by dogs 30 minutes apart. The skin of a wounded minnow releases a pheromone called *schreckstoff* which causes other minnows to disperse, thus avoiding the predator. A 2-microgram skin fragment containing approximately 0.001 micrograms of *schreckstoff* is enough to disperse an entire school of minnows from a feeding place.

Other modes of communication among animals, such as posture, gait, and expression, convey important visual signals. A wolf's facial expression and the position of his tail inform other wolves about the mood of the individual (aggressive, submissive, and so forth). An elk threatens his attacker by holding his head high and his ears back, while stamping with his front feet. An elk's frozen stance denotes surprise, and a distinct, high-stepping, marching gait denotes warning to other members of the herd, perhaps of the approach of a predator.

Certain species of mormyrids and gymnotids, tropical South American and African freshwater fish, possess weak electric organs which are believed to function in communication as well as in orientation. When a second mormyrid was placed into a tank containing an already established resident, both fish released synchronous discharges, indicating that they had detected each other's presence.

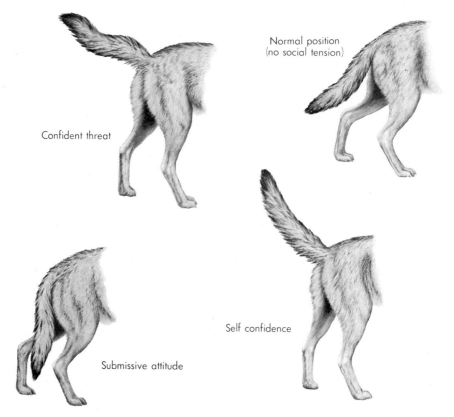

Normal position
(no social tension)

Confident threat

Self confidence

Submissive attitude

Figure 89   Posture, gait, and motion supply important signals in inter-species communication. In wolves, the position of the tail, the facial expression, and the movement of the ears convey information about the mood of the animal.

QUESTIONS FOR DISCUSSION

1. Why is it difficult to define behavior precisely?
2. Define the term *stimulus.* Do all stimuli arise outside of an animal body? If not, give examples of internal stimuli. Can an animal perceive a stimulus but not respond to it? What is your basis for concluding this?
3. In addition to the gene, and the behavioral types mentioned in the text, what other biological "entities" are recognized and used by biologists?
4. Why is the simplest explanation of bat orientation, echolocation, the preferred explanation? Would *hypothesis* be a suitable substitute for the word explanation as used here?
5. Animals find their way by means of landmarks, the position of the sun, and the detection of echoes. What other means of orientation might be used?

6. What reasons can you give for susceptibility of imprinting being greatest in the species in which it is found? What hazards exist for a species in which the young are capable of being imprinted?

7. What other functional categories of behavior can you suggest?

8. In what ways do you think behavior might affect the future evolution of a species of animal?

9. What kinds of structural and physiological specialization would you expect to accompany the exceptional olfactory activity of animals such as rats, dogs, and pigs?

10. Give 3 examples of animal communication that would correspond to "lying" in human communication.

11. Draw a diagram of the relationship of food, hive, and sun which would exist if scout bees performed the following waggle dance patterns.

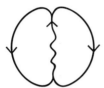

12. What would be the pattern of dance expected when the sun was *directly* overhead above the hive?

13. Does the human species communicate by means of odors?

SECTION SIXTEEN

ANALYSIS OF BEHAVIOR

In the preceding material we saw that it was possible to generalize about the behavior patterns of animals and to group similar appearing kinds of behavior, such as kineses and taxes, and patterns that were alike in function. From the total repertoire of behavior traits of a single species we now wish to select a single pattern, and to analyze this pattern in detail.

A careful description of the behavior is required first. Precisely what does the animal do? Is there a sequence or pattern of acts? Is this sequence invariably maintained, or is there variation in the order of the actions of the pattern?

How does the expression of the pattern vary with time of day? with the season? with the life cycle of the animal?

Is the pattern modified by the earlier experience of the animal? What role does learning play in the expression of the behavior?

What is the nature of the stimulus which elicits the behavior? To what, precisely, is the animal responding? Does the environmental setting of the animal affect the nature of the response? What receptors are involved in the response? Where are they located?

In what way does the internal state of the animal effect the response? What is the role of nutrition, hormones and other chemicals in effecting the response?

Is the ability to express the pattern inherited? If so, in what way does the genetic mechanism control the behavior?

What is the function of this pattern in the life of the animal?

How did the pattern evolve? How does the expression of the pattern affect the evolution of the animal?

We shall select for our analysis the feeding behavior of the black blowfly *Phormia regina*. The blowfly is an ideal animal for laboratory investigation; it is easily cultured and reproduces rapidly in the laboratory. In nature, this non-biting fly is a scavenger, feeding on carrion and other dead organic matter, and also on plant sugars. Female blowflies lay their eggs on the carcasses of dead animals, on which the maggots (larvae) feed after hatching. Depending upon the temperature and other environmental factors, the cycle, egg (2 days) $\longrightarrow$ larvae (8 days) $\longrightarrow$ pupa (4 days) $\longrightarrow$ adult, takes about two weeks. Adults live approximately two months. In feeding, the fly detects a source of food with its chemosensitive receptors, extends its proboscis and sucks up the food until it is satiated. At that point the proboscis is retracted.

Figure 90   A breeding cage for flies.

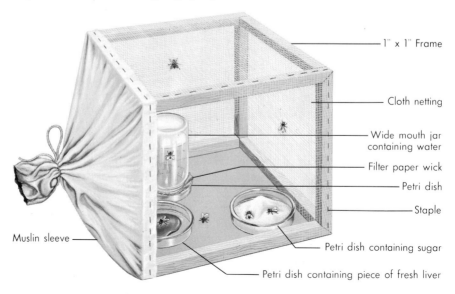

1" x 1" Frame

Cloth netting

Wide mouth jar containing water

Filter paper wick

Petri dish

Staple

Muslin sleeve

Petri dish containing sugar

Petri dish containing piece of fresh liver

| PREPARATORY TECHNIQUE 1 | **Culturing Blowflies** |

The equipment and technique necessary for the culture of blowflies is shown in the illustrations of a breeding cage (Figure 90, page 290), and of a flow diagram (Figure 91), both showing steps in culturing flies from eggs to adults.

Figure 91   Raising flies.

Petri dish with piece of fresh liver and fly eggs

Eggs removed from liver and placed in sterile pint jar containing sterile medium

Add sterile sawdust and substitute screening for metal jar top

LARVAE HATCH PUPATE

After larvae pupate pour sawdust and pupae on white paper and separate pupae from sawdust

After pupae hatch insert paper towel moistened with 1/10 M aqueous sucrose into quart jar and replace lid

Transfer pupae to empty clean quart jar and cover with screen lid

Particular attention must be paid to directions for the care and handling of adult flies. Water and a source of energy (sugar) must be supplied at all times to insure a normal life span. Paper toweling kept moistened with 0.1 M sucrose solution is advised. Usually, application of the sugar solution twice a day will suffice. Time can be saved by using as a feeder a small jar containing sucrose solution with a wad of paper for a wick.

The flies should be kept at a fairly constant room temperature; ideally it should be maintained at about 22 to 25°C. This is not always feasible, however, and a minor fluctuation of temperature is not harmful.

Flies are positively phototactic (move toward light), and, therefore, should be exposed to uniform lighting during experiments in order to eliminate the effect of light as an unwanted variable.

PREPARATORY TECHNIQUE 2	**Anesthetizing Flies**

Experimental flies must be anesthetized in order to prepare them for investigation. The choice of an anesthetic depends upon safety, ease of use, effect upon the organism, and cost. Ether is effective but is highly inflammable and if used in excessive amounts, is toxic to the organisms.

Figure 92   A CO_2 tank anesthetizer.

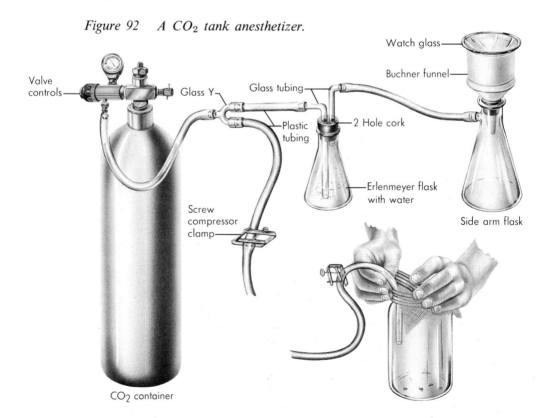

Valve controls

Glass Y

Glass tubing

Watch glass

Buchner funnel

Plastic tubing

2 Hole cork

Erlenmeyer flask with water

Side arm flask

Screw compressor clamp

CO_2 container

One of the safest anesthetics to use is carbon dioxide. It is nonflammable and essentially nontoxic to flies. The flies can be kept in a CO_2 environment for several hours without harmful effect. An efficient method is to arrange a system consisting of a tank of CO_2 with plastic tubing leading to the anesthetizing chamber. (See Figure 92.)

The free tubing is used to deliver CO_2 into a jar of flies. After movement has ceased, place the flies in the Buchner funnel and cover with a watch glass. Close the clamp on the free tube and allow a small volume of CO_2 to flow continuously into the side arm flask and through the holes in the funnel. Thus the flies are kept under anesthesia throughout the laboratory period, or longer if desired. It is important to regulate the flow so that only a small volume of CO_2 passes into the anesthetizing chamber. The rate of flow is easily controlled by observing the bubbling in the water trap.

Dry ice may be substituted for the tank of CO_2. As the dry ice sublimates, gaseous CO_2 can be fed through the same system. Flies can also be anesthetized by placing them in the freezing compartment of a refrigerator for several minutes. Whichever method of anesthesia is used, flies remain anesthetized for several minutes only; therefore, speed in the preparation of flies for experimental use is very important.

PREPARATORY TECHNIQUE 3	**Handling Flies**

Fix an anesthetized fly to the waxed end of an applicator stick as illustrated in Figure 93. This technique requires considerable care and dexterity. The dorsal surface of the fly should adhere tightly against the wax with the wings at right angles to the body. A touch of a warm needle to each wing will serve to fix the wings to the wax. Prepare the waxed applicator stick by successively dipping it into melted paraffin and then allowing it to cool until the desired thickness of wax is obtained.

Figure 93   *Attaching a fly to an applicator stick.*

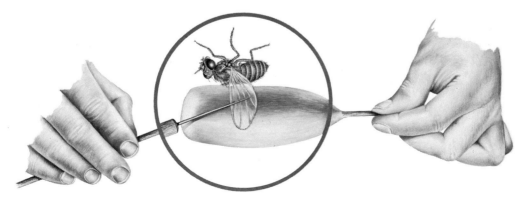

If this preparation is properly done, the awakened fly should be able to move its legs and mouth parts freely. The captive fly may now be subjected to microscopic examination.

1. Hold the fixed fly under a dissecting microscope and observe the following: general body plan; abdomen, thorax, head; compound eyes. Practice identifying the sex of flies by observing the spacing of the eyes. The eyes of the female are spaced far apart while the eyes of the male are close together. Practice sexing flies without the aid of a microscope.

2. Hold an applicator stick as illustrated with the mouth parts of the fly just touching the surface of a 1 M sucrose solution. Carefully observe the extension of the proboscis when the fly is drinking. Practice this several times. The ability to detect the proboscis extension is essential to future investigations.

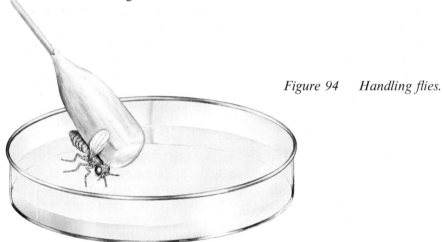

Figure 94   Handling flies.

INVESTIGATION FOR FURTHER STUDY

What patterns of behavior can you discern in the blowfly? Begin with an empty cage. Add a single fly. Observe and make careful notes of the fly's actions in each of the following steps: add 9 or 10 more flies; add a watering jar; add a piece of raw liver; add a petri dish containing sugar; place a single light source at one end of the cage.

| INVESTIGATION 34 | **Effect of Food Contact on Locomotion** |

With a fine-pointed scissors remove wings from several flies that have been fed a minimal diet (0.1 M sucrose solution). Allow flies to adjust to this wingless condition overnight. During the adjustment period, flies should be kept in a bottle together with a circle of filter paper or paper toweling soaked in distilled water. *No food should be given during this period.*

Procedure

1. Place a dewinged fly on the table. Note the general pattern of walking. Does it walk in relatively straight lines? Continue your observations for several minutes while carefully recording its walking behavior.
2. Place a small drop of 1 M sucrose solution in contact with the mouth parts of a fly, or place a drop so that the fly will contact the sugar-water solution for an instant. Remove the fly from the source of sugar water. Now note the general pattern of walking. Does it continue to walk as it did before exposure to sugar? Describe its walking behavior; if no difference is detected, discard the fly, select another from the jar, and repeat the procedure.

QUESTIONS FOR DISCUSSION

1. Suggest a hypothesis that would account for the behavior of the fly under these two different conditions.

2. Suggest a possible adaptive mechanism implied by this behavior. That is, in what way might this behavior be of survival value to the fly?

INVESTIGATION FOR FURTHER STUDY

1. Compare the walking behavior of wild flies with that of flies raised in captivity. Catch several wild flies and repeat Investigation 34. Record, and attempt to account for, any differences between the behavior of wild and captive flies.

2. Is there a relationship between feeding and activity in flies? Place 10 flies in a well-lighted cage, containing water and a petri dish with a 1 M sucrose solution. After the flies have fed to satiation, remove the dish, and, periodically for the next 72 hours, record the number and duration of their walks and flights within a 10-minute period. Replace the sucrose solution for one hour each day.

| INVESTIGATION 35 | **Detection of Food** |

Procedure

1. Using a camel's hair brush, draw concentric circles of distilled water and sugar solutions on typing paper as shown in Figure 95.

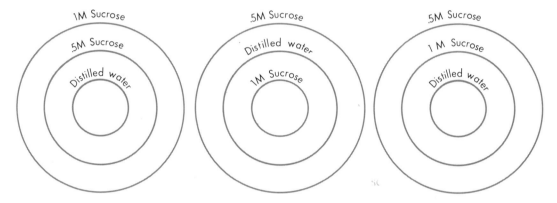

Figure 95   *Concentric circles of distilled water and sugar solutions.*

2. Place a wingless fly in the center circle of diagram 1 and observe its behavior continuously until it leaves the outer circle. Continue this procedure for diagrams 2 and 3 using a new fly each time. Repeat the experiment ten or more times.
3. Describe the behavior of the fly in each of the three situations. What explanation can you give for the behavior of the flies in each case?
4. Select a fly that has *not* reached a food satiation level. Draw an SOS trail of 1 M sucrose solution. Can the fly follow the message? If so, have you "trained" the fly to behave in this fashion? Could you at this point suggest how the fly detects the presence of sugar?

Figure 96   *A trail of*
1 M sucrose.

As a result of your investigations thus far, you have been able to observe at least a portion of the repertoire of the fly's behavior. You have seen how a fly responds when he detects a food source, including food sources of differing concentrations, and the effects of feeding on the type and rate of his activity. We shall now examine some of the characteristics of the sugar receptors.

INVESTIGATION 36	**Sensitivity to Sucrose**

Procedure

1. Fix at least 50, and preferably 100, anesthetized flies to applicator sticks. If this responsibility is divided evenly among four or five teams, it should be possible to complete the preparation during one class period. The sticks should be placed in holding boards as illustrated.
2. The flies should be given plain water until used for the experiment on the following day. Devising a method of watering the flies will require careful thought and technique.
3. Prepare 8 different concentrations of sucrose solution ranging from 0.008 M to 1.0 M. This is easily done by serial dilution. Pipette 5 ml of plain water into each of seven petri plates. Pipette 5 ml of 1 M sucrose into the first dish containing 5 ml of plain water; this will give a 0.5 M solution. Pipette 5 ml of the 0.5 M sucrose into the second dish of plain water; this will give a 0.25 M solution. Continue this serial dilution process until a final concentration of 0.008 M is obtained. Then arrange ten petri plates as illustrated for each team.

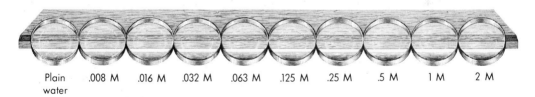

Plain water   .008 M   .016 M   .032 M   .063 M   .125 M   .25 M   .5 M   1 M   2 M

Figure 97   Serial dilution of sucrose.

4. Determine the sensitivity to sucrose solution for each of the flies that were prepared on applicator sticks the previous day. When testing for sensitivity, the legs of the fly are immersed in the liquid as shown in Figure 98, page 298. It may be necessary to wiggle the fly several times to make sure that good contact has been made. The first extension of the proboscis indicates sensitivity to the specific concentration. Always test each fly for a possible response to plain water before testing for sugar. If the fly extends its proboscis into plain water, allow it to drink

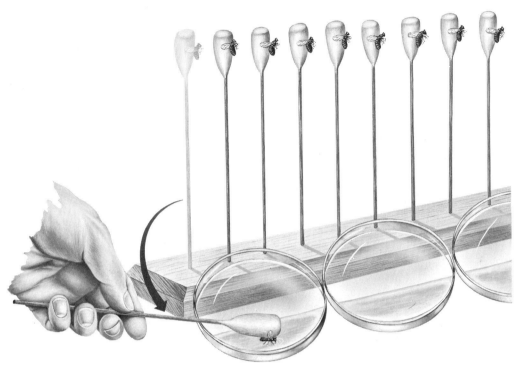

Figure 98   Flow diagram: determining sensitivity level.

until the proboscis is retracted and is no longer stimulated to extend by contact of the legs with plain water. Next, determine the lowest concentration to which each fly is sensitive. When a fly no longer responds to a sucrose solution, retest the fly's ability to respond by presenting it with a more concentrated solution. The flow diagram illustrates several techniques involved in determining the food sensitivity levels of flies.

5. Both team and class results should be recorded on charts by using plus (+) signs to indicate positive reactions.
6. Plot the data on graph paper to determine the distribution of sensitivity. Use the vertical axis to record the number of flies that respond to each concentration and the horizontal axis to express molar concentration. Plot the combined data from all teams in the same manner.

QUESTIONS FOR DISCUSSION

1. Calculate the mean and standard deviation for the class data. What per cent of the flies fall within 1 and 2 standard deviations of the mean? Does the distribution of sensitivity for the

class data approach a normal distribution expected in a population?

2. Are the graphs prepared by each team similar to the graph prepared from the combined data from all teams?

3. Analyze the graph of distribution in terms of sample size, experimental variables, and error.

INVESTIGATIONS FOR FURTHER STUDY

1. Is the sensitivity of flies to sugar inherited? Carefully remove from the wax several male and female flies which are known to be highly sensitive to sucrose. Place them in a breeding cage and attempt to produce another generation. Repeat this procedure with several male and female flies known to be relatively insensitive to sucrose. Test the offspring of both groups for sensitivity to sucrose. By means of a t test, compare the mean level of sensitivity of each of these groups to each other and to the parental population. Is there a significant difference? Interpret the meaning of your results.

2. By now you may have surmised that chemoreceptors sensitive to sucrose are located on the leg and that stimulation of these receptors elicits the response, proboscis extension. Can you determine on what part or parts of which of the fly's legs the receptors are located? Devise your own experiment and plan of observation.

3. What factors affect the sensitivity of flies to sucrose? Repeat the procedure employed in testing for sensitivity to sucrose, but divide the flies into two groups, males and females. Compare your results by means of a t test. Repeat again, using flies fed 6 hours before testing and flies fed 24 hours before testing. Repeat with a group tested at a high temperature and another group tested at room temperature. How does sensitivity vary with sex, hunger, and temperature?

4. How does a fly determine the quantity of food to be imbibed? How does a fly know when it is hungry? Design and carry out experiments that might lead to possible solutions and further hypotheses. You might try feeding the fly sugar solutions of increasing concentration until a point is reached where it will no longer extend its proboscis and feed. Allow it to drink to satiation at each concentration before proceeding to the next higher concentration.

So far our investigations of feeding behavior have centered about sucrose as the food substance that can be detected by the fly. This stimulus has nutritional value. The purpose of the next two investigations is to examine other sugars, substances similar to sucrose, which may or may not be of nutritional value to the fly. This new information will be related to the fly's ability to discriminate between a substance high in food value and a substance low in food value. The following investigations begin our inquiry into the nature of the stimuli which elicit feeding behavior.

INVESTIGATION 37	The Relation of Food Selection to Nutrition

Flies will be given a choice between two substances, one sweet tasting but low in food value and the other high in food value but lacking a sweet taste. Arabinose is very sweet but non-nutritious; sorbitol is very rich in nutritional value but practically tasteless. Before beginning the experiment, predict which of these two food substances will be selected by the fly.

The basic technique of this investigation is measurement of the quantity of different sugars consumed by a number of flies over a specific period of time. Selection of a suitable feeding arrangement is critical. If a large number of flies is used, the feeding pipettes may be large. If the number of flies is small, a small feeder is necessary.

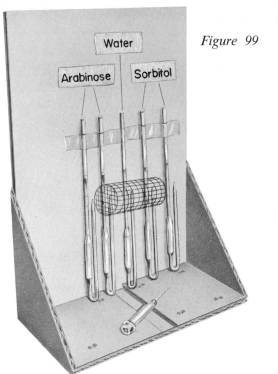

Figure 99   *Maintaining blow-flies.*

Procedure

1. Prepare a cage containing one feeding pipette for each solution: plain water, 1.0 M arabinose, and 1.0 M sorbitol. Each of the pipettes must contain the same volume of liquid. (See Figure 99.)
2. Add 25 young flies that have been fed 0.1 M sucrose for several days.
3. Provide an evaporation control by placing identical feeding pipettes outside the cage but in the same immediate area.
4. After several days, terminate the experiment and measure the quantity of liquid remaining in each container. This can be done by successively pouring the remaining liquid from each pipette into a graduate cylinder and recording the difference in volume of each. Compute the amounts of liquid lost through evaporation from the control pipettes and subtract these from the experimental volumes.

QUESTIONS FOR DISCUSSION

1. Which of the two solutions was consumed in the greatest quantity?

2. Are flies able to choose tasteless but nutritionally valuable liquids over sweet but nutritionally poor liquids?

3. What implications for survival are indicated by your results?

INVESTIGATIONS FOR FURTHER STUDY

1. Determine how long flies will live on a diet of sorbitol or arabinose.

2. Test the sensitivity of flies to other sugars and to sugar substitutes such as saccharine. Does the threshold of sensitivity for sugars which elicit responses differ from the threshold determined for sucrose?

QUESTIONS FOR DISCUSSION

1. Flies evolved long before man began processing sugar cane and beets into sugar. What sugars did they eat and where could they have found them?

2. Construct an hypothesis or series of hypotheses to explain the evolution of flies in terms of their feeding behavior.

| INVESTIGATION 38 | Selection of Protein and Sugar |

So far the investigations have indicated that sugar is the essential diet of blowflies. All living things, however, require nitrogen in order to build amino acids; otherwise, the organisms must feed upon protein, a material made up of amino acids. Are blowflies an exception to the rule? This investigation may provide an answer to this question.

Procedure

1. Into a cage, place two, open, wide-mouth jars, one containing protein (a piece of liver will do) and the other containing dry sucrose. At random, select about 50 three- or four-day-old flies, and place them in the cage.
2. When ten or more flies enter each of the jars and feed, quickly cover the jars, anesthetize the flies in each, and examine them. Record any differences, and return the anesthetized flies to the cage.
3. Repeat step 2 several times.

QUESTIONS FOR DISCUSSION

Do you find any pattern of differences in the flies which are found in the two different food substances? Can you explain the significance of your findings?

This analysis of feeding behavior should provide an insight into the ways in which single patterns of behavior come to be understood, paving the way to further hypotheses which will lead to greater understanding. Whether or not the questions asked regarding these insects have been answered depends on the experimental technique used in the investigation and the interpretation of experimental results.

Your study of behavior need not be ended with these few investigations. Behavior is an area of science that can be examined almost anywhere: at home, in school, or on a vacation trip. The selected references listed in Appendix G extend this introduction to animal behavior.

Genes and Behavior

To what extent is the behavior of animals regulated by genes? We know that the expression of behavior depends upon the structure and the physiology of animals, including both receptors and effectors. These characteristics are under genetic control. However, it is equally clear that both the development of structure and the functioning of an animal are continuously dependent upon oxygen, nutrients, and the nature of the environment. Evidently, we can expect both genetic composition and environment to affect the expression of animal behavior.

It is erroneous to conclude that learned behavior is environmentally determined, while unlearned behavior is genetically determined. What is inherited is a framework of possibilities, or limits, within which changes in the environment, or experience, affect the expression of a behavioral trait to a greater or lesser degree. A chick or duckling has the genetically determined potentiality to be imprinted during a critical period shortly after hatching. The object upon which it will be imprinted is determined by the environment.

The relative contribution of heredity and of environment to the expression of behavior can be expected to differ from trait to trait. The variability in behavior observed within a population of animals permits the determination of the role of genes in affecting behavior or the heritability of behavior traits. Where there is uniformity in the expression of a trait within a population, or between closely related species, we cannot conclude that the effects of the environment are negligible, without experimentation.

Evidence for the heritability of behavior comes from observations of strain differences, response to selection for a particular trait and from observation of the effects of specific genetic changes.

Inbred strains of mice have been maintained in biological laboratories for use in studies which require animals of similar genetic background. Comparison of the performance on tests of exploratory activity among 15 mouse strains shows a 23-fold difference between the highest and lowest average score. This difference in behavior among mouse strains is especially impressive inasmuch as these strains were established without conscious concern for behavioral traits. In rats, the onset and amount of hoarding differs between strains, while in rabbits the nature of maternal care differs from strain to strain.

Selection experiments with *Drosophila* have been successful in producing two strains, one showing negative response to gravity (geotaxis), the other, positive response to gravity. Tests were initiated on a population that had a neutral response to gravity, but contained some individuals which responded positively, and some negatively, to gravity. In the apparatus used, the flies responded by climbing upward, or climbing downward in a chamber in which all other environmental factors were as uniformly distributed as possible.

After the initial testing, negative responding flies were selected and bred, and positive responding flies were selected and bred. Offspring from these two populations were repeatedly tested, selected and inbred. At the end of twenty generations of flies reared and tested under identical conditions, the two populations illustrated in Figure 100 had been developed.

Complex traits, such as the ability of rats to learn a maze, also respond to selection. By testing, selecting and inbreeding rats that score few errors,

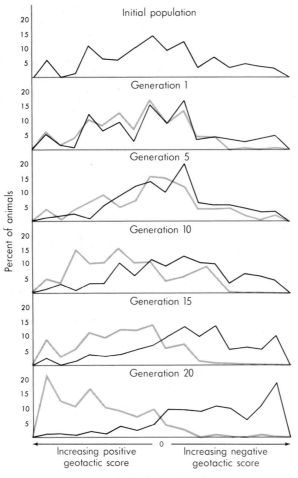

Figure 100   Selection for positive geotactic response, and negative geotactic response produced two distinct Drosophila populations with the desired trait by generation 20.

and repeating this procedure with rats that score many errors on a series of maze trials, it has been possible to develop a "maze-bright" strain and a "maze-dull" strain within a few generations from an initial foundation population. Conditions of rearing and testing were maintained unchanged throughout the experiment. The "maze-bright" rats did not perform better on all types of learning.

The ability of behavior traits to respond to selection, such as geotaxis in *Drosophila* and maze learning in rats, is important evidence for the effect of genes upon behavior. As the genotype changes with selection, the variability within the population in the expression of the trait also changes.

Much of our knowledge of the effects of individual genes upon behavior results from studies with *Drosophila*. In this fly it has been possible to determine that the gene *w* (white eye) decreases copulation frequency, while the gene *y* (yellow body color) reduces the strength and duration of wing vibration, important in male courtship. Another gene *e* (ebony body

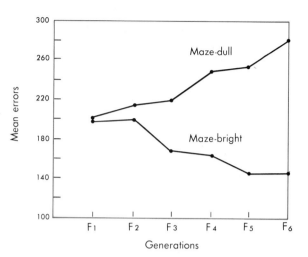

Figure 101   Selection for low-error maze performance and high-error maze performance from an initial population containing both low-error and high-error individuals produced the two populations illustrated in a few generations.

color), reduces the mating activity of males in the light, but not in the dark. All of these genes have morphological effects, in addition to their action upon behavior, and the action of the gene is not independent of the conditions of the environment.

Genes act to affect behavior through several patterns. Some traits, as *phenylketonuria,* a type of mental retardation in man, result from the action of a single pair of genes. Other traits, such as the opening of brood cells on the comb and removal of diseased brood by honeybee workers, appear to be under the control of two pairs of genes, one pair affecting opening, the other the removal of the larvae or pupa. Most traits that have been investigated, however, appear to be influenced by genes at several loci, so-called polygenic inheritance.

The mechanism or the pathway through which genes affect behavior is currently under intensive investigation. In phenylketonuria, homozygous individuals lack an enzyme essential for the metabolism of the amino acid phenylalanine. The chemical products which accumulate from the enzyme deficit appear to be responsible for the mental retardation. A single-gene trait in mice, characterized by a peculiar motion, called "waltzing," results from a brain lesion. For most traits, the paths between genes and the behaviors they regulate remains to be discovered.

Figure 102   In response to the disease, American foul-brood, worker bees uncap cells (left) and remove infected larvae (right). This behavior response is controlled by 2 pairs of independently inherited genes.

We conclude that a sizeable body of evidence indicates that behavior, like structure and physiology, is under the control of genes, and is influenced by the nature of the environment. As gene controlled traits, behavior patterns are subject to the action of natural selection. Thus behavior evolves and contributes to the continuous adaptation of animal populations to their environment.

SUMMARY

Your concepts of science in general, and of biological science in particular, are probably somewhat different now than they were at the beginning of this course. You have studied a number of problems in which biologists have long been interested. You have seen that when an investigator is successful in answering one question, that answer will immediately raise a new one. Early studies in genetics and cytology gave us the concept of the gene as the determiner of heredity. But what is the gene and how does it work? It was found that chromosomes contained a great deal of DNA. What relation, if any, does DNA have to transmission of hereditary traits. Still later Watson and Crick worked out the structure of DNA and showed how it might duplicate itself exactly. But how could DNA determine the hereditary traits. Evidence was obtained that DNA in the nucleus could determine the arrangement of the bases as RNA was synthesized and that certain arrangements of the bases on RNA would cause amino acids to be joined in certain orders during protein synthesis in the cytoplasm. But why do the same cells produce different proteins (enzymes) at one time than at others?

You have also seen that most of the results obtained in the laboratory are variable and there is often the probability that sampling errors are involved. And you have seen that it is very difficult to "prove" any hypothesis; we simply cannot test all alternatives.

How are the knowledge and understandings which scientists have uncovered to be used for the best purposes? In fact what are the best purposes? These are often questions which the scientist cannot answer. Some may involve moral issues. Scientists claim no more insight into these problems than that possessed by other intelligent and educated persons.

The next part of this book considers some questions of this sort. You may note that in each case, more knowledge and understanding is needed. But you might consider the problems as they are now, and as they might be if we had the added knowledge.

PART THREE CONCLUSIONS
AND BEGINNINGS

SCIENCE AND SOCIETY

RESPONSIBILITIES OF THE SCIENTIST

Scientists have an obligation to explain their ideas and investigations to those who support their work. The responsibility of the scientist to inform the public and the responsibility of the public to learn about science is the subject of the following contribution by a noted educator, Dr. L. A. DuBridge, President of California Institute of Technology.[1] Dr. DuBridge attempts to answer the questions: (1) What goals do scientists seek? (2) What do scientists work for and how do they achieve their ends? (3) What is a desirable relationship for scientists with the everyday world in which they, too, participate? (4) How can obstructions to understanding between scientists and nonscientists be removed?

Evaluate Dr. DuBridge's, opinions but do not be dictated to by them. Formulate independent ideas as to the role of science and scientists in society.

THE INQUIRING MIND[2]

by L. A. DuBRIDGE

In 1798 a monk by the name of Thomas Robert Malthus published a paper with a long and complex title which attempted to analyze man's future on this planet. Examining past experience and bringing to bear on this experience the brilliant logic of an analytical mind, he came to some rather dire conclusions about the future. It was quite obvious to him that men had to eat; that the only major source of food was the arable land; that the area of such land was limited. Therefore, there was a limit to the potential food supply, and hence to the population that could exist on the earth.

On the other hand, he noted that the human population tended to grow at an ever-increasing rate. Any sort of voluntary birth control, it seemed to him, would be either unnatural or immoral. Therefore, the only possible future was one in which the population eventually outgrew the food supply, and thereafter death by starvation, disease and war would take over to balance a birth rate which knew no control.

Clearly, a world in which most of the people would assuredly die of one of these causes was not a very pleasant one to contemplate.

[1] DuBridge, L. A. "The Inquiring Mind." *Engineering and Science,* vol. 18, October, 1954. California Institute of Technology, Pasadena, Calif. pp. 11–14.
[2] Reprinted by permission from *Engineering and Science.*

DuBridge   However, here we are 156 years after the Malthusian prediction, and the
portion of the world that we live in does not face the Malthusian death
sentence. Our population is expanding at a rate never dreamed of in
Malthus' time. There are four times as many people on the earth now as
then. At the same time, here in the United States at least, we have far more
trouble with food surplus than with shortage. We buy potatoes and dye
them blue, butter and let it spoil, wheat and give it away, in our desperate
effort to avoid the economic consequences of growing more food than we
can eat.

Surely Malthus was the most mistaken man in history. Or was he?

Actually, as Harrison Brown points out in his recent book (from which
I shall now borrow heavily), *The Challenge of Man's Future*, Malthus'
reasoning and logic were entirely correct. His only misfortune was that his
observations and assumptions were later rendered obsolete by unforeseeable new developments. What were these new developments? They were
of two kinds—technological and social. On the technological side men
learned how to raise more pounds of food to the acre, learned to get more
nutritive value to the pound, and learned how to transport food quickly
from areas of surplus to areas of shortage. On the social side, great segments of the human race came to regard voluntary birth control not as a
sin but as a virtue.

Now I think it is quite evident that without this latter factor—voluntary
population control—the Malthusian disaster can be only postponed, and
not finally prevented, by any advances in technology. We must admit that
the supply of land is limited, that the productivity of land can *not* be expanded beyond all limit. But population, if not controlled, does expand
without limit, and sooner or later—in 50, 250, 500 or 5000 years—a population which is doubling every 75 years or so is bound to outrun any given
food supply.

This makes it clear that the primary need of the world is to insure that in
all parts of it the population recognizes the need for growth that is controlled by voluntary action rather than through starvation. Clearly, this is
not primarily a job for science and technology, but rather for education.

But science and technology do have some terribly important tasks to
perform in this field. First, there is the task of improving the technology of
producing, processing and preserving food so that the food supply will
keep pace with population for the 25, 50 or 100 years required to complete
the educational job. Second, there is the task of improving standards of
living over a larger part of the world—for increased education goes only
with increased living standards and increased disposable wealth. Finally,
science and technology have the task of providing the necessary tools so
that any segment of the population that has overcome the starvation limit
can then proceed to help men and women lead happier and richer lives.

Now I claim that these constitute quite substantial and immensely
challenging tasks. Another way of expressing them is to say simply that if

men are to attain those social, moral and spiritual goals which we of the   DuBridge
Christian nations believe desirable, then science and technology must
provide the physical tools to make their attainment feasible.

This being about as important a goal as I can think of, it behooves those
of us who are working in the fields of science and technology to ask ourselves how we are doing. Have we properly visualized our task and our
goals? Have we properly analyzed and evaluated the steps which need to
be taken, the prerequisites for progress? Are we putting first things first and
do we know which things *are* first? Are we creating within science and
technology itself, and within the community at large, the conditions most
likely to nurture progress and success?

Now it would be presumptuous of me to attempt to answer these questions or to try to solve the problems they suggest. But I can presume to
raise the questions and ask you to think about them, in the hope that if
enough people think about them, we may some day get them answered.

The goals we seek

It seems to me obvious from the way in which I have stated the problem
that it is important that we keep in mind the goals we seek. As I have suggested, these goals are not merely more food, more products, more gadgets.
Our goal in the last analysis is a moral goal—more happiness for individual
human beings, expressed in whatever terms their own philosophy of life
dictates.

I emphasize and repeat this matter of ultimate goals precisely bcause it
is so obvious to us that it is often forgotten. We become so absorbed in our
gadgets, our machines, our new foods, new medicines, our new weapons,
that only too often we think of them as ends in themselves—forgetting
what they are *for.*

Now if we ourselves—if we scientists—forget the ends in our absorption
with the means, that is bad enough; for then our work loses its meaning.
But it is even more dangerous if we let the public believe that our machines
and our mechanisms are ends in themselves. For then our work, which in
the end depends upon public support, will surely be destroyed. And it will
be destroyed by the public even though the public itself, rather than the
scientists, would be the principal losers.

Let us bring this closer home. It is a paradoxical fact that, in these days
of the mid-20th century, science and technology are being simultaneously
praised to the skies and dammed with religious fervor; they are being
handsomely supported and heartily kicked. Scientists are publicly acclaimed as a group and privately slugged as individuals.

Why is this?

Clearly, we have not told our story adequately. Our physical achievements are evident. But, because they are physical, we are accused of being
materialists. Because the tools of science are powerful, their power is
feared and those with the power are suspected of evil motives. Because

weapons have been produced to help men fight in their own defense, it is assumed that they also make men *want* to fight. So we see that as we brag about our knowledge but are silent about our aims, then the public will come to ignore our knowledge and denounce our aims.

What scientists work for

So my first plea is that scientists shall throw off their reticence in speaking of their feelings and come out boldly and unashamedly to say, "We are working for the betterment and happiness of human beings—nothing less and nothing more."

But, in spite of the romanticism of the poet, we know full well that for most human beings *happiness* is not attained solely by sitting under a tree with a loaf of bread and a jug of wine. And even if it were, someone has to bake the bread and bottle the wine. The poet was right in suggesting that the essential elements of happiness consist of food, shelter, companionship and leisure. He only forgot to mention that these must be achieved by effort, and that the effort itself may bring happiness, too.

In any case, we are forced at once to consider how human effort can be most effectively employed to provide the physical elements for happiness and also the leisure to enjoy them. Nor are we content—as were those of medieval and ancient times—to have *many* people exert the effort and a few people enjoy the leisure. We have proved that *all* may work and *all* may play.

Now what is it that has made it possible for us today to think of a modest amount of happiness coupled with a reasonable amount of work as a possible goal for *all* people, rather than just a few? The answer is, clearly, that a series of *intellectual achievements* have enabled men to enlarge, to expand, and to dream of achieving a moral goal.

What are the intellectual achievements?

I think it is fair to say that the essential cause of the difference in the physical and the moral outlook of the western world in the 20th century, as compared to the 10th is simply that, along some time between those dates, men invented a new process of thinking.

Men had, of course, always thought, always observed, always speculated, always wondered, always asked questions, always explored. But along about 1700 men began to do these things in a new way. Men began to realize that by making observations carefully and analyzing them quantitatively, it could be shown that nature behaved in a regular manner and that these regularities could be discovered, reduced to mathematical form and used to predict future events.

This was an astonishing discovery. And as this new concept, outlined by Francis Bacon, was pursued—first by Galileo, then by Newton, then many others—a new world of understanding was opened to men's minds. Nature was partly comprehensible, not wholly mysterious and capricious. The falling stone and the moving planets became suddenly not only under-

standable but miraculously and simply related. Men couldn't *affect* the   DuBridge
motion of the planets, but they *could* control the motion of the stone and
of other objects.

And so, machines were invented, the concept of energy emerged, steam
was put to work—and suddenly, after thousands of years of doing work
only with the muscles of men and animals, men found that a piece of burning wood or coal could take the place of many slaves or horses or oxen.

From that time on, happiness and leisure for all men became a possible
goal, not a crazy dream.

A limitless quest

But that was only the beginning. The scientific method led from physics
to astronomy to chemistry to biology. A beachhead on the shores of
ignorance became a vast area of knowledge and understanding. Yet, as the
frontiers of knowledge advanced, the area of ignorance also seemed to
enlarge. Nature was not simple after all. A literal eternity of new frontier
was opened up. The quest for understanding, we now see, will, for finite
man, be limitless.

I need not recount the way in which this new understanding has
spread—often slowly, often with startling rapidity—from one field to
another.

But I would like to direct your attention to the conditions that are required for knowledge and understanding to grow and to spread. Intellectual advancement does not come about automatically and without
attention. There have been throughout human history only a few places
and a few periods in which there have been great advances in knowledge.
Only under certain special conditions does the inquiring mind develop and
function effectively. Can we identify these conditions? Certainly we must
try.

The first condition, of course, is that at least a few people must recognize
the value of the inquiring mind. Here we all take for granted that new advances in understanding come only from the acts of creative thinking on
the part of individual human beings. We know that, and we respect and
admire the men who have shown the ability to think creatively. But we
mustn't get the idea that our admiration for original thought is shared by
all people.

Even in this country, the man who thinks differently is more often
despised than admired. If he confines his new thoughts to the realms of
abstruse theoretical physics or astronomy, he may not be molested. For
then he will be speaking only to those who understand him. But if he
wanders into biology or medicine, into psychology or sociology or politics,
then he should beware.

Now in recognizing the virtues of thinking differently, we do not mean
that we must encourage the idiot, the criminal or the traitor. Honest, truly
intellectual inquiry is perfectly easily recognizable by those who have some

DuBridge   training in the field. But just here we run into difficulty. Those who are in-
competent to judge may nevertheless render judgment and pass sentence
on those with whom they disagree, or whom they fear.

One of the great unsolved problems of a democracy is how to insure
that, in intellectual matters, judgments are left to those who are competent,
and the people will respect that competence. But when uneducated
fanatics presume to choose and to censor textbooks, when government
officials impose tests of political conformity on the scholars that may leave
or enter a country, and when the editors of a popular magazine set themselves up to judge who had the proper opinions of nuclear physics, then
the inquiring mind finds itself in an atmosphere not exactly conducive to
maximum productivity.

Fortunately, for the past 100 years in Western Europe and in the United
States the impediments to creative scholarship have been less important
than the great encouragements. In the past 10 years the physical conditions
necessary for research in the sciences have enormously improved. More
opportunities have been created to study, to travel, to carry on research,
than ever before existed.

The needs of the inquiring mind

But physical conditions are not enough. Big, beautiful laboratories do
not themselves produce research—only the men in them can think. And
if conditions are such as not to attract men who think or such as to impede
their thinking, then the laboratory is sterile. Such laboratories, as you well
know, do exist. There is no use storming and raging at the perverseness of
scientists who refuse to work when conditions are not just to their liking.
We don't call a rose bush perverse if it fails to bloom when deprived of
proper water and soil. A community or a nation which wishes to enjoy
the benefits that flow from active inquiring minds needs to recognize that
the inquiring mind is a delicate flower, and if we want it to flourish we
are only wasting our time if we do not create those conditions most conducive to flowering. The cost of doing so will be well repaid.

The inquiring mind then needs, first of all, some degree of understanding
and sympathy within the community. And if there are those who cannot
understand, then at least they must be insulated by those who do, so that
they do the least harm. As someone has said, we can stand having a few
idiots in each community—as long as we don't put them on the school
board.

As I have already suggested, it is not enough for the scholar or the
scientist to wring his hands and wish that there were fewer idiots or that
they had less influence. He must also, to the extent of his ability, explain to
those who can understand what he is doing and why. We now see that an
intelligent and informed segment of public understanding is essential to
the progress of scholarly endeavor.

Scientist and government   DuBridge

This leads me to another subject which has become timely to the scientist and to the citizen in recent years; that is, the relation of the scientist and the government. This is obviously a very large subject which I cannot attempt to explore here. But as the scholar needs an informed community to support him, so he owes an obligation to that community.

The prime obligation of the scholar, of course, is to pursue scholarship. That is, he must seek answers to important questions, observe carefully, analyze accurately, test rigidly, explain imaginatively, and test and test again. Then he must publish his results, fully, fearlessly, objectively, and defend them enthusiastically unless or until the facts prove him wrong. Through such intellectual struggle does the truth emerge.

But in these days the results of science impinge so heavily on public affairs that the public—in particular the government—needs the scientist's help in so many ways. Obviously, the government needs the direct services of thousands of scientists and engineers to carry on work in public health, standards of measurement, agriculture, conservation of resources and in military weapons, to name a few.

But when there is developed a new weapon, a new treatment for a disease, a new way of using public resources, does the scientist's responsibility end there? I think not. There are so many ways in which important matters of public policy are affected by these new scientific achievements that scientists must stand by as advisers at least to interpret, explain, criticize and suggest on policy matters.

Scientific advice

We would not think, of course, of allowing a new law affecting public health to be passed without asking a physician's advice on whether it is wisely conceived. Yet I am sure state and federal legislatures *have* thought of it—in the various antivivisection bills, for example. Fortunately, (for this purpose at least) the medical profession has great influence and can make its opinions heard. And most of the public respects its doctors.

But when national security matters are being discussed which involve the nation's strength in atomic weapons, it is clear that those in charge of forming policy will need to have much help on questions of what atomic weapons really are, what they do individually, and what would be the effects of setting off the whole stock pile. I am not saying that such scientific advice is not sought (though I think it is not always adequately used). But I do say that scientists need to be ready to help. Yes, they may need to be ready to intrude with their advice even if it is not asked for.

This problem has, of course, caused much recent trouble and misunderstanding. Many prominent citizens, including many politicians and editors, apparently feel that scientists should stick to the laboratory and let public policy matters be handled by others. Now no one argues that

DuBridge   *decisions* on public matters must be made by the properly constituted responsible officials. But *advice* and *information* on scientific aspects of the problem is often essential and must come from scientists.

It is often true that the scientific aspects of a problem are so important that they overshadow all else—and the scientist's advice becomes adopted as a decision. But in other cases, other factors may appear important and the scientist's advice may be wrong, or many not be taken. Even the scientist, being human and being a citizen, will take non-scientific matters into account in rendering his advice. He may be just as competent to do this as anyone else. Being a scientist does not disqualify a person from being an intelligent citizen. But the possibilities of disagreement and misunderstanding are very great.

A risky course

A very great and admittedly loyal scientist is right now being persecuted partly because, though he gave advice of surpassing value on many, many occasions, he gave on one occasion advice which some (but by no means all, then or now) believe was wrong. The sad part of this case is not so much the harm to the individual, as the harm to the country that will result if scientists cannot give honest advice to their government officials, or will be no longer asked for advice, or listened to. Dire disaster could indeed follow from such a course pursued in the thermonuclear age.

I fervently believe that the world has been remade the past century—remade physically, socially, and spiritually—by the work of the inquiring scholars. These scholars have sought new knowledge and new understanding; they have sought to use this understanding to produce those things that men needed—or thought they needed—to improve their health, their comfort, their happiness, their security.

Scholars will continue these activities and the world will continue to change. Their efforts must be aided; for though what they do may yield dangers, the dangers are far greater if they do less. And since what they do affects the world, affects you and me and our community and our country, we should have these inquiring and active minds around all the time to direct their attention to the most difficult of all problems—how to help men make better use, in their relations with each other, of the great new areas of knowledge which can yield so much to make men happier and better.

End of Article

SECTION EIGHTEEN

THE ROLE OF CONTROVERSY IN SCIENCE

Controversy . . . a discussion of a question in which opposing opinions clash; . . . *Webster's New World Dictionary, College Edition.*

Science has been emphasized as a process of inquiry, but because the conclusions derived from inquiry may often be diverse, science involves controversy as well as inquiry. This is so true that *constructive controversy* is a major mechanism in the growth of science.

History shows that scientific achievement along with its resulting technological advances has grown under the freedom of controversy and has become restricted (or extinct) by the restraint of free debate.

However, the society which permits free debate must be an educated society if it is to choose wisely among the alternatives offered it. Survival itself demands a society objectively familiar with the ways in which science and scientists affect it.

When we look at the past and attempt to evaluate the knowledge and attitudes of previous centuries, we find many examples of superstition and ignorance masquerading as science, and scientific inquiry not only being neglected, but even prohibited. Compare that darkness with the brilliance of our times—but what of our times? Are we really able to rationalize current controversies with scientific candor? Are we honestly wiser than our ancestors in the exercise of rational thought and emotional control? Are we able to make the decisions that will affect our future and the future of all others as yet unborn, or will our descendants look back and remark on the "ignorance of the past"?

We have the opportunity to become a better educated society through the use of constructive controversy and through understanding its contribution to the progress of science.

How does controversy contribute to the rational progress of science? The conclusions of science depend on the results of its experiments. Experiments constantly attempt to establish the correctness or fallacy of ideas. Thus, experimentation is the way science approaches controversy. While well-designed experiments may settle one controversy, often new knowledge derived from these experiments engenders new controversy, and this becomes, in turn, a part of the growth of science.

The following essays represent two examples of current scientific controversy. No guide questions or suggested points of discussion will be given. Read them, individually deliberate their contents, and then collectively and freely discuss these opinions. It will be strange if your discussions do not bring out ideas and solutions which would not even have been suggested by the authors.

The Use of Insecticides In 1962, the late Rachel Carson's book, *Silent Spring*, appeared on the nation's bookshelves. *Silent Spring* became a bestseller overnight, for it introduced an important scientific controversy: the use of chemicals, specifically insecticides and herbicides, to protect certain plant life from insects or other plants. Miss Carson skillfully and convincingly leads the reader to the conclusion that the continuation of life on earth may well depend on halting the use of insecticides. Her book was acclaimed almost unanimously by book reviewers.

For years before the talented Miss Carson's debut into the field of insecticides, however, other biologists had been debating the dangers and merits of these chemicals used in such huge quantities throughout the country. Many felt that the use of insecticides was not an "all-or-none" proposition. Trained scientists believed that perhaps the use of insecticides could be justified under certain conditions, but just what conditions justify this use presented an area for a many-sided controversy. Some favored the application of insecticides on a rather broad scale and others preferred a very restricted use of these chemicals. Undoubtedly all shades of opinion between the "all-or-none" extremes could be found in the scientific community.

Biologists' continuing interest in insecticides is well illustrated in an article, and subsequent letter to the editor in reply, which appeared in two issues of *The AIBS Bulletin* during 1960.[1] In the April issue, Dr. George Decker, Head, Section of Economic Entomology of the Illinois Natural History Survey, takes a strong stand for a realistic attitude toward the necessity of insecticides in our modern world. Dr. Samuel A. Graham, School of Natural Resources, University of Michigan apparently favors a somewhat more restricted use of insecticides than does Dr. Decker. We have reprinted both scientists' articles for your examination.

In both extracts from *The AIBS Bulletin*, we witness scientific literature functioning as a medium for free and open controversy. Neither scientist takes as extreme a view of the evils of insecticides as does Miss Carson. Neither see the issue as "black or white," for both are trying to settle on a shade of grey that could represent adequately the many pros and cons of this very controversial subject. Perhaps an ultimate test of discretion is to be able to distinguish, and to compromise capably, moderate views. Certainly very little insight is required to distinguish an extremist position from its opposite, such as the indiscriminate use of insecticides as opposed to a complete abandonment of their usage.

Read the articles by these two scientists and discuss the merits of each point. You should be familiar with Carson's *Silent Spring* for yet a third view on the use of insecticides.

[1] For reference, the *Bulletin* was renamed *Bioscience* in January, 1964.

INSECTICIDES IN THE
20th CENTURY ENVIRONMENT[1]

by GEORGE C. DECKER

WHEN THE FIRST white men came to North America, they found a race of rather primitive men living in reasonable harmony with a relatively stable environment. Under those conditions, this continent supported a population of about one million persons and provided in excess of 2000 acres per capita. Then, as now, literally dozens of insects attacked every crop that grew and neither man nor beast escaped their ravages. In the years that followed, with agriculture on a subsistence basis and a seemingly endless supply of land available, there was plenty for all, and farmers raised only feeble objections to share cropping with the insects. Later, as urban populations increased, each farmer was called upon to meet the food and fiber requirements of an ever-increasing number of individuals and to do so on an ever-decreasing number of acres per capita. This trend continued until at present we have only a little over ten acres per person, seven of which are classified as farm land but only two of which are devoted to crop production.

The early American farmers had little choice but to rely upon nature to control their insect enemies. Then, as losses mounted and the standards of perfection demanded by an increasingly more discriminating consuming public rose, farmers began to clamor for governmental aid and scientific guidance to solve their insect control problems. The early state and federal entomologists were essentially naturalists, and they preached a gospel of biological and cultural insect control methods. For years such measures dominated all entomological endeavor, but finally when natural controls proved wholly inadequate, entomologists reluctantly turned to chemicals, and thus we entered an age of chemical insect control.

The Advent of Insecticides

The large-scale practical use of insecticides is in reality one of the important technological developments of the 20th century. While it is true that numerous nondescript concoctions of lye, lime, soap, turpentine, brine, vinegar, fish oil, and even some tobacco, pyrethrum powder, mineral oil, and arsenic were reportedly used as insecticides prior to the year 1800, effective use of agricultural insecticides had its origin with the use of Paris green to control the Colorado potato beetle in 1867. For the next seventy-five years, arsenical compounds played an ever-increasing role in insect control. Thus, considering the many insecticidal uses for white arsenic,

[1] Condensed from a paper presented at a Symposium sponsored by the Ecological Society of America. "Ecological Problems of Pest Insects," given at the AIBS-sponsored meetings in Bloomington, Indiana. August, 1958. Reprinted from *The AIBS Bulletin*, April, 1960. pp. 27–31.

Decker sodium arsenite, lead arsenate, calcium arsenate, and other arsenical salts, it is not surprising to find that from 1939 to 1948 the domestic consumption of white arsenic averaged over 35,000 tons per year. It must be noted also that the arsenicals were not the only chemicals used as insecticides in the pre-DDT era. To obtain a fair estimate of the extent of insecticide usage in the early 1940's, we would have to add about 15 million pounds of cryolite and related fluorine compounds, some 15 million pounds of pyrethrum flowers, 8-10 million pounds of rotenone-bearing roots and powders, and at least one million pounds of nicotine. Then to all of this we must add literally millions of gallons of petroleum oils, unestimated quantities of tars, cresols, fish oil, and many lesser products.

With the advent of DDT for agricultural use in 1945 and the large array of chlorinated hydrocarbon and organophosphate insecticides that followed in quick succession, many of the older materials suffered a rapid decline in popularity and they were largely replaced by the more effective synthetic organic insecticides. It appears that the actual tonnage of primary insecticidal chemicals produced for domestic consumption each year may not have changed materially. However, with the use of newer and more effective materials at much lower rates of application, the acreage treated has increased several fold in the last decade. Moreover, prior to the advent of DDT the use of insecticides was for the most part confined to fruit, vegetable, cotton, and a few miscellaneous crops of high-per-acre value, they are now used quite extensively on several field crops, pastures, meadows, and forests.

When DDT and at least a dozen other new chemicals became available for general use, a number of competent and distinguished scientists expressed concern that widespread use of these materials might create a public health problem. Immediately a number of publicity seekers and misguided individuals seized upon the idea that the public was being poisoned, and the country was deluged with an amazing flood of scare stories. Then, as the general public began to show some concern, the witch hunt got underway in earnest. As absurd charges and counter-charges were hurled back and forth in congressional committees and in the press, the scientists settled down to a detailed analysis and factual study of the problem. The public health aspects were reviewed by several scientific bodies, notably the World Health Organization (1, 12), the U. S. Public Health Service (7), and the Food Protection Committee of the National Research Council (4, 6). The general conclusions drawn in each instance were: (a) The large-scale usage of pesticides in the manner recommended by manufacturers or competent authorities and consistent with the rules and regulations promulgated under existing laws would not be inconsistent with sound public health programs, and (b) although the careless or unauthorized use of pesticidal chemicals might pose potential hazards requiring further consideration and study, there was no cause for alarm.

These encouraging conclusions notwithstanding, the fact that insecticides may be misused remains a matter of concern to a considerable segment of the American public. This is true particularly of conservationists who quite correctly insist that many forms of wildlife are subjected to certain potential hazards not shared by man and his domestic animals.

Clarification of Terms

As a prelude to any attempted evaluation of the hazards which may be inherent in the use of insecticides, a few frequently unused [sic] terms must be clearly defined. To avoid endless confusion, a careful distinction must be drawn between the terms hazard and toxicity. As the Food Protection Committee of the National Research Council has repeatedly pointed out: "Toxicity is the capacity of a substance to produce injury; hazard is the probability that injury will result from the use of the substance in the quantity and in the manner proposed." Therefore, to be at all reliable, an estimate of the hazard involved in the use of any substance must be based upon a knowledge of its inherent toxicity and upon the details of its proposed use.

It is also imperative to recognize and understand the equally clear-cut difference between the terms acute and chronic toxicity. In general, *acute toxicity* refers to toxic effects (either lethal or profound) occurring immediately after, or at least definitely attributable to, a single exposure by any route of administration, but usually referring to ingestion. *Chronic toxicity* refers to toxic effects resulting from repeated or multiple exposures extending over a period of time and is generally considered to be accumulative in nature.

Elm trees killed by Dutch elm disease. Tree lovers insist this should not have been permitted; bird lovers insist trees should not be sprayed if birds and other wildlife may be adversely affected. (Photograph Courtesy of Illinois Natural History Survey.)

As noted earlier, the hazards to man and his domestic animals resulting from approved uses for insecticides in public health and agricultural insect control programs have been extensively studied and the general sum and substance of all research in this field has failed to indicate any significant public health hazards. It is generally conceded that safety factors ranging from 10 to 100 fold have been included in most recommendations and at times such factors have been superimposed one upon another until the possibility that an actual hazard may exist is fantastically remote. Whereas man and his domestic animals are afforded much protection by the labeling requirements of the Insecticide, Fungicide, and Rodenticide Act of 1947, which specifies definite time-lapse intervals between insecticide applications and the harvest or consumption of the crop, it is generally recognized that most forms of wildlife can hardly be expected to avail themselves of such precautions. It is also recognized that fish, reptiles, amphibians, and numerous arthropods are more susceptible to insecticide poisoning than are mammals and birds, and in fact there have been a number of cases where fish were killed following the direct or inadvertent contamination of streams and lakes.

As a matter of fact, entomologists, toxicologists, and wildlife biologists alike recognize that some species of wildlife are subjected to hazards not encountered by man or by his domestic animals and thus they present special problems requiring special research attention. For example, it is well known that in general the food consumption of animals is more or less inversely proportionate to their size; thus birds, rabbits, and other forms of wildlife receiving the same diet as much larger animals actually ingest larger amounts of pesticidal chemicals in terms of mg/kg of body weight. Then too, in many treated areas the intake of insecticides by various forms of wildlife may be by ingestion, inhalation, or absorption, and under some conditions certain species may be subjected simultaneously to exposure by all three routes of administration. Finally, it is obvious that relatively small species moving in, around, and under a vegetative cover are subjected to greater and more prolonged exposure than are larger domestic animals standing well above the contaminated vegetation.

In view of the foregoing factors, it is not surprising that there have been numerous instances where wildlife of varied types has been adversely affected by insecticides. At the same time, the preponderance of evidence to date indicate that such incidents can usually be traced to carelessness, to accidents, to instances of outright experimentation, or to non-agricultural programs involving anticipatable hazards. Considering the thousands of tons of insecticides that have been used—and misused—in the control of agricultural pests during the last 50 years, it can be concluded that to date the impact of insecticide usage on wildlife has neither been great nor disastrous. This holds true for orchards, market gardens and cotton fields, which represent the most extensive and intensive agricultural usage of insecticides. Actually, considered from the broad point of view, the impact of agricultural and public health insecticide use on wildlife has been insignificant when compared with many of the other everyday activities of man.

In contrast to these remarkably safe agricultural practices, the existence of some very specialized insect control programs that call for per-acre insecticide dosage rates as much as 5 to 10 times those required in most agricultural uses must be recognized. These do involve calculated risks insofar as wildlife is concerned. The spraying of elms for the control of phloem necrosis or the Dutch elm disease, and the fire ant control program are examples. In such cases the interested parties must, or at least should, with the aid of competent experts, weight the facts pro and con and then adopt a course of action that will best serve overall interests.

The Balance of Nature

Not infrequently insecticides are accused of upsetting the balance of nature, when in many instances it would be more accurate to say they were used to suppress an organism already out of balance. Actually, man himself has been the primary factor in upsetting the so-called natural balance. When he cleared the forest, plowed the prairies, drained a marsh, or dammed a stream, he altered an entire environmental complex and set up an entirely new set of opposing forces which if left uninhibited would establish an entirely new biotic equilibrium. Presumably it is obvious to all that nature's balance is not a static condition, but is rather a fluid condition changing from day to day, and at the same time constantly moving forward in response to the forces of changing geologic time and advancing culture. Insecticides represent only one minor element of these dynamic forces.

In nature, every living organism is engaged in the most ruthless kind of competition with every other organism upon which its interests impinge. Man is a part of that environment. That he has been eminently successful is evidenced by the fact that the human population of this country has risen from less than one million to over 170 million in some fifteen to twenty generations. It now becomes apparent that to clothe and feed this vastly increased population, man must maintain his position of dominance, and our agricultural production must continue to increase even at the expense of the further displacement of native plants and animals. It may be news to some that these pressures are now intensified by the fact we have at last absorbed and brought into production most of the lands suitable for agricultural production. As a matter of fact, 1954 marked a turning point in our history because then for the first time the withdrawal of agricultural land for use as home or industrial sites, airports, and highways exceeded the land reclaimed, and the number of acres in farms showed a decline. While America is presently blessed or, as some say, plagued, by overproduction, with populations increasing and the area of farm land tending downward, it will be a matter of only a few years until agricultural scientists and farmers will have to make ever-increasing use of new advances in agricultural technology, including even greater use of insecticides and other pesticides, to meet the nation's food and fiber requirements.

Population and Land Use

In a recent discussion of population dynamics and land use problems, H. B. Mills (9) said: "When we think of the future of recreational lands in all of this competition for land use, we cannot get away from zoning. We must think of areas where people will live, where they will work, where their roads will go, where they will produce their food, where they can find outdoor relaxation, and where wildlife can live and prosper. We may not like the idea of such regimentation; it will be an expression of restriction of personal freedom due to increased population density."

In 1954, the United States Department of Agriculture (11) estimated that to offset the pest losses in agricultural production, an extra 88 million acres must be cultivated, and that losses subsequent to harvest equal the production of an additional 32 million acres. Is it not possible that the benefits to be derived by diverting these acres to soil and wildlife conservation would far exceed any foreseeable damage that might accrue from the approved use of insecticides? The recent amendment of the duck stamp law is a step in the right direction, but this is apparently not enough. There is still some talk of a land bank, and the disposition of submarginal lands is still an open question. But 10 years hence may be too late. Is it possible that while dissipating our energies pondering potential hazards that may never materialize, we are missing the opportunity of a lifetime to secure and preserve an adequate representation of our native fauna and flora to be forever maintained in suitable conservation and recreational areas?

Difficulties of Evaluation

Those familiar with the excellent reviews on wildlife-insecticide relationships by Brown (2), Rudd and Genelly (10), and Cope and Springer (3) must be aware of the fact there is a considerable volume of excellent field and laboratory research, much of which tends to pinpoint areas of considerable concern where further research is needed. Nevertheless, at times it is difficult to evaluate properly many of the criticisms directed against insecticides and certain insect control practices. For example, some authors frequently note that a certain insecticide such as aldrin or heptachlor, is 5, 10, or even 20 times as toxic as DDT and then, after commenting in a matter-of-fact way that it may persist for several years, they imply that the hazard involved is tremendous, when actually the hazard may be insignificant because the dosage is low and the residue is rapidly lost. All too often

the results of some laboratory or field experiments are cited as if they were
typical of conditions to be encountered following the legitimate use of the
insecticide in the field. Then, too, one frequently encounters vague references to mass applications of insecticides without any further detail. Some
attempt should be made to distinguish between the treatment of a million
acres of cotton with X insecticide at 2 ounces per acre, and an equal area of
marsh or timberland at 2 pounds per acre. A million acres is a lot of
ground, but, after all, it represents considerably less than $\frac{1}{10}$ of one per
cent of the land area of the United States.

Pre-testing Insecticides

It is frequently asserted that new insecticides are introduced and released
for large-scale insect control operations without adequate pre-testing, but
apparently these critics are unaware that as early as 1948, Dr. A. J. Lehman
(8) clearly and with amazing accuracy set forth the toxicological characteristics of DDT and related compounds. Then, too, the very fact that the
review by Rudd and Genelly (10) contains a bibliography in excess of
a thousand titles would indicate that the characteristics of insecticidal
chemicals are not entirely unknown. As a matter of fact, there are experts
who would testify that few if any chemicals known to man have undergone
the toxicological scrutiny to which DDT has been subjected. It is true that
all questions and problems have not been entirely resolved "beyond
a shadow of a doubt," but that is not surprising, for after all, science is
seldom if ever static and there are few instances where a scientist can
claim he has established all of the answers finally, conclusively, and
irrevocably.

Actually, there are many problems related to insecticidal chemicals that
cannot be anticipated or resoved in advance in any laboratory or small
plot experiments. As a matter of fact, in establishing the principles to be
observed in the evaluation of new insecticides, the Food Protection Committee of the National Research Council (5) acknowledged this basic truth
when it said: "Complete knowledge of many factors pertaining to pesticide
usage, performance, and ultimate safety can be developed only through
actual use in large scale performance tests. Hence, any system proposed
for regulating the distribution of new materials should provide for their
orderly release with recognized steps between strictly controlled small plot
experiments and full scale commercial operations." This being the case,
one must anticipate certain adverse reactions and responses in the early
large-scale usage of a pesticide. The correct procedure is to make sure such
instances are detected and corrected as soon as possible. While the occurrence of such incidents is disturbing and regrettable, it seems reasonably
certain the adverse effects will rarely if ever be disastrous or permanent.

Not infrequently the wildlife specialist and the conservationist feel that
they are placed at a disadvantage in presenting their case because in a large
degree the values with which they deal are intangible and thus the recon-

Decker   ciliation of divergent points of view which often elicit strong emotional
          responses becomes doubly difficult. Even here, there are at least some
          entomologists who can lend a sympathetic ear, for insect control also has
          its intangible considerations which can likewise induce violent emotional
          eruptions.

          Many of the most dreaded diseases of man are insect-borne, and there
          are those who regard the continued control of insect disease vectors as
          essential to the maintenance of successful public health programs. The
          hundreds of phone calls that besiege public health officials when nuisance
          mosquitoes become annoying lend ample testimony to the public interest
          in and the demand for local mosquito control programs.

          Then, too, a large segment of the American public is profoundly
          interested in the protection of shade trees, ornamental plantings, and
          forests. Literally thousands of individuals, recalling with profound regret
          the demise of the chestnut tree because no effective disease control
          measures were available, vociferously demand that every possible effort
          be made to assure that the same fate does not befall the American elm, the
          most common and perhaps the most beloved shade tree in America. In the
          battle for the elms we approach the tragedy of civil war, for here we have
          entomologist pitted against entomologist, conservationist against conser-
          vationist, and neighbor against neighbor. Last but not least, the fact that
          the Congress of the United States and a score of state legislatures,
          normally reluctant to appropriate funds, except in response to great pres-
          sure, have approved plans and appropriated funds for several large-scale
          insect control programs, testifies to the public interest in phases of insect
          control which do not affect its diet and only indirectly its pocketbook.

          Considering All Sides

          Any fair and impartial appraisal of the impact of insecticides on wildlife
          must give equal consideration to both the good and bad side effects that
          may occur, and if we are to be honest we must look for the good as
          diligently as we look for the bad. Unfortunately, harmful side-effects are
          usually readily apparent, whereas indirect beneficial results are apt to pass
          totally unobserved. Nevertheless, the impartial observer may be pardoned
          if he considers the loss of a few song birds attributable to the spraying of
          elm trees less harmful than the permanent loss of such trees, with the
          accompanying disappearance of nest sites.

          Unfortunately, the ultimate effect of insecticide usage on animal life
          cannot always be measured in terms of initial mortality of individual
          species. In reality it must reflect and encompass the long-term effects on
          both plant and animal life. Since the latter are largely dependent upon
          plants for both food and shelter, is it not possible that the destruction of
          timber, range vegetation, or cultivated crops by insects may produce a
          chain reaction that will ultimately affect all of the forms of life in the area?

Conclusions

There is no question but that the future food, fiber, and public health needs of this country will assure the continued, if not, indeed, the greatly expanded use of insecticides for generations to come.

Despite the widespread use of insecticides totaling billions of pounds in the last decade, profound fears that the large-scale usage of modern pesticidal chemicals would seriously upset the balance of nature and result in disastrous losses of wildlife have not been realized. To quote from the most comprehensive and complete study of the problem (10), "Considered in its broadest scope, at the present time pesticides seem to be only minor influents in nature compared to other factors in land and water development and use."

Favorable results notwithstanding, the many diverse and complex problems of wildlife conservation in a chemical world must be kept under continued surveillance. Particular attention should be devoted to the welfare of rare species of restricted habitat, to the impact of new chemicals as they are introduced, and to pest control programs involving the widespread application of insecticides over large contiguous areas.

Since most of the unfortunate incidents, problems, and differences of opinion that have arisen or are likely to arise, involve insecticide usage (unintentional or otherwise) that was not covered by label approval, it appears that the solution of the problem at hand rests in the detection, isolation, proper evaluation, and eventual elimination of malpractices rather than indulgence in wholesale condemnation of insecticides and insecticide usage *per se.*

Bibliography

(1) Barnes, J. M. 1953. Toxic hazards of certain pesticides to man. World Health Organization Monograph Series N. 16. 129 pp.

(2) Brown, A. W. A. 1951. Insect control by chemicals. John Wiley & Sons, Inc., London. 817 pp.

(3) Cope, O. B., and P. F. Springer. 1958. Mass control of insects: The effects on fish and wildlife. Bulletin of the Entomological Society of America. 4(2):52–56.

(4) Food Protection Committee. 1951. Use of chemical additives in foods. National Research Council. Food and Nutrition Board. 23 pp.

(5) ———. 1952. Safe use of chemical additives in foods. National Research Council. Food and Nutrition Board. 26 pp.

(6) ———. 1956. Safe use of pesticides in food production. National Research Council. Publication 470. 16 pp.

(7) Hayes, Wayland J., Jr. 1954. Agricultural chemicals and public health. U. S. Dept. of Health, Education, and Welfare Public Health Reports. 69(10):893–898.

(8) Lehman, A. J. 1948. The toxicology of the newer agricultural chemicals. Bul. Assoc. Food & Drug Officials. 12(3):82–89.

(9) Mills, H. B. 1959. The importance of being nourished. Trans. Ill. Acad. Sci. 52 (1, 2).

(10) Rudd, Robert L., and Richard Genelly. 1956. Pesticides: Their use and toxicity in relation to wildlife. State of California Department of Fish and Game, Game Bulletin No. 7. 209 pp.

(11) United States Department of Agriculture. 1954. Losses in agriculture. Agricultural Research Service. 190 pp.

(12) World Health Organization. 1956. Toxic hazards of pesticides to man. Tech. Report Series No. 114. 51 pp.

End of Article

LETTER[1]

by Dr. SAMUEL A. GRAHAM

July 26, 1960

George Decker's article on insecticides and their use in the 20th Century, (*AIBS Bulletin* April, 1960) is an excellent presentation of the agricultural entomologist's viewpoint on this controversial subject. One can find little to criticize either in the logic of his argument or the general conclusions reached, in so far as they relate to the production of human foods. There are, however, some apparent implications inferring blanket approval of the widespread application of insecticides which deserve comment, in view of the current controversy between bird lovers and control agencies. Knowing Dr. Decker as I do, I feel sure that these implications were not intended, and were the natural result of time and space limitations that prevented adequate coverage of a very complex subject. This letter to the editor is written, not to criticize but rather to amplify and clarify.

We must agree that insecticides will continue to be used, perhaps in increasing quantities, in the artificially simplified environment of our fields, gardens and orchards. This seems inevitable. We have no desire to eat wormy apples, and most of us object to too many aphids in our spinach. Furthermore, one would encounter difficulty in persuading the potato grower to desist from using insecticides when he has seen per acre production rise from 75 to 500 or even 1000 bushels as a result of his use of agricultural chemicals, of which insecticides and fungicides are outstandingly important.

But when we depart from the fields and orchards, conditions are by no means comparable. The widespread application of poisons cannot be justified by the fact that the use of these chemicals on farms is necessary. Most of the controversy about the use of toxicants is centered around projects involving large areas, often under multiple ownership. Usually the projects which are questioned are conducted by public agencies, municipal, state, or federal, and therefore are not subject to regulations that apply to projects conducted by individuals or corporations.

[1] Reprinted from *The AIBS Bulletin,* October, 1960. pp. 5–7.

Graham

Decker points out correctly that DDT has received a tremendous amount of research attention and he seems to imply that all insecticides have been subjected to similar careful scrutiny before they are approved for use. Actually, DDT is the only chlorinated hydrocarbon insecticide that has been adequately evaluated in terms of side effects on many organisms that are either of direct value to man, or appreciated for their beauty or aesthetic value. The widespread use of toxicants cannot be justified until small scale tests have proved their worth and their shortcomings. That is the reason that forest entomologists, while experimenting with other materials on a limited scale, have used only DDT on extensive projects.

We know that DDT used at dosages greater than one or possibly two pounds per acre may cause injury to certain terrestrial organisms. $\frac{1}{2}$ pound per acre or even less many cause serious damage to fish. Why unexpected mortality of fish from low dosages sometimes happens is difficult to explain, especially when the mortality is delayed until several months or more after spraying. Possibly the death of organisms on which they feed results in malnutrition of fish, but more likely the toxicant is concentrated in the bodies of organisms used by fish for food. We know this to be true in the case of earthworms feeding on materials contaminated with insecticides of the chlorinated hydrocarbon family, and that robins feeding upon such worms are poisoned (Barker, 1958). The cherry orchardist may be happy about the reduction in the robin population, but others may not be.

The question of when, how, and where to use insecticides on a widespread scale is not easy to answer. Decker suggested that benefits to be derived should be weighed against the damage that may be done. Obviously this evaluation should not be entrusted to individuals or organizations which will do the actual control work and thereby stand to benefit. Sincere though they may be, such people are likely to be biased in viewpoint, and unwise decisions may result. The recklessness with which insecticides have sometimes been applied by public agencies, especially municipalities, for the control of the Dutch elm disease is a good illustration of carelessness. Dosages have ranged from one pound to over 100 pounds of DDT per acre. In one locality with which I am personally acquainted a private operator sprays the elms at so much per tree per treatment, and instead of one treatment when the trees are dormant and birds are least likely to be injured, three treatments are applied, thus tripling the income of the operator, but causing needless injury to birds. The residents, whose trees are sprayed without their direct authorization, are charged personally for the work.

Decker inadvertently infers by the photograph of elms in his article that economic entomologists approve without reservation the Dutch elm disease spraying program, as it is conducted. This is not altogether true because we know that the disease cannot be controlled by spraying alone, as Decker and his associates have elsewhere pointed out. (I.N.H.S.) The

Graham   difficulties encountered in controlling the Dutch elm disease are evident on
the campus of The University of Illinois, where, in spite of spraying, the
elms have died in great numbers, not only from the elm diseases but from
the scale insects which almost always increase following the application of
DDT. Control of the Dutch elm disease can only be accomplished by
intelligent use of insecticides combined with sanitation. Furthermore,
sanitation does not mean merely the prompt removal of dead wood, as we
are inaccurately told by control agencies, but rather the prompt removal of
dying or recently killed branches and dying trees, regardless of the cause
of mortality, before the elm beetles have had a chance to breed in them.
The beetles cannot breed in trees or branches that have been dead long
enough for the inner bark to have become darkened, and without the bark
beetles the Dutch elm disease would be without its primary means of dis-
semination. These facts have almost never been fully publicized by those
responsible for the Dutch elm disease control on the local level.

The actual decision to spray or not to spray is all too often in the hands
of inadequately-trained men, who can only see the pros. The Dutch elm
disease situation is only one illustration of this. We need some provisions
that will assure wise and dispassionate decisions on whether or not the
broadcast use of an insecticide is justified in a specific instance.

Decker may seem to imply that insecticides must always be the "backbone" of insect control, although he recognizes that cultural practices and
natural enemies of insects are helpful. Some of us feel that other means of
insect control are even more important than insecticides, especially in
forests, and judging from the research program under his supervision
Decker himself is among these. Some research even in orchards, has shown
that in certain localities proper selection and timing of insecticidal applications can increase the effectiveness of natural enemies in limiting the
multiplication of some pests. The result is a material reduction in the
amount of toxicants needed. (Pickett, 1956) Much more ecological work
along this line should be encouraged.

Admitting, as we must, that the use of toxicants is essential to man's
well-being, we need not assume that broadcasting these poisons is the best
way to apply them. Widespread application from the air is spectacular and
attractive because it makes news, but it inevitably entails a certain amount
of risk. Fortunately we have some researchers looking for safer ways of
using toxicants; among them are F. S. Arant and Sidney Hays in Alabama
who are developing a technique for poisoning the imported fire ant that
seems safe. The "catch" is that the technique must be applied by individuals who wish to control the ants on their property, and not by the
widespread and spectacular treatments under federal aid, so attractive to
some public agencies.

Unfortunately space does not permit the enumeration of other work
leading toward the safer application of insecticides, but fortunately con-

siderable effort is being directed along this line. These efforts should be Graham encouraged.

I have raised a question concerning the wisdom of the Dutch elm disease program as currently conducted. Now let us look at the fire ant situation. We know that the toxicants used in the broadcast applications to "eradicate" this insect are highly destructive to some birds and mammals. That this is recognized by proponents of the program is indicated by the warnings issued. These include, covering of fishponds, keeping pets and small children off treated ground for a certain length of time after treatment, covering leafy vegetables in the garden, and preventing pets from drinking from pools of water standing after a rain.

Only a major emergency could justify a widespread program that requires such precautions. Can the fire ant be so classified? Many entomologists think not. In fact it appears from personal conversation with one entomologist who has studied the insect intensively, that the fire ant is chiefly a nuisance. On the credit side it is highly predatory upon other insects such as the cotton boll weevil and boll worm. Furthermore, it appears to be less destructive to ground nesting birds than is our native fire ant, which it seems to be replacing, and with which we have lived for generations. These facts cause us to wonder whether or not the pros and cons were carefully weighed before the fire ant program was undertaken.

Also, the program to eradicate the gypsy moth is open to question. Would it be practicable to eradicate this insect? Most forest entomologists who are acquainted with the situation believe not. I do not question the sincerity of those who proposed the project, but I do question their judgment and their competence to weigh the pros and cons. In support of this viewpoint, we in Michigan have been trying unsuccessfully to eradicate the gypsy moth from a small area around Lansing since 1954. If, after five or six years of spraying, a small infestation such as this has not been eradicated, what chance is there that the New York-New England program can succeed?

Some entomologists seriously question whether or not the eradication of *any* thoroughly established insect can be accomplished with means now at our disposal. The case of the Mediterranean fruit fly in Florida is often cited as an example of successful eradication, but actually the results there signify little if we accept Hopkin's (1938) conclusion that the climate in Florida is unsuited to the year in year out survival of the insect.

Still other widespread control projects supported by public funds might be mentioned, some justifiable and some not. But from the examples mentioned, the evidence is clear that enough mistakes have been made to raise questions concerning the infallibility of some publicly-supported insect control agencies.

My conclusion is this and I hope that Dr. Decker will agree: that the use of insecticides is a necessity for production of foods in the quantity and

Graham quality that we require. However, numerous widespread projects involving the broadcasting of insecticides that have been endorsed enthusiastically by the public-supported control agencies, are open to question. Apparently the decision to spray or not to spray cannot be safely left to these control agencies. The temptations of empire building are too great. The pros and cons should be weighed by persons with broad training and experience, who can evaluate all available information dispassionately, thus reaching a decision that will be in the best long-term interest of mankind and as nearly unbiased as possible. The viewpoint of forest entomologists on the broadcasting of insecticides deserves special comment because it is a sensible one. It is this: All agree that the application of insecticides over large areas must be regarded as an emergency treatment, comparable to extinguishing a fire or removing a man's appendix. Control projects involving the broadcasting of insecticides should not be entered upon lightly.

References

Arant, F. S., Kirby L. Hays, and Dan W. Speak. 1958. Facts about the imported fire ant, Highlights of Agricultural Research. The Alabama Polytechnic Institute, Auburn, Ala. 5: #4

Baker, Roy J. 1958. Notes on some ecological effects of DDT sprayed elms. Jour. Wildlife Mgt. 22: 269–274

DeWitt, J. B. 1956. Chronic toxicity to quail and pheasants of some chlorinated insecticides. Jour. Agric. and Food Chem. 4: 863–866.

Hays, Kirby L. 1958. The present status of the imported fire ant in Argentina. Jour. Econ. Ent. 51: 111 & 112.

Hopkins, A. D. 1938. Bioclimatics. U.S.D., Misc. Pub. 280, p. 64.

George, John L. and Robert T. Mitchell. 1947. The effects of feeding DDT-treated insects to nestling birds. Jour. Econ. Ent. 40: 782–789.

Illinois Natural History Survey Publications—by several authors, Jour. Econ. Ent. 47: 624–627—Plant Reporter, 44: 163–166-etc.

Pickett, A. D., et al. 1956. Progress in harmonizing biological and chemical control of orchard pests in eastern Canada. Proceedings of the Tenth International Congress of Entomology, 3. 169–174.

Wallace, G. J. 1959. Insecticides and birds. Audubon Mag. 61: 10–12.

End of Article

	Next to the problem of controlling nuclear energy,
Too Many	perhaps the most urgent controversy of our age is
People?	the exploding world population. There are many

opinions on what to do about this problem, and the only positive statement that can be made is that the problem remains. Inquiring minds, free to express opinions, must provide solutions.

Two essays by contemporary scientists follow as an illustration. These scientists do not necessarily agree on all points, but they write in the spirit of free controversy, each hoping that someone will break through the barrier of universal ignorance to offer sound counsel to guide our future.

FORECASTING THE FUTURE[1]

by SIR CHARLES DARWIN

WE NONE OF US CAN HELP hoping that when anyone undertakes to prophesy the future, the facts will prove him wrong. I share this taste myself, and yet it may appear that I too am starting to prophesy. In fact I am going to try and do something much more modest. Forecasting is the word used for the predictions that the meteorologists make about the probable future weather, and this is the analogy I am going to follow. Through the reports he receives the meteorologist knows better than the rest of us what is happening in other parts of the world, and though he is very conscious that there are a great many things he does not know, with the information and experience that he has, he is in a good position to forecast the *probabilities* of future weather.

The present director of the British Meteorological Office, Sir Graham Sutton, recently wrote an article which describes the situation admirably. In making his forecast the meteorologist is doing the same sort of thing that a player does when he bids his hand at the game of bridge. If he were required to predict what tricks he would take with absolute certainty, he would not get very far; for example, if he had the ace and king of a suit he would only be *absolutely* certain of two tricks if that suit were trumps.

In fact, he does not declare that he will get two tricks, but he makes the estimate that he will probably get say eight or nine tricks. He reckons that this is the probability; he knows that one or two of his strongest cards may possibly fail to win the tricks he expects, but then he knows that this will most likely be compensated by tricks from some of his other cards he was not so confidently counting on. He estimates probabilities, and if he is an experienced player he is usually not far from right in a general way, even though some of his details may be wrong.

That is the sort of prediction that the meteorologist makes about the weather, and it is the sort of prediction that I am going to try and make about the future prospects of the world.

I want to work out this analogy with meteorology rather further. There are two separate branches of that subject, called respectively weather-forecasting and climatology. In forecasting, the meteorologist uses all the detailed knowledge of conditions in the world at the present moment and applies to them the laws of mechanics and also a good deal of personal experience and personal judgment, and from all this he says what things will be like twenty-four hours hence, and he usually gets it fairly right. He also tries to do forty-eight hours, but has a good deal less confidence about that, because as time goes on the things he does not know get proportionately more and more important.

[1] Reprinted by permission from *Engineering and Science*, April, 1956. pp. 22–36.

Sir Charles Darwin.

Darwin The subject of climatology is quite different. In this there is no forecasting of what things will be like tomorrow, but instead there are general
statements such as that this place will be a desert, that place a tropical
jungle, while yet another one has a climate which will support good agriculture most of the time. It is much less detailed but a much more general
subject, and it is one that must always be in the back of the mind of the
forecaster when he makes his predictions.

I am going to try and make a forecast for the fairly close future, say fifty
or a hundred years, but before coming to that I must say something about
what I call the climatology of my subject, because that really is a deeper
part of it. I will begin this by taking a simplified example. Suppose that
somewhere in the ocean there is an island that is completely isolated from
contacts with other parts of the world. I am told, in a general way, such
things as what its climate is, how hot it is, how much rainfall it has, and
what the soil is like. I am also told a little about the inhabitants and their
state of culture—say that they know about the use of metals, but have only
rather inferior food crops.

With only this information I could say a great deal about the life of the
island; for instance, I could make a very fair estimate of the numbers of its
population. To do this I should take as my principle that the normal way
that any living species of animal survives is by producing too many offspring, of which only a fraction survive. With many lower animals the
excess is often enormous, with a million produced of which only one may

survive, but the same rule holds for the higher animals, too; the excess production is much less, but it is still there.

The same rule applies to man. The families on the island will mostly each produce several children and the parents will do all they can to keep their children alive and to bring them up. Now, simply to replace the numbers of the two parents, two children would be enough, but most peasant families surely produce more than two children, so that there is a tendency for the population to increase.

What is it that determines the total population then? The whole island will have come under cultivation, and it will be yielding all the food it can. Through the uncertainties of the weather, in some years there will be good harvests and in some years bad, and the peasants will accumulate a certain amount of reserve food against the bad harvests. But sometimes there will be two or three bad years running, and then they will get short of food, and perhaps two or three times in a century there may be four bad years running, and then there will be real famine. It will be these occasional famines that will determine the average number of people on the island.

This is not the sort of thing we see now anywhere in the world, but, for example, it was what used to control the population of India until about a hundred years ago. All this may seem rather obvious, but it is worth noting that we can say with some confidence that one of the most important features in the life of the island will be famines at the rate perhaps of three a century, and it is these famines that will mainly determine the number of people on it.

Now, suppose that the island has settled down into this state, but that its perfect isolation is broken by a ship which is wrecked on its coast and in which there happens to be a cargo of potatoes or some such crop. The new crop will give a much better yield than any of the previous food crops of the island, and it will be gradually adopted by the inhabitants. Every acre of ground will now yield twice as much food as it did previously.

Man is a rather slow breeder, so that the most conspicuous thing first to be noticed is that there is plenty of food for everyone. The bad old days of famines have disappeared and the population starts to increase. The historians of the island will record that it is a Golden Age, with an easy life very different from that of their parents. They will probably have a very human failing; they will forget about the cargo of potatoes, and they will claim how clever the present inhabitants are in overcoming the difficulties of life that used to afflict their ancestors.

This Golden Age will go on for a century or two, while the population increases to double its previous numbers, but at the end of that time the old troubles will begin all over again, because now again the yield of the crops will only be about enough to provide food for the new numbers of the population. There will be the old trouble over occasional successions of bad harvests which will produce famines again, and this will limit the population in the same old way. Something very like this was what happened in Ireland in the 1840's.

I have developed this imaginary example at some length, because it has a most important application to the present condition of the whole world. The world is just now in a highly abnormal condition, as is shown by the consideration of the increasing numbers of humanity. We are living in a Golden Age, which for man may well be the most wonderful Golden Age of all time. The historians have made fairly reliable estimates of the numbers of world population at different periods of history, and these numbers reveal it rather clearly. At the beginning of the Christian era the population of the world was about 350 million. It fluctuated up and down a bit, and by A.D. 1650 it was still only 470 million. But by 1750 it had risen to 700 million, and now it is 2500 million. That is to say that for 1700 years it was fairly constant, and then in 200 years it has suddenly quadrupled itself.

The increase of world population is still going on at a rate of doubling itself in a century, but it is a most menacing thing to think about. Year in year out the increase is at a rate of about one percent, and this means that every day there are 80,000 more people on the earth. That is the daily difference between the number of babies born and the number of people dying. Even those who are not conscious of this fact are unconsciously used to it, and accept it as natural, but it quite obviously cannot go on forever like this, and the most crucial question for us all is how long it *can* go on.

An abnormal state of affairs

This will be the main thing I shall want to discuss, but to see how abnormal the present condition is, I will imagine for a moment that it was the normal condition and I will look at the consequences that would follow. If the population were going to be able to double itself in each century, it would only be two thousand years before it was a million times what it is now, and two thousand years is only a short time in the period of human history. As a matter of simple arithmetic, if the population were a million times what it is now, there would be just about standing room on the land surfaces of the earth, but not room for the people to lie down! This would obviously be a fantastically impossible state of affairs, but it illustrates what an abnormal state the world is in just now with its population increasing at this rate.

It is obvious what has produced this present abnormal state of the world. There have been two chief causes. One of them was the discovery of the New World, much of it barely inhabited, which has provided enormous areas for possible expansion, in particular for the white races. The other is the development of science, through which it has been possible for man to find ways of producing a great deal more food, and in particular of transporting it from the places where it is produced to the places where it is needed. The Scientific Revolution, which began about three hundred years ago, must rank as one of the two really great episodes in human history; the only thing comparable with it in importance is the Agricultural Revolution. This happened in about 10,000 B.C., when man learned how to become a food grower instead of merely a food collector.

Darwin

The climatology of humanity

I want to give more consideration to what I have called by analogy the climatology of humanity. As I have shown, the present time is very abnormal, and so present conditions cannot be of much help in this. Are there any deeper principles that can be used? I think there are sufficient of them for us to be able to say a good deal about it. The first point is that the climate—and here I mean the actual climate—of the earth has been fairly constant for something like a thousand million years at least. It is eminently reasonable, then, to expect that we can count on it for say at least one more million years. Here is one constant datum we can use in our estimates.

A second thing is the finite size of the earth, and the fact that its whole surface is now fairly well known. This knowledge, of course, is quite a new thing; even a century ago there were great areas in Africa and South America that were hardly known, and they might have held something quite unexpected. There may, of course, still be many things to be discovered; there might possibly be other gold fields like the South African one, or perhaps great ore-fields of other, more practically valuable metals, but we can now be fairly confident that there is not room on the earth for anything, at present unknown, on a scale that would materially alter the possibilities of our ways of life.

The third principal we can use is much the most important. It is human nature. The characteristics of mankind are conveniently, though only roughly, divided into two parts, which have—as I think, rather clumsily—been called nature and nurture. Nurture signifies the environment in which people grow up and live, and it is, of course, what determines most of their day-to-day behavior. It is thus immensely important in making the short-term forecast, but the conditions of life have varied enormously from century to century, and they will surely continue to do so, and therefore nurture gives little reliable help in estimating what the long-term character of human life will be.

The matter is quite different when we consider nature. Here, as we know from the study of many types of animals heredity plays a predominating part, and so for as long as any of us can really care about—say a hundred thousand years at least—we must accept that man will be just like what he is now, with all his virtues and all his defects. There is simply no prospect at all of any millennium in which pure virtue triumphs, because that is not in the nature of the species Homo Sapiens. In so far as heredity

Darwin   determines man's behavior, we can take this as a constant in making our
predictions about his destiny.

The most important human characteristics, for my present purpose, are
the deepest instincts which human beings have. These are the instincts
which are directed towards the perpetuation of the species. One of them is
the fear of death, shared by such a vast proportion of humanity that even
under the most dreadful catastrophes very few people do actually commit
suicide. This instinct serves to help in keeping the individual alive.

Equally important are the instincts serving to reproduce the species. In
man and in the higher animals this characteristic falls into two rather
separate parts, the sexual instinct and the parental instinct. Among the
animals these two instincts suffice to perpetuate the species, and until very
recently the same has been true of man. Things have, however, been
changed by the developments of methods of birth-control, which have revealed a curious gap in our equipment of instincts.

Most people feel the sexual instinct with a force almost as great as the
fear of death, and most people, when they have got children, have a very
intense instinct to care for them and bring them up, but a good many
people lack the desire to have children in advance; or at any rate, if they
have the instinct, it is very much weaker than the other two. The parental
instinct seems to be evoked mainly by the presence of the children, and
thus it has come about that the sexual instinct can be satisfied without
leading to the consequence it ought to have of ensuring the creation of a
next generation. This third instinct, coming between the sexual and the
parental, may be called the procreative instinct; it is much weaker than the
other two, and indeed seems to be absent in a good many people.

Long-range forecast

The really important condition essential for human life was first fully
described by Thomas Malthus in 1799, in his celebrated book, *An Essay on
Population.* In this he drew attention to the necessity of a balance between
the numbers of a population and the food it will require. He pointed out,
with numerous examples, that there is a tendency for population to increase in geometrical ratio, whereas the area from which they will derive
their food cannot possibly increase in this ratio.

Malthus could not be expected to have foreseen the consequences of the
Scientific Revolution, which was going for a time entirely to upset the
balance between the two sides of his account. During the 19th century it
was possible to take the view that the disasters foretold by him had not
occurred and that, therefore, his principles had been proved wrong.

This comfortable view overlooked the fact that all through that century
population was, in fact, increasing geometrically, just as he had said, but
for a time this was being balanced by the opening up for agriculture of
barely inhabited regions in the New World, from which the newly invented

railways and steamboats could convey the food to the places where it was
needed.

It was the developments of the Scientific Revolution that for a time
upset Malthus's balance, but now once again the balance is coming into
effect, because we are now very fully conscious of the finiteness of the
earth. There are few more regions that can be opened out for agriculture,
and once again we have to face the problem of how our rapidly increasing
populations are to be fed.

Population and food production

I have noticed that most people, when for the first time they face the
population problem, at once think about the possibilities of producing
more food. They first think perhaps of the fields we all notice here and.
there that are not being properly cultivated. Then they may think of improved breeds of plants that will produce two or three crops a year instead
of only one. Then there is the possibility of cultivating the ocean. And there
is the Chlorella, an alga which might be grown on a sort of moving belt in
a factory; it can produce proteins perhaps ten times more efficiently than
the garden vegetables do, but unfortunately at a hundred times the cost.
Finally with the rapid progress in our knowledge of chemistry, it is not to
be excluded that one day the foodstuffs necessary for life will be synthesized in factories from their original elements, carbon, nitrogen, phosphorus and so on.

All these things are possible, and I do not doubt that some of them will
be done, but to accomplish them is no help, because of the central point
made by Malthus, that there has to be a balance between food production
and population numbers. Until population numbers are controlled, it will
always continue to be true that, *no matter what food is produced there will
be too many mouths asking for it.* New discoveries in the way of food production may make it possible for many more people to keep alive, but what
is the advantage of having twenty billion hungry people instead of only
three billion?

In the light of these considerations it seems to me that the food problem
can be left to look after itself and that all attention must be given to the
other side of the balance. Can anything be done about it? Frankly, though
perhaps for a short term something might be done, in the long run I doubt
it. My reason is this. Nature's control of animal populations is a simple,
brutal one. In order to survive, every animal produces too many for the
next generation, and the excess is killed off in one way or another. It is a
method of control of tremendous efficiency, and during most of his history
it has also applied to man. To replace a mechanism of this tremendous
efficiency it is no use thinking of anything small; the alternative we must
offer, if we want to beat nature, must also be tremendous.

The difficulty is even greater than it appears at first sight, because there
would be an instability about any alternative scheme deliberately adopted.

Darwin Thus, suppose some really good solution was found, and was adopted by half the world. For a generation or two this half would prosper. Its numbers would stay constant and the people would not be hungry, but all the time the numbers in the other half of the world would be increasing, so that in the end they would swamp the first half. That is the terrible menace of the matter; there is a strong survival value in being one of those who refuse to limit population.

The most easily imagined solution would be the establishment of some *world-wide* creed prohibiting large families, but when we reflect how many rival religious creeds there already are, all largely subsisting on account of their mutual differences, there seems little hope for any universal creed which would permanently limit population in this way.

It is very much to be hoped that a great deal of thought will be given to this matter on the chance that someone may hit on a solution, but I must repeat that nature's method of limiting population is so brutally tremendous that it can never be replaced by any such triviality as the extension of methods of birth control. It calls for something much more tremendous if there is to be any prospect of success.

Short-range forecast

I have said all I want to say about what by analogy I called climatology, and I will turn to weather forecasting; that is to say, I will attempt to forecast what will happen in the near future of say 50 or 100 years. I would remind you of the description of forecasting that I gave at the start, that it is like declaring a hand at bridge, where one makes a general estimate on incomplete data and one only expects to be right in general and not in detail. The weather forecaster can only do his work by receiving a great deal of information coming from all over the earth, and I need similar information for my forecasting. I have derived this from a fairly wide variety of sources. One of the most useful sources was a book entitled *The Challenge of Man's Future*, by Prof. Harrison Brown of Caltech. As a geochemist his study of the prospects of shortages in the future supply of various minerals led him on to study other shortages facing the world. A second book, *The Future of Energy*, by P. C. Putnam, deals very usefully with a narrower subject, the rate of exhaustion of our present fuel supplies and the various possible alternatives to them. Another very valuable source of information came from attendance at the UNO Conference on Population which was held in Rome in 1954. I may also refer to a book, *World Population and Resources*, recently composed in England by the organization known as P.E.P.

Cautious estimates

As I have already shown, we have been living during the past hundred and fifty years or so in a period of history of quite unique prosperity. Ex-

pert demographers estimate that our present two and a half billion population will have become four billion by A.D. 2000 and six billion by A.D. 2050.
These estimated increases will be fairly equally distributed among the
different races and among the social classes in each. For example, one of
the most rapidly increasing groups at present consists of the moderately
well-to-do Americans, who are increasing at a rate faster than the peoples
of India or Japan. I may say that these estimates should be regarded as
cautious ones.

The first thing we may think of which might reduce the numbers is war,
but most war is not nearly murderous enough to have any effect. Thus we
should count as a really bad war one in which five million people were
killed, but this would only set back the population increase for less than
three months, and that hardly seems to matter. I doubt if even an atomic
war would have any serious influence on the estimate, unless it led to such
appalling destruction of both the contestants that the economy of the whole
world was so entirely ruined that barbarism and starvation would ensue.
There is perhaps some hope that man will be wise enough not to embark on
such a war, but anyhow I shall refuse to consider it in my forecast.

Some people may feel that methods of birth control might upset the
whole forecast. This is a most important matter, which must be considered.
The proponents say a contraceptive may be discovered which would put
in our hands the possibility of completely controlling population numbers.
It is very possible that such a discovery may be made, and I hope it will,
but I do not think it seriously affects the forecast. This is because of the
time scale in human affairs. Even if we already possessed the full knowledge of what I may call the "contraceptive pill," a good deal of time would
be taken in building factories to make it on a scale large enough to provide
pills for the whole world population and the world-wide distribution would
take some arranging; but there are other more serious troubles which
would also have to be overcome.

It is hardly likely that the physiologists could be absolutely confident
that such a drastic medicine would have no collateral effect at all, and to
verify this, many years of experiment on a smaller scale would be necessary. For example, it would take two or three decades to verify that when
the habitual users of the pill did decide to have children, those children
would grow up into normal adults. It would be necessary to verify that
there were no unforeseen collateral effects, such as a premature aging of
the habitual user, or perhaps a special liability to some disease. I may quote
as a parallel the liability of people exposed to X-rays to develop cancer
a good many years later.

Furthermore there would need to be an enormous educational campaign, and the number of educators would have to be so vast that it would
take all of a generation to train them, and therefore two generations for
them to produce their results.

Darwin On all these counts I think it is safe to say that no large-scale effects could possibly be seen under two generations or so, and therefore the contraceptive pill—which in fact we have not got yet—would have little influence in affecting the forecast for fifty years, though it might for a hundred. But things are unlikely to be even as favorable as this; there are religious doctrines that might prohibit the use of the pill and there is a tremendous stock of unreasoning emotion in such intimate matters that would make a lot of unforeseeable difficulties.

A population of four billion

In the light of these considerations I see no escape from the estimate that by A.D. 2000 the world population will be four billion.

It is time to turn to the other side of the Malthusian account. Malthus only thought of actual food production as the balancing item, but since his day there are a lot of other things to be included which he could not have foreseen—such things as the supply of energy and the metals which are essential for the city life which alone can carry large populations.

First, the agriculturists at the 1954 Rome Conference on Population claimed that a doubling of food production can probably be achieved, but to do so everything has got to be exactly right. There must be no creation of dust bowls by the exhaustion of poor soils, and the stores of artificial fertilizers must not be distributed freely, but must be controlled so that they are only used in the places where they will give the most advantage. I am not competent to discuss this matter, but I do wonder how far this strict control will be possible.

In connection with agriculture I may refer to a thing of the recent past which is at least suggestive. Between 1947 and 1953 the world's agriculture made the most tremendous strides; in these seven years it increased by 8 percent, a truly wonderful performance, which we owe largely to the brilliant work of the scientific agriculturists. *But*—during those seven years the world's population increased not by 8 percent, but by 11 percent, so that the world was hungrier at the end than at the beginning. So, as I have said, I forecast there will be four billion people in fifty years from now, but I forecast that they will be hungrier than the two and a half billion we have now.

Now, to turn to other matters, Malthus needed only to think about agriculture, but we have to consider the provision of a lot of other things, because since his day the enormously increased numbers can only exist by living in large cities, and these demand all sorts of equipment like good roads, railways, water supply, electricity and so on. If some of these things could not be supplied it would be quite impossible to maintain the large numbers we have. So we must add to the right-hand side of Malthus's balance sheet things like energy and metals, and consider whether the supply of these will be adequate to keep us going for the next fifty years.

The prospects for energy

As to energy, as far as we can see the prospects are not too bad. There are only three sources which can provide power in quantities sufficient to be important. They are the "fossil fuels" coal and oil, nuclear energy, and the direct use of sunlight. Notice that water-power is not in the list; this is because the total quantity yielded, if all the rivers of the whole earth were fully exploited, would be only 12 percent or so of even the present energy developed.

At present, of course, practically all the power comes from coal and oil, and it is being used up at an ever-increasing rate. It is not possible to estimate the reserves with any great accuracy because it would be necessary to take some standard of the ease with which the coal can be won; for example, would it ever be worth while to mine a seam only a foot think? But an estimate very definitely on the optimistic side predicts that the coal will be all gone in 500 years. Since it took some 500 million years to make the coal, it may be said—speaking only very loosely, of course—that we are living on our capital at the rate of a million to one. Is it surprising that we can create wonderful prosperity for a short time? Oil is won much more easily than coal, and it is expected it may at most last for a century.

The prospects for nuclear energy are good, but the construction of nuclear power stations will inevitably take a good many years. It has been estimated that at the end of 30 or 40 years something like a quarter of the power developed in Britain will come from uranium instead of coal. Even at the present rates of consumption of power this would still mean a very large demand for coal, and as the demand in fact is growing year by year, there seems little prospect of the coal situation improving. Indeed, I would not be surprised if there was going to be a rather awkward period for us in about 50 years, when the expense of winning the remaining coal has in-increased a good deal, while there are still not enough nuclear power stations.

These difficulties apply specially in Great Britain. In America the situation is much easier in respect to coal. It is being consumed at an almost fantastic rate here, but there would seem to be enough easily mineable coal to last you a century. I have called the rate fantastic, and this can be justified by the following consideration. In the history of the world man has burnt up a very considerable amount of coal in all, but half of this total has been burnt in the United States since 1920.

Favorable prospects

As far as we can judge in these rather early days there is not likely to be any shortage of uranium for many centuries, and there is also always the possibility that the fusion of deuterium into helium may be made to occur slowly instead of, as now, only in the form of a super-bomb. The prospects

Darwin   for the supply of energy are therefore rather favorable, but it must be noticed that it may make very considerable changes in our ways of life. Nuclear power units are likely to have to be very large, and this may mean that there will have to be far fewer small units such as motor-cars. This suggests that in the nuclear age the population will be concentrated in the great cities even more than it is now.

The energy arriving at the earth day by day in the form of sunlight is quite enormous, and if it could be turned into mechanical power it would supply many times over the needs of mankind. A square yard facing the sun receives energy at a rate of about a horse power, but this implies that a great area would be required in order to make any reasonable power station. It may well be that improving techniques will solve this problem, but there is certainly a long way to go. Indeed it is rather humiliating to know that at the present time the most efficient way of collecting solar energy is to plant a row of trees, let them grow, cut them down and burn them.

If the provision of energy is not necessarily going to be a great difficulty, the same cannot be said of many other raw materials, in particular many of the metals, though even the supply of such a common thing as fresh water is going to be a formidable problem. Of course, strictly speaking, the metals, unlike coal, are indestructible; once won they can be used again and again, but in fact there is always some wastage due to wear or to actual loss, and this wastage must be allowed for. There has been the same enormous increase in the extraction of metals as of coal; in fact, of all the metal mined from the earth, half has been dug up in the last 30 years.

The possession of metals in great quantity seems to be essential for industrial development. It would appear likely that there simply is not enough of many of them, such as lead or tin or copper, to permit the underdeveloped countries to become industrialized on a scale at all equivalent to that of the highly developed ones. It is true that substitutes can often be found, but usually they will be inferior; for example, an electric transformer could be made with aluminum wires to replace the copper, but it would be less efficient. The underdeveloped countries which are trying to improve their industrial power are already handicapped in two respects. They lack capital, and they lack engineering experience, and to these difficulties must be added a third, the expected world shortage of constructional materials. So I forecast that at the end of this century industrialization will not have spread very greatly over the less developed parts of the world.

My general conclusion then is that in fifty years the population of the world will be four billion. They will be a rather hungry four billion, busily engaged in straining the resources of the earth to yield enough food, but they will not have succeeded very much in their present ambitions about becoming more industrialized.

I regard the forecast for a century with a great deal more doubt. The   Darwin
demographers forecast six billion for the year 2050, but my own guess is
that the world will not have succeeded in yielding enough food for this, and
that by then the world will have begun to go back into what I earlier called
its normal state, the state in which natural selection operates by producing
rather too many people, so that the excess simply cannot survive.

A gloomy picture

I fear this is a gloomy picture, and I ought to say that there are many
people who forecast quite the opposite. They are the technological
enthusiasts. They claim that whenever a shortage has declared itself the
technologists have produced a substitute and that things will go on forever
like that. To me they do not seem to appreciate the overwhelming importance and difficulty concerning the population numbers, and that is why
I must disagree with them. If they are right and I am wrong the world can
look forward longer than I expect to a continuance of the present era of
prosperity.

I hope that they will prove right, and that I shall be proved wrong, but
I must repeat my opinion that the central problem is that of world-popula-
tion. I do not see any happy solution of this, but I earnestly hope that if
many people face the difficulties, someone may possibly be inspired to find
an acceptable solution.

End of Article

FORECASTING THE FUTURE?[1]

by FRED HOYLE

Readers of Sir Charles Darwin's challenging article, "Forecasting the
Future" (*E & S—April 1956*), can scarcely avoid wondering whether any
answer can be given to it. Indeed I suspect Sir Charles of deliberately trying
to provoke us all into offering some answer to his dire prognostications.
At all events this is the effect his cheerful pessimism had on me, so I resolved to set down what counter-arguments I could think of.

First, a brief repetition of the argument itself. It is convenient to group
the ideas under several headings.

(1) Animal populations are governed by food supplies, the number of
animals of a particular type that are alive at a given time being just the
number that can be supported with the food supply available at that time.
Let the food supply increase and the number of animals increases.
Let the food supply decrease and the number of animals decreases, starvation being the controlling factor.

[1] Reprinted by permission from *Engineering and Science*, June, 1956. pp. 8–10.

Hoyle   (2) During the last 6,000 years or so, and particularly during the last few centuries, human knowledge has developed in an astounding degree. With increasing knowledge have come improved techniques, and with improved techniques has come a sharp increase of food production. Always accompanying the increase of food production there has been an increase of human population. Indeed, the rise of human population has followed the availability of food so consistently and closely that one cannot avoid the unpleasant suspicion that the human animal is responding to biological conditions in a manner not a whit different from that of other animals.

(3) The argument that improvements of technique will always keep pace with the rising human population is arrant nonsense. The human population is rising so rapidly today that *if the rate is maintained,* the amount of standing room on the surface of the Earth will be reduced in about 1100 years to a ration of one square yard per person; in 5,000 years the mass of humanity will exceed the mass of the Earth itself; while in about 11,000 years humanity will exceed the mass of the whole universe visible with the 200-inch Hale telescope.

(4) The rate of increase of the human population must therefore decline. The word 'must' is unqualified. What will cause the decline—starvation or a voluntary decrease of the birth rate?

(5) Decline through starvation is a natural process, the natural law whereby animal populations are governed. A decline through a voluntary decision by the human species will require some powerful basis in emotion and logic if it is to compete in strength with natural law. It is to be doubted whether any such strong basis will be found.

(6) Even if a voluntary limitation of the birth rate were seriously considered, it is doubtful whether it would be accepted by the whole of humanity. Those who accepted it would limit their numbers, while those who were unwilling to accept it would increase their numbers. The effect would be that those who refused limitation of numbers would automatically swallow up the others, so that in the result there would be no controlled check at all on the human population.

(7) The conclusion is that the human being is an animal and that at root he lives like an animal, controlled by exactly the same natural processes as other animals. The rise of food production occasioned by improved techniques cannot continue indefinitely. We live today in an exceptional age, a Golden Age, in which for a little time the inexorable march of natural law is not immediately apparent. Sooner or later, however, perhaps in a century, perhaps in half a dozen centuries, man will be forced to conform to the selfsame conditions that the rest of the animal kingdom conforms to. Eventually he must return to a semi-bestial existence.

This is a powerful argument, but it seems to me that not all of its links are of the same strength. Points (3) and (4) are quite unassailable, point (2) is, I think, correct, point (1) I would accept with some reservation.

On the other hand, point (6) seems to me to be a *non sequitur,* while the   Hoyle
last sentence of (5) seems open to serious question. Since the final conclusion turns on the acceptance of (5) and (6), I do not feel that the conclusion is logically compelling. It may, of course, turn out to be correct,
.nonetheless.

The ideas underlying point (6) would be correct under conditions of
primitive technology but do not seem to me to be consistent with modern
technology. A community that adjusts its population in a rational manner
cannot nowadays be overwhelmed by sheer force of numbers, but only by
a superior technology. And this is not likely to be possessed by an overpopulated community. Rather is the situation the other way round; an
overpopulated community with large concentrations of humanity would
be more vulnerable to modern weapons.

Starvation is not the only way

The reservation I have about point (1) is that I do not believe starvation
to be the *only way* in which populations become adjusted to food supplies.
I have read on good biological authority that certain species of songbirds
automatically limit their populations without starvation's necessarily intervening. The territory available for food is divided not into a number of
units equal to the number of contending birds, but into the number that
can adequately provide enough food for the rearing of a brood of chicks.
If the number of contenders exceeds the number of territorial units, then
fighting takes place until the birds are separated into two groups, those
with territory and those without. The ones with territory breed, while those
without territory do not. In this way the birth rate is automatically
governed to the availability of food, and this is done without the starvation
of unsuccessful birds, since enough feeding grounds are left over to support
the latter.

I mention this example at length because it comes near the crux of the
whole business. It must be granted that a feedback has to exist between
food supplies and population, but this feedback need not involve starvation. Starvation is a crude form of control in which the feedback mechanism operates directly on the population. If the population gets too large,
individuals die, thereby reducing the population. In the case of the birds,
no individuals die. The feedback is a more sensitive system in which the
food supplies operate on the birth rate, which then affects the population
at one stage removed, as it were. Instead of the excess of individuals dying,
they simply are not born.

Human feedback processes

Herein lies the root of my disagreement with Sir Charles. I think there
is evidence to show that humans are susceptible to even more subtle feedback processes than are the birds. For instance, I think the fact that Sir

Hoyle   Charles wrote his article, that I am writing this reply, that Harrison Brown
wrote his book, *The Challenge of Man's Future,* are all examples of feedback. Once a man grasps the unassailable qualities of points (3) and (4),
some sort of feedback along these lines becomes inevitable. Should this
happen to men on a sufficiently large scale, Sir Charles will have the
"strong basis" that he requires in point (5).

Of course the feedback may not happen on a large enough scale to produce important effects, but I think there are some considerable indications
that it may. An appreciation of the seriousness of (3) and (4) is undoubtedly growing very rapidly; indeed, there is every reason to suspect
that the growth has some similarities to a chain reaction. If this is so, then
the feedback will almost certainly win out, for the reason that the characteristic multiplication time of the chain reaction (probably one or two
years) is far shorter than the characteristic time of the rise of population
(about 70 years).

An example of feedback can be given that has controlled the birth rate
of a whole nation. During the last 30 years there has been a stability of the
birth rate in Britain. This stability is not governed by starvation, but by the
threat of a lowered standard of living—a far more subtle feedback than is
required if points (3) and (4) are to exercise their influence on the world
population.

In conclusion I would like to stress that nothing that I have said is intended to minimize the problems raised by Sir Charles Darwin. These
problems are in my view far more important, and lie far deeper in the
fabric of civilization, than are and do the Communist-Anti-Communist
issues we hear so much about in the daily paper. Mankind in its public
discussions seems to have a penchant for irrelevancy. Where I do not agree
with Sir Charles is in the position that because the problems are severe they
are well-nigh incapable of solution.

End of Article

THE COURSE IN RETROSPECT

If this course has served its purpose, you now have an increased awareness that science is a major force in the destiny of living things. Through
science, man will continue to accumulate knowledge, and with that knowledge he will acquire the ability to design the future according to his aspira-
tions.

The BSCS Second Course in biology has not attempted to define science
precisely; such a definition may be neither possible nor useful. Rather, the
course was designed to broaden your understanding of science as a constantly growing and changing process which defies precise definition. If

you elect a career in science, you will be enlarging continually on your understanding of what science is. If you are not going to be a scientist, we hope you can grasp the potentials of science now. If you can, your year's work has been worthwhile.

As a process, science includes the recognition of problems, the formation of hypotheses, and the designing of experiments. Scientific progress depends on carefully controlled experiments evaluated as objectively as possible. This evaluation thrives on publication. Published experiments can be studied by others, evaluated, and re-evaluated. Their methods and conclusions can be applied to new problems. Thus, an intellectual history of science has accumulated, and it continues to grow.

The evaluation of scientific progress continues as new insights are continuously being acquired and recorded. Even now, the accumulated knowledge of the past has resulted in new instrumentation and techniques which allow scientists to probe the inner structure of molecules and to speculate on the basic physical structures of life. More important in science than knowledge and instrumentation, however, is man's unique ability to reason. It is responsible for his past successes and failures and will certainly determine his destiny. Even though man's destiny must depend on his purpose, that purpose in turn must depend on his capacity for clear and rational thought. We hope this course has enabled each of you to increase that capacity.

APPENDIX

APPENDIX A   General Laboratory Requirements
APPENDIX B   Laboratory Requirements for Each Investigation
APPENDIX C   Preparation of Chemical Solutions
APPENDIX D   Preparation of Culture Media
APPENDIX E   Maintenance of Living Organisms
APPENDIX F   Math Tables
APPENDIX G   Bibliography

APPENDIX A

GENERAL LABORATORY REQUIREMENTS

A complete list of equipment and materials needed for a class of 24 students is given below. Orders for material should be placed well in advance of their projected use. Orders for living material should be scheduled so that organisms arrive close to the time they are needed.

Quantity	General Equipment
1	Autoclave or pressure cooker (22 qt)
1	Balance, analytical or torsion
6	Balances, triple beam (0.01 g sensitivity)
1	Brooder, chick
6	Burners, Bunsen
1	Burner, Fischer
1 roll	Cellophane, dark blue (MSC 300 or equivalent)
1 roll	Cellophane, dark green (MSC 300 or equivalent)
1 roll	Cellophane, dark red (MSC 300 or equivalent)
6	Coleoptile cutters
5 lbs	Cotton, absorbent
5 lbs	Cotton, non-absorbent
6	Counters, mechanical (optional)
1	De-ionizing column
40	Dishes, round covered polyethylene (8 oz) for use with temperature gradient box
6	Dissecting kits, each including
	1 Forceps (medium), medium points
	1 Forceps (fine), sharp points
	2 Needles, dissecting

Quantity	General Equipment
	Dissecting kits (cont.) 　1 Scalpel
	1 Scissors (medium size), sharp point
	1 Scissors (small size), fine point
1	Incubator
24	Loops, inoculating
1	Meter, footcandle (optional)
12	Microscopes, compound monocular
12	Microscopes, stereo binocular
6	Needles, hypodermic ($\frac{3}{4}$ inch-18 gauge)
6	Needles, hypodermic ($\frac{3}{4}$ inch-22 gauge)
3 yds	Netting, mosquito
2 boxes	Paper, filter (10 cm)
1 large roll	Polyethylene film (.004-.006)
400 assorted	Polyethylene plugs, flask size
1000 assorted	Polyethylene plugs, test tube size
1	Pump, aquarium
1	Refrigerator
12	Rubber stoppers, 2-hole, No. 4
2	Rubber stoppers, 3-hole, No. 7
15 ft	Rubber tubing, 6 mm
24	Rulers, plastic (mm)
1	Stop watch (optional)
12	Spatulas
1	Stove or hot plates
6	Syringes, hypodermic (0.1 ml accuracy)

1	Temperature gradient box
10	Test tube racks
12	Thermometers, centigrade (0-100°C range)
1	Ultraviolet light source
6	Volumeters

Quantity	Glassware
24	Beakers, Griffin low form (100 ml Pyrex or Kimax)
12	Beakers, Griffin low form (500 ml Pyrex or Kimax)
6	Beakers, Griffin low form (1000 ml Pyrex or Kimax)
1 oz	Cover glass (No. 1)
40	Dishes, culture (4 inch fingerbowls or round 8 oz polyethylene refrigerator dishes with covers)
24	Dishes, culture (10 inch fingerbowls or round 64 oz polyethylene refrigerator dishes with covers)
24	Flasks, Erlenmeyer (125 ml Pyrex or Kimax)
24	Flasks, Erlenmeyer (250 ml Pyrex or Kimax)
12	Flasks, Erlenmeyer (500 ml Pyrex or Kimax)
24	Flasks, Erlenmeyer (1000 ml Pyrex or Kimax)
1	Flask, side arm (500 ml Pyrex or Kimax)
1	Funnel, Buchner
1 lb	Glass beads
10 ft	Glass rod, solid
1	Graduated cylinder (1000 ml)
6	Graduated cylinders (100 ml)
6	Graduated cylinders (50 ml)
6	Graduated cylinders (25 ml)
6	Graduated cylinders (10 ml)

Quantity	Glassware
12	Hemocytometers and cover glasses
1 box	Microscope slides, regular
12	Microscope slides, single depression
24	Pipettes (1 ml)
6	Pipettes (10 ml)
6	Pipettes, Pasteur (with rubber bulbs)
72	Plates, petri (glass)
12	Serum vials
100	Test tubes (22 mm × 175 mm)
100	Test tubes (13 mm × 100 mm)
30 ft	Tubing, glass (6 mm)

Quantity	Chemicals
1 g	Adenine (6-amino purine)
1 lb	Agar
1 qt	Alcohol, 95% ethyl
1 gal	Alcohol, methyl
5 g	Ammonium oxalate
5 g	D-arabinose
5 g	L-arabinose
1 lb	Ascarite, coarse
10 mg	Biotin
1 g	Boric acid (H_3BO_3)
25 g	Calcium chloride
75 g	Calcium nitrate
10 g	Chloretone (1,1,1-trichloro-2-methyl-2-propanol)

10,000 I.U.	Chorionic gonadotrophin
1 pt	Chloroform (optional)
1 g	Copper sulfate
5 g	Crystal violet
1 pt	Ether (anesthetic)
5 g	Ferric chloride
25 g	Fructose
100 mg	Gibberellic acid
1 lb	Glucose
100 g	Glycerol
1 oz	Gram's stain
3 oz	Hydrogen peroxide (30%)
1 g	Indoleacetic acid
1 g	Indolebutyric acid
10 g	Iodine crystals
0.1 g	Janus green
3 g	Lactose (optional)
$\frac{1}{4}$ lb	Lanolin
150 g	Magnesium sulfate
3 g	Mannose (optional)
1 g	Malachite green
5 g	DL-methionine
5 g	Methylene blue
1 qt	Mineral oil
16 g	Mold inhibitor (Tegosept or equivalent)
1 g	Para-aminobenzoic acid
5 g	Peptone (optional)

Quantity	Chemicals
10 g	Potassium chloride
100 g	Potassium hydroxide
100 g	Potassium iodide
75 g	Potassium nitrate
225 g	Potassium phosphate, monobasic
10 g	Potassium phosphate, dibasic
5 g	Purine (optional)
5 g	Pyrimidine (optional)
20 mg	Pyridoxine HCl (vitamin B_6)
1 g	Safranin
1 qt	Sesame oil
· 10 g	Sodium azide
10 g	Sodium carbonate
1 lb	Sodium chloride (noniodized table salt)
140 g	Sodium hydroxide pellets
100 g	Sodium phosphate, monobasic
100 g	Sodium phosphate, dibasic
50 g	D sorbitol
1 lb	Starch, corn
1 pt	Sulfuric acid, concentrated
5 lb	Sucrose, commercial grade
5 g	Thiourea
1 roll	Tes-Tape
500 mg	Testosterone propionate
1 g	L-thyroxin
1 g	L-triiodothyronine

5 g	2,3,5-triphenyltetrazolium chloride
10 g	Tryptone
15 g	Yeast extract
1 g	Zinc sulfate

Quantity	Biological Materials
	Animals
26	Chicks (1- or 2-day old cockerels of the same strain)
26	Chicks (1- or 2-day old pullets of the same strain)
10	Frogs, mature females
30–50	Frogs, mature males (check number required for particular season)
25	Tadpoles, small *Rana pipiens* or *clamitans* (if not saved from earlier investigation)
10	Tadpoles, large (hindbud stage)
300	Fly pupae (*Phormia regina Meig*)
	Microorganisms
1 culture	*Aspergillus nidulans,* strain 180
1 culture	*Aspergillus nidulans,* strain 183
1 culture	*Bacillus subtilis*
1 culture	*Sarcina lutea*
1 culture	*Serratia marcescens,* strains D1, 933, and WCF
12 pkgs	Dry yeast (active)
	Plant Items
2200	Seeds, Alaska pea
300	Corn grains
3 g	Great Lakes lettuce seeds
3 g	Grand Rapids lettuce seeds

Quantity	Biological Materials (Plants)
640	Kentucky Wonder bean seeds
620	Little Marvel dwarf pea seeds
900	Oats (*Avena sativa*), variety Victory, seedlings
450	Pinto bean seeds
50	Sorghum RS610 seeds

Quantity	Miscellaneous Materials
2 rolls	Aluminum foil (18 inches $\times$ 20 inches)
5 lbs	Baby chick feed
25	Boxes, sweater or shirt (for germination trays)
25	Boxes, corrugated (for growing flats, 3 inches to 5 inches high)
—	Box and heat source for young chicks (if no brooder)
—	Bristle probe (bristles from an inexpensive paint brush mounted in a handle)
1 roll	Cellophane or plastic tape
—	Carbon dioxide source (CO_2 bottle with regulator or dry ice)
1 qt	Detergent, commercial
12	Flowerpots, 3 inches in diameter
1 bottle	Food coloring
1 gal	Hexol or Lysol
10	Jars, large and small mouth (gallon)
6	Light bulbs (7.5 watts)
6	Light bulbs (15 watts)
6	Light bulbs (50 watts)
5 rolls	Masking tape
1 qt	Molasses
4	Pans, Pyrex cake (8 inches)

—	Paper towels
1 set	Pens, marking
100	Pipe cleaners, colored
2 pkgs	Razor blades
1 lb	Washed sand (if no glass beads)
1 box	Saran wrap
1	Storage container, plastic (5 gal)
1 cu yd	Vermiculite
5 gal	Water, distilled

APPENDIX B

LABORATORY REQUIREMENTS FOR EACH INVESTIGATION

In the following lists the quantities specified are requirements for each team unless they are preceded by an asterisk, which indicates that the quantity is for the class.

When quantities are not specified, review the investigation and determine the amount required.

INVESTIGATION 1   THE PROBLEM

1 pkg	dry yeast
1	100 ml graduate cylinder
10	test tubes (22 mm × 175 mm)
10	test tubes (13 mm × 100 mm)
—	test tube racks
—	cotton stoppers
* 1 pt	commercial molasses
* 1	1000 ml Erlenmeyer flask
*—	distilled water

INVESTIGATION 2   A NEW HYPOTHESIS

10	test tubes (22 mm × 175 mm)
10	test tubes (13 mm × 100 mm)
1	100 ml graduate cylinder
1	millimeter ruler
—	test tube rack
* 2	Erlenmeyer flasks (125 ml or 250 ml)
* 1	1000 ml Erlenmeyer flask

* 1 pkg	dry yeast (active)
*—	sucrose

INVESTIGATION 3   A STUDY OF VARIABLES

10	test tubes (22 mm × 175 mm)
10	test tubes (13 mm × 100 mm)
1	test tube rack
2	Erlenmeyer flasks (125 ml or 250 ml)
*—	sucrose
*—	molasses
* 1	1000 ml Erlenmeyer flask
* 1 pkg	dry yeast (active)

INVESTIGATION 4   A NEW PROBLEM

Materials are the same as those used in Investigations 1, 2, and 3.

INVESTIGATION 5   TEMPERATURE AS A VARIABLE

10	test tubes (22 mm × 175 mm)
10	test tubes (13 mm × 100 mm)
—	a 4% solution (by weight) of glucose in distilled water
1 pkg	dry yeast (active)
2	temperature gradient tube holders, one with $7\frac{1}{2}$ watt bulbs and another with a 15 watt bulb
—	thermometers calibrated from 0°C to 100°C
*—	millimeter rulers
* 1	1000 ml Erlenmeyer flask
*—	refrigerator
* 1	incubator with a constant temperature of 20°C to 25°C

INVESTIGATION 6 **ENZYME CONCENTRATION AS A VARIABLE**

7	test tubes (22 mm × 175 mm)
7	test tubes (13 mm × 100 mm)
1 pkg	dry yeast (active)
1	250 ml Erlenmeyer flask
—	a 4% solution (by weight) of glucose in distilled water
1	graduated 1 ml pipette
1	graduated 10 ml pipette

INVESTIGATION 7 **MEASURING RATES OF RESPIRATION**

1	volumeter (complete)
1	thermometer
100	Alaska pea seeds
1	germination tray (sweater box and polyethylene liner)
1	100 ml graduate cylinder
—	glass beads
3	150 ml beakers
—	solution of vegetable dye (food color)
—	cotton
—	ascarite
—	eyedroppers

INVESTIGATION 8 **GROWTH OF A YEAST POPULATION**

1	microscope
1	hemocytometer (counting chamber)
1	250 ml flask

2	150 ml flasks
1	volumetric pipette, 1 ml accuracy
—	mechanical counters
* 1	1000 ml flask
* 1 pkg	dry yeast (active)
*—	12°C and 22°C incubators

INVESTIGATION 9	**DETERMINING MUTATION FREQUENCY IN BACTERIA**
1	stock culture of *Serratia marcescens,* strain D1
11	tubes of *S. marcescens* broth
1	sterile pipette, 1 to 10 ml size
8	sterile petri plates with 15 ml *S. marcescens* agar each
6	sterile 9 ml water blanks in test tubes
1	glass dally (5 inch piece of rod)
1	wire loop
—	incubator

INVESTIGATION FOR FURTHER STUDY

—	peptone media
—	sugars media
—	purine
—	pyrimidine
—	yeast extract
—	mineral mixtures
—	ultraviolet light or X-ray source
—	suspension of *S. marcescens,* strain D1
—	*Bacillus subtilis* culture

—	hydrogen peroxide
—	Gram's stain
—	acetone
—	crystal violet
—	malachite green

INVESTIGATION 10   **THE INTERACTION OF TWO MUTANTS OF A BACTERIUM**

—	stock cultures of *S. marcescens,* strains 933, WCF, and D1
—	wire loop
4	petri plates with *S. marcescens* agar
4	tubes of sterile *S. marcescens* broth
—	incubator

INVESTIGATION 11   **A VERIFICATION OF RESULTS**

—	stock cultures of *S. marcescens,* strains 933 and WCF
3	tubes of *S. marcescens* broth
1	glass dally
3	petri plates with *S. marcescens* agar
—	incubator

INVESTIGATION 12   **A STUDY OF INTERACTIONS BETWEEN UNKNOWN MUTANTS**

—	stock cultures of WCF and white isolates from Investigation 10
3	tubes of *S. marcescens* broth
2	sterile Pyrex cake pans with aluminum foil covers
—	wire loop
200 ml	*S. marcescens* agar
—	incubator

INVESTIGATION 13   **PREPARATION OF A**
                      SCIENTIFIC PAPER

Materials are the same as those used in Investigations 10, 11, and 12.

INVESTIGATION 14   **CONFIRMATION OF STRAINS**
                      AND GENOTYPES

100 ml	sterile distilled water
50 ml	wetting solution
2	pipettes, 1 ml capacity
2	Pasteur pipettes fitted with rubber bulbs
3	test tubes, 10 and 20 ml capacity, plugged with cotton, aluminum foil, or slip-on metal caps
—	70% alcohol
—	autoclave
—	thermometer
—	cultures of *Aspergillus nidulans,* strains 180 and 183
—	inoculating needle
—	glass marking pen or wax pencil
2	dissecting needles (Mount a No. 13 sewing needle in a stick of balsa wood.)

INVESTIGATION 15   **HETEROKARYOSIS AND**
                      COMPLEMENTATION

—	microscope
—	hemocytometer
—	heavy spore cultures of *A. nidulans,* strains 180 and 183 (5 to 7 days old) in petri plates of YAG agar medium
—	sterile tube
—	transfer loop

3	test tubes, sterile
8	petri plates, sterile
1	inoculating needle
1	marking pen
100 ml	sterile distilled water
2	pipettes, sterile (1 ml capacity)
2	sterile Pasteur pipettes with rubber bulb
—	wire rack
2	dissecting needles, fine

INVESTIGATION 16 **GENETIC RECOMBINATION AT MEIOSIS**

—	dissecting microscope
—	dissecting needle
—	inoculating loop
—	marking pen
1	petri plate of 3% agar
—	glass dally
50 ml	95% alcohol
10	test tubes containing 8% saline solution
20	petri plates containing M media
10	petri plates of YAG media
—	refrigerator

INVESTIGATION 17 **SELECTION AND ISOLATION OF DIPLOIDS**

5	cultures YAG medium
7	plates of M medium with pyridoxine and biotin

8	plates of YAG medium
—	dissecting microscope
—	sterile wetting solution
—	sterile test tube
—	sterile Pasteur pipette
—	inoculating needle

INVESTIGATION 18   **GENETIC RECOMBINATION AT MITOSIS**

4	plates of YAG medium from Investigation 17
—	dissecting microscope
7	sterile plates of fresh YAG medium
7	sterile plates of M medium
—	inoculating needle

INVESTIGATION 19   **ENZYME ACTIVITY IN GERMINATING SEEDS**

—	corn grains, soaked
1	razor blade
3	culture dishes
50 ml	starch agar
1 roll	Tes-Tape
25 ml	tetrazolium solution
1	100 ml beaker

INVESTIGATION 20   **ISOLATION OF AN ENZYME**

2	plates of starch agar
2	petri plates or culture dishes

1 roll	Tes-Tape
25 ml	tetrazolium solution
1	razor blade

INVESTIGATION 21   **TESTING FOR SEED VIABILITY**

—	pea seeds
25 ml	tetrazolium chloride
2	100 ml beakers

INVESTIGATION 22   **EFFECTS OF LIGHT ON GERMINATION OF SEEDS**

—	Grand Rapids and Great Lakes lettuce seeds
—	germination trays
—	blue, green, and red filters or sheets of cellophane
—	daylight fluorescent light source
—	incandescent light source

INVESTIGATION 23   **THE EFFECTS OF DIFFERENT WAVELENGTHS OF LIGHT ON GERMINATION OF SEEDS**

The materials vary with each design, but germination trays, seeds, and a light source are necessary.

INVESTIGATION 24   **MINERAL REQUIREMENTS OF SORGHUM PLANTS**

8	test tubes (22 mm × 175 mm)
20	seeds of RS610 sorghum
—	cardboard box and styrofoam lid
—	mineral solutions (see Appendix C)

—	cotton for plugging test tubes
—	distilled water
—	detergent
—	germination tray and toweling
—	razor blade

PREPARATORY TECHNIQUE 1 — **OBTAINING FROG PITUITARIES**

1 to 10	male frogs
—	chloroform
—	cotton
1	fine scissors
1	fine forceps
—	10% Holtfreter's solution

PREPARATORY TECHNIQUE 2 — **INJECTING PITUITARIES**

—	hypodermic syringe and No. 18 needle
1 to 5	female frogs
—	plastic containers and lids
—	70% alcohol solution
—	cotton

PREPARATORY TECHNIQUE 3 — **FERTILIZATION *IN VITRO***

1	female frog previously injected with pituitary glands
1	male frog, mature
10	plastic dishes and covers
—	fine, sharp scissors

—	fine forceps
—	cotton
—	medicine dropper
—	10% Holtfreter's solution

PREPARATORY TECHNIQUE 4   **ESTABLISHING AND MAINTAINING FROG EMBRYO CULTURES**

—	temperature gradient box
10	plastic dishes
—	pond water or 10% Holtfreter's solution
—	*Elodea*
—	refrigerator
—	fertilized eggs from Preparatory Technique 3

INVESTIGATION 25   **DEVELOPMENT OF THE FROG EMBRYO**

10	plastic dishes with embryos from Preparatory Technique 4
—	lettuce or *Elodea*

INVESTIGATION 26   **OBSERVATION OF REGENERATING TISSUE**

1	fine scissors
1	fine forceps
6	tadpoles
6	petri plates
—	anesthetic MS-222 or Chloretone
—	lettuce or *Elodea* for tadpole food

INVESTIGATION 27   **HORMONAL CONTROL OF THE DEVELOPMENT OF FROG EMBRYOS**

7	flat culture dishes or large plastic bowls (1 liter capacity)
7	stones or bricks
1	1 liter graduated cylinder
—	stock solutions of thyroxin, triiodothyronine, and iodine
35	tadpoles
3	10 ml graduated pipettes
—	pond water

INVESTIGATION 28   **CONTROL OF DEVELOPMENT IN CHICKS**

5	1-day-old male chicks
5	1-day-old female chicks
*—	brooder or several boxes of sawdust and heat source
* 4	hypodermic syringes graduated to 0.1 ml with No. 21 or 22 needle
*—	solutions of hormones (testosterone propionate and chorionic gonadotrophin)
*—	chick food and water trays
*—	marking pencils
*—	colored pipe cleaners
*—	millimeter ruler
*—	scale or balance
*—	70% alcohol
*—	sesame oil
*—	centigram balance

INVESTIGATION 29	**THE GONADS OF HORMONE-TREATED CHICKS**
—	chick-killing jar and chloroform, or a scalpel, knife, or scissors
—	medium size scissors
—	sharp pointed forceps
—	small glass dishes and covers
—	paper toweling
—	centigram balance

INVESTIGATION 30	**THE EFFECT OF LIGHT ON THE GROWTH OF SEEDLINGS**
—	germination trays
—	Alaska pea seeds
—	sand or vermiculite
—	paper toweling

INVESTIGATION 31	**A BIOLOGICAL ASSAY**
—	*Avena sativa,* variety Victory, seedlings
—	germination box with red cellophane and light shield
—	indoleacetic acid
—	sucrose
—	coleoptile cutter
6	petri plates
—	millimeter ruler
1	10 ml pipette

INVESTIGATION 32	**EFFECT OF GIBBERELLIC ACID**
—	Alaska and Little Marvel pea seeds
4	4 inch flower pots or other containers

—	solution of gibberellic acid (100 mg per liter)
—	germination tray
—	sand and soil

		EFFECTS OF GROWTH

INVESTIGATION 33   EFFECTS OF GROWTH REGULATING SUBSTANCES ON PLANTS

60 to 80	pinto bean seeds
1	germination tray
21	bottles (baby food jars)
—	plant growth regulators (indoleacetic acid, indolebutyric acid, and gibberellic acid)
—	4% ethyl alcohol
—	lanolin
—	toothpicks
—	dropper pipettes

PREPARATORY TECHNIQUE 1   CULTURING BLOWFLIES

—	blowfly media in sterile mason jars
—	blowfly breeding cage (16 inches × 16 inches)
—	mosquito netting
2	petri plates
2	food dishes
—	water supply (petri plate, lid, and so on)
1	blowfly culture (about 300) or zoo cultures if you do not raise flies
—	mason jars with mosquito netting
—	sterile sawdust
—	constant temperature device and uniform lighting

PREPARATORY TECHNIQUE 2   ANESTHETIZING FLIES

—	CO_2 bottle and regulator
—	glass *y* tube
2	Erlenmeyer flasks
1	Buchner funnel
1	side arm flask
2	clamps
1	watch glass
—	rubber tubing

PREPARATORY TECHNIQUE 3   HANDLING FLIES

—	applicator sticks
—	wax
—	dissecting probes

INVESTIGATION 34   THE EFFECT OF FOOD CONTACT ON LOCOMOTION

—	fine pointed scissors
—	minimal diet solution (0.1 M sucrose)
—	filter paper or paper towel
—	24 hour dewinged flies
—	CO_2 anesthetic

INVESTIGATION 35   DETECTION OF FOOD

—	camel's hair brush
—	sucrose solutions (1 M and 0.5 M)
—	distilled water
—	24 hour dewinged flies (these may be the flies from Investigation 34)

INVESTIGATION 36   SENSITIVITY TO SUCROSE

50 to 100	flies
—	CO_2 anesthetic
—	applicator sticks
—	distilled water
—	water trough
—	paper towels
—	holder for applicator sticks
—	sucrose solutions (8 concentrations from 1 M to 0.008 M)

INVESTIGATION 37   THE RELATION OF FOOD SELECTION TO NUTRITION

—	graduate cylinders
—	feeding pipettes
—	solution of 1 M arabinose
—	solution of 1 M sorbitol

INVESTIGATION 38   SELECTION OF PROTEIN AND SUGAR

2	wide mouth jars
—	liver
—	sucrose
50 flies	flies (4 days old)
—	CO_2 anesthetic

APPENDIX C

PREPARATION OF CHEMICAL SOLUTIONS

A. General Information

Solutions are used in many scientific investigations; therefore, it is necessary to become familiar with what certain solutions contain and with some of the techniques used in preparing them. In the laboratory one uses many different solutions in varying concentrations. The term *concentration* means the amount of one substance that is contained within a definite amount of another substance. There are numerous way of expressing concentration, some of which follow:

1. Percent Concentration

The number of parts by weight or volume of one substance contained by 100 parts by weight or volume of solution.

2. Parts per Million

The number of parts of one substance contained in one million parts of solution; usually expressed by weight; 1 mg/liter = 1 ppm.

3. Molarity

The number of moles of one substance contained in one liter of solution. *Mole* means the molecular weight of a substance expressed in grams. *Liter* is a unit of volume in the metric system.

The terms *solute* and *solvent* are used to designate the components of a solution. The solute is the substance that is dissolved in the solvent. A *solution* is obtained when a solute is dissolved in a solvent.

The following conversion factors will aid you in understanding the discussion of a *dilution,* which is used to obtain weights of amounts of chemicals too small to be weighed on the balances in the laboratory:

$$1 \text{ gram (g)} = 1000 \text{ milligrams (mg)} = 1,000,000 \text{ micrograms } (\mu g)$$
$$1 \text{ mg} = 1000 \text{ } \mu g$$
$$1 \text{ liter} = 1000 \text{ milliliters (ml)}$$

B. Preparation of Solutions of Low Concentrations by Serial Dilutions

The scientist uses extremely small quantities of chemicals—amounts less than the finest balances can weigh accurately. For accurate measurement, then, it is necessary to start with a volume of a solution containing an amount of the chemical which can be weighed accurately. Assume you have prepared 1 liter of a uniform solution containing 1 g of solute. Since 1000 ml of this solution contains 1000 mg of the chemical, 1 ml contains 1 mg. 1 mg is less than can be weighed accurately on a triple beam balance. Can you see how *volume measurements* may be used to obtain the weights of small quantities of a substance?

Even smaller weights of the chemical can be obtained easily by preparing more dilute solutions. Assume that 1 ml of the above solution (thus, 1 mg, or 1000 μg, of the chemical) is diluted in 999 ml of distilled water. We can now obtain 1 μg of the chemical by using 1 ml of this second solution. This is known as the serial dilution technique.

Serial dilution techniques may be applied to such diverse materials as chemicals, microbial cultures, serums, and so on, in the laboratory. In this case we have used 1000-fold dilutions, but any convenient dilution factor (2-fold, 4-fold, 10-fold, and so on) may be employed as the occasion demands. Solutions which contain a known weight per volume, and which are kept on hand to provide a definite quantity of material, are often called *stock solutions.*

C. Sterilizing Solutions

In biological work it is often necessary to use solutions which do not contain pathogens (disease-causing organisms). This is particularly true when one is working with microbes or with solutions which are to be injected into living tissue. Two common methods of heating solutions for such studies are autoclaving and pasteurizing.

Autoclaving. Autoclaving sterilizes (kills all life) in the material so treated. To autoclave, prepare the solution and place it in the container. Place a cap on the container, loosely so that steam can escape, and place it in an autoclave or pressure cooker. Bring the temperature of the autoclave to 120°C and maintain it for 20 minutes. If a pressure cooker is used, a pressure of 15 pounds will approximate this temperature. After 20 minutes, remove the heat source and allow the apparatus to cool. Allowing the pressure to go down suddenly may cause the caps or stoppers to blow off, so be certain to allow the apparatus to cool slowly by itself. Remove the solution from the autoclave or pressure cooker and secure the caps or stoppers immediately.

Pasteurizing. Pasteurization kills unwanted organisms but usually does not kill all life in the product. Prepare the solution and place it in the container. Cap it loosely so that air resulting from its expanding contents can escape. Place the container of solution in a pan of water on a heat source or in a constant-temperature water bath and bring the temperature of the water to 62°C. Maintain this temperature for 30 minutes, then remove the container from the water and secure the cap or stopper. This is the temperature and time often used for pasteurizing milk. Other products may require different temperatures and times to be pasteurized effectively.

D. Preparation of Solutions

1. Tetrazolium Test Solution

2,3,5-triphenyltetrazolium
chloride   0.5 g
Distilled water   10.0 ml

Solution should be used within 3 to 6 hours after its preparation.

2. Iodine-Potassium Iodide Solution

Iodine (crystals)   5.0 g
Potassium iodide   10.0 g
Distilled water   100.0 ml

Dilute this stock solution one part to ten parts water before using.

3. Growth Regulator Solution

Specific regulator   100.0 mg
Ethyl alcohol (95% absolute)   40.0 ml
Distilled water   960.0 ml

This is for the preparation of a solution of 100 ppm of growth regulator (indoleacetic acid, indolebutyric acid, and gibberellic acid). For each separate solution, dissolve the regulator in the alcohol and dilute with water, stirring constantly.

5. Growth Regulator Paste

Specific regulator   0.1 g
Lanolin   9.9 g

For a preparation of a 1.0% growth regulator paste, melt lanolin in a small beaker placed in a water bath and add regulator, stirring for several minutes. (For a 0.1% paste, use 1.0 g of the 1.0% preparation and 9.0 g of lanolin.)

6. Thyroid Hormone Solutions

a. *Thyroxin Stock Solution.* Dissolve 0.1 g thyroxin in 10 ml of 0.1 M sodium hydroxide and combine this with 90 ml of distilled water. Combine 1 ml of this solution with 1 liter of distilled water to prepare the final stock solution which contains 1 μg of thyroxin per ml.

50 μg/liter solution: Combine 50 ml of thyroxin stock solution with 950 ml of pond water.

25 μg/liter solution: Combine 25 ml of thyroxin stock solution with 975 ml of pond water.

10 μg/liter solution: Combine 10 ml of thyroxin stock solution with 990 ml of pond water.

b. *Triiodothyronine Stock Solution.* Substitute triiodothyronine for thyroxin and follow the directions given for preparing the thyroxin stock solution.

c. *Iodine Stock Solution.* Dissolve 0.1 g of iodine crystals in 10 ml of alcohol, and combine this with 90 ml of distilled water into which has been dissolved 0.1 g potassium iodide. Combine 1 ml of this solution with 1 liter of water to prepare the final stock solution which contains 1 μg of iodine per ml of solution.

2 μg/liter solution: Combine 2 ml of iodine stock solution with 1 liter of pond water.

1 μg/liter solution: Combine 1 ml of iodine stock solution with 1 liter of pond water.

d. *Thiourea Culture Solution.* Prepare a 3.3 g/liter culture solution by dissolving 3.3 g of thiourea in 1 liter of pond water.

7. Holtfreter's Solution

a. *Standard Stock Solution.* Combine 3.5 g sodium chloride, 0.05 g potassium chloride, and 0.2 g sodium bicarbonate with 1 liter of distilled or deionized water.

b. *10% Holtfreter's Solution.* Prepare this solution by combining 1 part standard stock solution with 9 parts distilled water.

8. Narcotic Solution

a. *100 mg/liter Chloretone.* Dissolve 100 mg of Chloretone (1,1,1-trichloro-2-methyl-2-propanol) in 1 liter of pond water or 10% Holtfreter's solution.

b. *50 mg/liter Chloretone.* Combine equal volumes of the above solution and either pond water or 10% Holtfreter's solution.

9. Respiratory Inhibitor

a. *Sodium Azide Stock Solution.* Dissolve 780 mg sodium oxyide (NaN_3) in 1 liter of acidified physiological saline (prepared by combining 2 parts 0.9% sodium chloride with 1 part of the phosphate buffer solution C listed under No. 11). This will give a 1×10^{-2} (0.01) M sodium azide solution.

b. *1 × 10⁻³ M Sodium Azide Solution.* 1×10^{-3} M Sodium Azide Solution. Combine 100 ml of stock solution with 1 liter of acidified saline.

c. *1 × 10⁻⁴ M Sodium Azide Solution.* 1×10^{-4} M Sodium Azide Solution. Combine 10 ml of stock solution with 1 liter of acidified saline.

10. Phosphate Buffer Solution

a. *Solution A.* Dissolve 9.5 g of disodium phosphate (Na_2HPO_4) in 1 liter of distilled or deionized water.

b. *Solution B.* Dissolve 9.07 g of monopotassium phosphate (KH_2PO_4) in 1 liter of distilled or deionized water.

c. *Solution C.* Prepare an acid solution with a pH of 5.8 by combining 7.8 parts of Solution A with 92.2 parts of Solution B.

11. Sex Hormones

a. *Testosterone Injection Solution.* Dissolve 250 mg of testosterone propionate in 10 ml of sesame oil. Place this solution in a serum vial and pasteurize it.

b. *Chorionic Gonadotrophic Injection Solution.* Chorionic gonadotrophin will be supplied in a sealed vial containing 500 Cortland-Nelson units (10,000 international units).

12. Physiological Saline

0.9% Saline Solution. Dissolve 9 g of sodium chloride in 1 liter of distilled water.

13. Preparation of Staining Materials

a. *Ammonium Oxalate-Crystal Violet Solution (for Gram's stain).* Make one solution by dissolving 2 g of crystal violet in 20 ml of 95% ethanol. Make a second solution by dissolving 0.8 g of ammonium oxalate in 80 ml of distilled water. Then mix the two solutions together and store.

b. *Gram's Iodine Solution.* Grind 1 g of iodine crystals and 2 g of potassium iodide in a mortar until they are finely dispersed. Then dissolve the mixture in 300 ml of distilled water.

c. *Safranin Counterstain.* Dissolve 0.25 g of safranin in 10 ml of 95%

ethanol. Then add 90 ml of distilled water to bring the volume up to 100 ml of solution.

d. *Methylene Blue (simple stain).* Dissolve 1 g of methylene blue in 99 ml of distilled water.

14. Preparation of IAA Stock Solutions

A stock solution of 100 mg/liter indoleacetic acid is prepared by dissolving 100 mg of indoleacetic acid in 1 to 2 ml of 95% ethyl alcohol and adding approximately 900 ml of water. Warm the mixture gently on a *hot plate* or *steam bath* to evaporate the alcohol; then dilute it with distilled water to one liter. This solution should not be used after it is two weeks old. It should be stored in a refrigerator, preferably in a brown bottle or flask and covered with aluminum foil to exclude light.

For Investigation 31, dilutions are needed of 20.0, 2.0, 0.2, and 0.02 mg/liter of indoleacetic acid. The following procedure is an accurate way to make up these stock solutions. Take 200 ml of the 100 mg/liter stock solution and dilute it to 1 liter; this is the 20 mg/liter solution. Take 100 ml of the 20 mg/liter solution and dilute to 1 liter; this is the 2.0 mg/liter solution. Take 100 ml of the 2 mg/liter indoleacetic acid solution and dilute it to 1 liter; this is the 0.2 mg/liter solution. Take 100 ml of this solution and dilute it to 1 liter; this is the 0.02 mg/liter solution. It is not advisable to make all of the solutions from the 100 mg/liter indoleacetic acid stock solution since it is very difficult to measure accurately the smaller quantities involved. Each class will need about 100 ml of each of the final solutions.

15. Preparation of 4% Solutions of Carbohydrates

The following formula may be used to make up carbohydrate solutions:

Specific carbohydrate	40 g
Distilled water	960 ml

16. Gibberellic Acid Stock Solution

Gibberellic acid	100 mg
Ethyl alcohol	3 ml
Distilled water	1000 ml

The gibberellic acid stock solution (100 mg/liter) may be prepared by weighing out the gibberellic acid, dissolving it in the ethyl alcohol, and then diluting the resultant solution with distilled water to 1 liter.

E. Sorghum Plant Mineral Requirements.

Chemical	Amount	Amount of distilled or deionized water
1. $Ca(NO_3)_2 \cdot 4\ H_2O$	23.6 grams	200 ml
2. KNO_3	10.0 grams	200 ml
3. $MgSO_4 \cdot 7\ H_2O$	4.2 grams	300 ml
4. KH_2PO_4	4.2 grams	300 ml
5. $CaCl_2$	5.6 grams	100 ml
6. KCl	1.6 grams	200 ml
7. Iron chelate (iron ethylenediamine-tetra acetate)	1.0 gram	100 ml

8. Trace elements (A stock solution should be made up to contain the following salts in the concentrations shown.)

a. $MnCl_2 \cdot 4\ H_2O$	1.8 grams
b. H_3BO_3	2.8 grams
c. $ZnSO_4 \cdot 7\ H_2O$	0.22 grams*
d. $CuSO_4 \cdot 5\ H_2O$	0.08 grams*
e. $Na_2MoO_4 \cdot 2\ H_2O$.	0.025 grams*

   f. Distilled or deionized water to make 1,000 ml.

* The difficulty in weighing these small amounts of material directly can be avoided by using aliquots of more concentrated solutions of each. For example,

Weigh out:	Dissolve in:	Use:
2.2 grams of $ZnSO_4 \cdot 7\ H_2O$	100 ml of water	10 ml per liter
0.8 grams of $CuSO_4 \cdot 5\ H_2O$	100 ml of water	10 ml per liter
2.5 grams of $Na_2MoO_4 \cdot 2\ H_2O$	100 ml of water	1 ml per liter

   Prepare the four mineral culture solutions in which you will grow the plants. Add each of the indicated stock solutions to about 500 ml of distilled or deionized water and then add enough water to make a total of one liter. (If you mix the stock solutions without diluting them, precipitates are likely to form, and these may be difficult to redissolve.)

Stock solution	Number of milliliters to be added for 1 liter of culture solution			
	Complete	Minus N	Minus P	Minus Fe
Ca(NO$_3$)$_2$ · 4 H$_2$O	10	—	10	10
KNO$_3$	10	—	10	10
MgSO$_4$ · 7 H$_2$O	10	10	10	10
KH$_2$PO$_4$	10	10	—	10
CaCl$_2$	—	10	—	—
KCl	—	10	10	—
Iron chelate	10	10	10	—
Trace element stock	10	10	10	10
Water (distilled or deionized) enough to make:	1 liter	1 liter	1 liter	1 liter

APPENDIX D

PREPARATION OF CULTURE MEDIA

Dehydrated growth media for microorganisms are commercially available. Commonly used media such as "nutrient agar," "nutrient broth," "potato dextrose agar," and others, can be purchased in this form. In addition, the components of many of these media may be purchased separately, including beef, yeast or malt extracts, peptone, and agar. Bouillon cubes are a dehydrated product, inexpensive and readily available in groceries. They need only be diluted three to four times more than called for on the label directions to serve as an excellent medium for many bacteria.

Although less convenient to prepare than dehydrated ones, "homemade" media are cheaper and sometimes better. Moreover, it is necessary on occasion to make media that are not available commercially. Detailed directions for the preparation of many media are provided in the references. Some simple, yet effective, media may be prepared from common food materials. Pieces of potato, turnip, and other bland tuber and root vegetables serve as a substrate upon which many bacteria can be grown. Boiled extracts of hay, lettuce, and other plant materials also furnish excellent media for growth of certain microorganisms. Sterilization of most media may be accomplished by autoclaving at 121°C for 15 to 20 minutes.

A. Procedures for Preparing Media

Media may be made in less than liter quantities by proportioning volumes and weights. To prepare either slants or tubes of medium, make up the medium as directed and heat by placing the flask in boiling water or in an autoclave with steam on and door slightly ajar. The liquified medium can be dispensed with a pipette to tubes; the plugged tubes are then autoclaved for sterilization. If slants are needed, the tubes are tilted while the medium is still in liquid form after sterilization. Otherwise, the sterilized medium is allowed to harden in upright tubes.

Pipettes should be sterilized by dry heat in stainless steel cans made for this purpose or wrapped in aluminum foil. It is possible to sterilize pipettes in the autoclave, by wrapping each one in newspaper. The pipettes will be wet but usable.

The glass dally is made by cutting pieces of solid glass tubing into suitable lengths of about 6 inches long. Then heat each in a bunsen burner to get an angle, so that the horizontal segment will be about 1.5 inches long.

Pasteur pipettes are prepared by heating pieces of glass tubing and drawing the ends apart while hot. The drawn end must be long enough to reach into test tubes for sucking up and ejecting the suspension of conidia. Pasteur pipettes may be sterilized in very long test tubes.

Plastic petri plates are less expensive than glass plates and are sterile when they arrive. When large orders are placed, volume discounts bring the price down to a still lower level. Do not attempt to sterilize plastic plates, for they melt at autoclave temperatures.

B. Formulas for Routine Microbiological Media Used in this Course

1. Fly Culture Medium

The culture medium used for raising flies consists of the following ingredients:

Bacto-agar	40 g
Whole powdered milk	200 g
Tegosept (mold inhibitor)*	16 ml
Dry active yeast	200 g
Boiling water	2 l

This will make enough for approximately 16 pint jars. Sterilize bottles and caps, and fill the jar slightly less than one half full of medium. Each jar will accommodate about 100 eggs covered with sifted, sterilized sawdust.

2. Nutrient Broth

Beef extract	3.0 g
Peptone	5.0 g
Distilled water	1000.0 ml

(Adjust pH from 6.8 to 7.2.)

3. Nutrient Agar

Beef extract	3.0 g
Peptone	5.0 g
Distilled water	1000.0 ml

(Adjust pH from 6.8 to 7.2.)

Add the above solution to 15 g of agar.

4. *Serratia marcescens* Agar

Add 0.05% glycerol to nutrient agar before sterilizing.

*Any other mold inhibitor in appropriate amount may be used.

5. Starch Agar

Agar	6.0 g
Corn starch	3.5 g
Distilled water	500.0 ml

Bring the mixture to a boil, stir briskly to dissolve.

6. Tryptone Glucose Agar

Tryptone	5.0 g
Yeast extract	2.5 g
Glucose	1.0 g
Agar	15.0 g
Distilled water	1000.0 ml

(Adjust pH from 6.8 to 7.2.)

7. YAG Medium

Yeast extract	5.0 g
Glucose	20.0 g
Agar	15.0 g
Distilled water	1000.0 ml

(Adjust pH from 6.5 to 7.0.)

The pH of microbiological media should be adjusted to their speci-fied values before they are used. This may be done by having on hand 1 N solutions of sodium hydroxide (NaOH) and sulfuric acid (H_2SO_4), and some pH paper. After dissolving all the medium in-gredients, take a sample of known volume from the medium (say 10 ml from a liter of medium) and check its pH. If no adjustment is necessary, proceed to sterilize the medium. If the sample is too acid, carefully pipette the necessary volume of 1 N sodium hydroxide to bring it to the proper pH. If it is too basic, add the needed amount of sulfuric acid. Now calculate the amount of acid or base needed to adjust the entire batch. Add this amount to the medium, recheck its pH, and if it is correct, proceed to sterilize. Some media may undergo pH changes during autoclaving. Check for this change by aseptically removing a sample of known size of the sterile medium and finding its pH. If pH adjustment is needed in sterile media, the acid or base used for this purpose must, of course, also be sterile.

8. M (Minimal) Medium for *Aspergillus nidulans*

To make the M (minimal) medium, prepare bottles of stock solu-tions A through F, and label carefully.

Prepare the medium by adding the indicated amounts of each stock solution to a 1 liter graduate. The total volume of the stock solutions added will be 162 ml. Next add 835 ml of distilled water and pour into a 2-liter flask. Now add,

$$\text{Glucose} \qquad 20 \text{ g}$$
$$\text{Bacto-agar*} \quad 18 \text{ g}$$

thus bringing the concentration of glucose in the medium to 2.0% and the concentration of agar to 1.8%.

Solution	Amount of solute in stock solution	Amount of stock solution/liter of medium	Concentration of minimal solution	
A KNO_3	37.5 g/liter	40 ml	1.5	g/liter
B $Ca(NO_3)_2 \cdot 4\,H_2O$	37.5 g/liter	40 ml	1.5	g/liter
C $MgSO_4 \cdot 7\,H_2O$	60.0 g/liter	40 ml	2.4	g/liter
D KH_2PO_4	60.0 g/liter	40 ml	2.4	g/liter
E H_3BO_3 $MnSO_4 \cdot 4\,H_2O$ $CuSO_4$ $ZnSO_4 \cdot 7\,H_2O$	1.0 g/liter 1.0 g/liter 0.1 g/liter 0.1 g/liter	1 ml	0.001 g/liter 0.001 g/liter 0.0001 g/liter 0.0001 g/liter	
F $FeCl_3$	4.0 g/100 ml (Keep in brown bottle in refrigerator.)	1 ml	0.04	g/liter

Autoclave the medium at 15 lb for 15 minutes. Start timing *after* the autoclave reaches 15 pounds. Do not pour the medium immediately from the autoclaved flask, but wait until it cools. The medium remains liquid until the temperature drops slightly below 45°C.

9. Supplements for M Medium

Genetic mutants require supplementation of the M medium to compensate for their genetic deficiency. The simplest method of supple-

*Bacto-agar is a product of Difco Laboratories, Inc., Detroit, Michigan. Other agars of high purity may also be used.

menting the M medium is to use stock solutions of the supplements. Add 1 ml of each supplement needed by a particular strain to the petri plate just prior to pouring the M medium into the plate. The following stock solutions are sufficient for approximately 100 plates:

methionine	500.0 mg/100 ml
adenine	40.0 mg/100 ml
para-aminobenzoic acid	2.0 mg/100 ml
pyridoxine	0.2 mg/100 ml
biotin	0.1 mg/100 ml

The solutions are made in distilled water in a pyrex bottle that can be closed with a screw cap. The bottles of solutions are sterilized with media in an autoclave, leaving the cap loose. After sterilizing, the cap is tightened and the solutions are stored in a refrigerator. Sterilized pipettes should be used in transferring the supplements from the stock bottles.

APPENDIX E

MAINTENANCE OF LIVING ORGANISMS

A. Maintaining Microorganisms in Culture

An organism can be maintained in culture for extended periods of time once it has been provided with a good medium for growth. Before attempting any of the procedures outlined below, the organisms must be permitted to develop on the medium until there is evidence of vigorous growth. In most cases two or three days growth after inoculation should suffice, but certain slow-growing organisms should be incubated longer. (See table on growth periods for representative bacteria.) When the microbe has grown sufficiently, one of the following techniques can be used to preserve the culture.

1. Storage at Cold Temperatures

A temperature of 4°C will maintain many microbes in a viable form for months. Some, however, will not survive under these conditions, so their viability at cold temperatures should be checked.

2. Storage Under Reduced Oxygen Tension

Dip a cork which fits into the culture tube into alcohol and flame it so that it is sterilized. Push it down the test tube containing the culture until it rests about an inch above the culture. Replace the cotton plug. If the cork fits tightly enough, it will restrict evaporation and access of oxygen, and cultures will last for six months.

3. "Pliofilm-Coating."

Push the cotton stopper into the neck of the test tube so that a small tuft remains for you to hold for its withdrawl. Wrap "Pliofilm" or the equivalent around the mouth of the test tube in order to prevent the agar's drying out.

4. Soil-Preservation*

Autoclave about a quarter-inch of soil in a test tube for at least half an hour. Transfer a rich suspension of the organism you wish to store, and mix it with the soil. This technique is one of the most effec-

---

* This technique is recommended as being most satisfactory.

tive and easiest to use, and works with a large number of organisms, including actinomycetes, fungi and some algae.

5. Storage Under Mineral Oil

Autoclave a bottle of "Nujol," or some other fine grade mineral oil, for an hour. Carefully pipette enough of this sterile oil over the surface of your culture so that about a half-inch of oil rests above the highest part of the agar. This technique, as well as the soil method, will preserve the viability of microorganisms, in some cases for years.

B. Table of Microorganism, Media, and Growth Time

Bacterium	Medium	Time for growth at room temperature (days)
Aspergillus nidulans	Potato dextrose agar	3–5
Bacillus subtilis	Tryptone glucose yeast	2
Sarcina lutea	Tryptone glucose yeast extract agar	3
Serratia marcescens	Tryptone glucose yeast extract agar	2
Staphylococcus albus	Tryptone glucose yeast extract agar	3

C. Culture of Microbes Required for this Course

1. *Aspergillus nidulans*

a. *A. nidulans,* strain 180. *w-3 pdx bio met-1 ade-*20 (white spores requiring pyridoxine, biotin, methionine, and adenine)
b. *A. nidulans,* strain 183. *y pdx bio pab* (yellow spores, requiring pyridoxine, biotin, and para-aminobenzoic acid)

The white strain will turn brown in old cultures and the yellow strain, dark yellow. Growth is good at ordinary room temperature but is somewhat more rapid at 31–33°C.

2. *Serratia marcescens*

Wild type, D1; and colorless mutants, 933, and WCF

3. *Saccharomyces cerevisiae*

As dried Fleischmann's active yeast

D. Care of Frog Embryos

Examine the embryos daily and remove any dead ones. When the water becomes cloudy or develops a foul odor, change it by decanting it through a strainer or fine mesh aquarium net which will catch embryos. Replace the old water with fresh water near the temperature of the original water. Replace any embryos which were caught in the strainer or net into the fresh water.

Frog embryos need no food until they have reached Shumway's Stage 25 of development. Once they reach this stage, follow the directions in "Maintaining Tadpoles in the Laboratory."

E. Induced Hibernation in Adult Frogs

Adult frogs can be maintained alive for several weeks in a moist environment in a refrigerator. Place about 6 frogs, along with plenty of wet cotton, in a gallon jar. Cover the jar with screen wire and place in a refrigerator. Examine the frogs periodically and remove any dead ones.

F. Maintaining Tadpoles in the Laboratory

Tadpoles are vegetarians and are relatively easily kept in the laboratory. They should be maintained in an aquarium or a similar container holding plenty of water. The water may be either pond water or tap water, but before using, tap water should be allowed to remain several days in the open so that the chlorine can escape.

Foods such as algae, boiled lettuce or spinach leaves, or any of the several canned, strained, green, baby-food vegetables are satisfactory for tadpoles. Algae have an advantage in that they do not cloud the water; therefore, the water can go as long as a week or more without changing. If the other foods are used, the water should be changed thirty minutes or so after each feeding. The animals should be fed three times a week, the amount depending on their size. Large tadpoles can eat as much as a teaspoon of vegetable matter per feeding.

G. Maintaining Baby Chicks in the Laboratory

A custom brooder is best for this work, but if one is not available, baby chicks can be kept in practically any warm enclosure. For the hormone work, a hair dryer with a brooder thermostat serves well as a heat source. (An electric light bulb cannot be used since the chicks must not be exposed to continuous light.) The chicks must be fed and watered daily. Regular baby chick feed from a feed store is best; however, finely ground cereals such as corn meal, rolled oats, or dried baby food cereal are satisfactory substitutes. A commercial feeding tray and watering device are the best appliances for maintaining a clean environment.

APPENDIX F

MATH TABLES

Common Logarithms

N	0	1	2	3	4	5	6	7	8	9
10	0000	0043	0086	0128	0170	0212	0253	0294	0334	0374
11	0414	0453	0492	0531	0569	0607	0645	0682	0719	0755
12	0792	0828	0864	0899	0934	0969	1004	1038	1072	1106
13	1139	1173	1206	1239	1271	1303	1335	1367	1399	1430
14	1461	1492	1523	1553	1584	1614	1644	1673	1703	1732
15	1761	1790	1818	1847	1875	1903	1931	1959	1987	2014
16	2041	2068	2095	2122	2148	2175	2201	2227	2253	2279
17	2304	2330	2355	2380	2405	2430	2455	2480	2504	2529
18	2553	2577	2601	2625	2648	2672	2695	2718	2742	2765
19	2788	2810	2833	2856	2878	2900	2923	2945	2967	2989
20	3010	3032	3054	3075	3096	3118	3139	3160	3181	3201
21	3222	3243	3263	3284	3304	3324	3345	3365	3385	3404
22	3424	3444	3464	3483	3502	3522	3541	3560	3579	3598
23	3617	3636	3655	3674	3692	3711	3729	3747	3766	3784
24	3802	3820	3838	3856	3874	3892	3909	3927	3945	3962
25	3979	3997	4014	4031	4048	4065	4082	4099	4116	4133
26	4150	4166	4183	4200	4216	4232	4249	4265	4281	4298
27	4314	4330	4346	4362	4378	4393	4409	4425	4440	4456
28	4472	4487	4502	4518	4533	4548	4564	4579	4594	4609
29	4624	4639	4654	4669	4683	4698	4713	4728	4742	4757
30	4771	4786	4800	4814	4829	4843	4857	4871	4886	4900
31	4914	4928	4942	4955	4969	4983	4997	5011	5024	5038
32	5051	5065	5079	5092	5105	5119	5132	5145	5159	5172
33	5185	5198	5211	5224	5237	5250	5263	5276	5289	5302
34	5315	5328	5340	5353	5366	5378	5391	5403	5416	5428
35	5411	5453	5465	5478	5490	5502	5514	5527	5539	5551
36	5563	5575	5587	5599	5611	5623	5635	5647	5658	5670
37	5682	5694	5705	5717	5729	5740	5752	5763	5775	5786
38	5798	5809	5821	5832	5843	5855	5866	5877	5888	5899
39	5911	5922	5933	5944	5955	5966	5977	5988	5999	6010
40	6021	6031	6042	6053	6064	6075	6085	6096	6107	6117
41	6128	6138	6149	6160	6170	6180	6191	6201	6212	6222
42	6232	6243	6253	6263	6274	6284	6294	6304	6314	6325
43	6335	6345	6355	6365	6375	6385	6395	6405	6415	6425
44	6435	6444	6454	6464	6474	6484	6493	6503	6513	6522

N	0	1	2	3	4	5	6	7	8	9
45	6532	6542	6551	6561	6571	6580	6590	6599	6609	6618
46	6628	6637	6646	6656	6665	6675	6684	6693	6702	6712
47	6721	6730	6739	6749	6758	6767	6776	6785	6794	6803
48	6812	6821	6830	6839	6848	6857	6866	6875	6884	6893
49	6902	6911	6920	6928	6937	6946	6955	6964	6972	6981
50	6990	6998	7007	7016	7024	7033	7042	7050	7059	7067
51	7076	7084	7093	7101	7110	7118	7126	7135	7143	7152
52	7160	7168	7177	7185	7193	7202	7210	7218	7226	7235
53	7243	7251	7259	7267	7275	7284	7292	7300	7308	7316
54	7324	7332	7340	7348	7356	7364	7372	7380	7388	7396
55	7404	7412	7419	7427	7435	7443	7451	7459	7466	7474
56	7482	7490	7497	7505	7513	7520	7528	7536	7543	7551
57	7559	7566	7574	7582	7589	7597	7604	7612	7619	7627
58	7634	7642	7649	7657	7664	7672	7679	7686	7694	7701
59	7709	7716	7723	7731	7738	7745	7752	7760	7767	7774
60	7782	7789	7796	7803	7810	7818	7825	7832	7839	7846
61	7853	7860	7868	7875	7882	7889	7896	7903	7910	7917
62	7924	7931	7938	7945	7952	7959	7966	7973	7980	7987
63	7993	8000	8007	8014	8021	8028	8035	8041	8048	8055
64	8062	8069	8075	8082	8089	8096	8102	8109	8116	8122
65	8129	8136	8142	8149	8156	8162	8169	8176	8182	8189
66	8195	8202	8209	8215	8222	8228	8235	8241	8248	8254
67	8261	8267	8274	8280	8287	8293	8299	8306	8312	8319
68	8325	8331	8338	8344	8351	8357	8363	8370	8376	8382
69	8388	8395	8401	8407	8414	8420	8426	8432	8439	8445
70	8451	8457	8463	8470	8476	8482	8488	8494	8500	8506
71	8513	8519	8525	8531	8537	8543	8549	8555	8561	8567
72	8573	8579	8585	8591	8597	8603	8609	8615	8621	8627
73	8633	8639	8645	8651	8657	8663	8669	8675	8681	8686
74	8692	8698	8704	8710	8716	8722	8727	8733	8739	8745
75	8751	8756	8762	8768	8774	8779	8785	8791	8797	8802
76	8808	8814	8820	8825	8831	8837	8842	8848	8854	8859
77	8865	8871	8876	8882	8887	8893	8899	8904	8910	8915
78	8921	8927	8932	8938	8943	8949	8954	8960	8965	8971
79	8976	8982	8987	8993	8998	9004	9009	9015	9020	9025
80	9031	9036	9042	9047	9053	9058	9063	9069	9074	9079
81	9085	9090	9096	9101	9106	9112	9117	9122	9128	9133
82	9138	9143	9149	9154	9159	9165	9170	9175	9180	9186
83	9191	9196	9201	9206	9212	9217	9222	9227	9232	9238
84	9243	9248	9253	9258	9263	9269	9274	9279	9284	9289

N	0	1	2	3	4	5	6	7	8	9
85	9294	9299	9304	9309	9315	9320	9325	9330	9335	9340
86	9345	9350	9355	9360	9365	9370	9375	9380	9385	9390
87	9395	9400	9405	9410	9415	9420	9425	9430	9435	9440
88	9445	9450	9455	9460	9465	9469	9474	9479	9484	9489
89	9494	9499	9504	9509	9513	9518	9523	9528	9533	9538
90	9542	9547	9552	9557	9562	9566	9571	9576	9581	9586
91	9590	9595	9600	9605	9609	9614	9619	9624	9628	9633
92	9638	9643	9647	9652	9657	9661	9666	9671	9675	9680
93	9685	9689	9694	9699	9703	9708	9713	9717	9722	9727
94	9731	9736	9741	9745	9750	9754	9759	9763	9768	9773
95	9777	9782	9786	9791	9795	9800	9805	9809	9814	9818
96	9823	9827	9832	9836	9841	9845	9850	9854	9859	9863
97	9868	9872	9877	9881	9886	9890	9894	9899	9903	9908
98	9912	9917	9921	9926	9930	9934	9939	9943	9948	9952
99	9956	9961	9965	9969	9974	9978	9983	9987	9991	9996

TABLE 10.   **Critical Values of χ^2**

Values of χ^2 equal to or greater than those tabulated occur by chance less frequently than the indicated level of p.

d.f.	$p = 0.9$	$p = 0.5$	$p = 0.2$	$p = 0.05$	$p = 0.01$	$p = 0.001$
1	.0158	.455	1.642	3.841	6.635	10.827
2	.211	1.386	3.219	5.991	9.210	13.815
3	.584	2.366	4.642	7.815	11.345	16.268
4	1.064	3.367	5.989	9.488	13.277	18.465
5	1.610	4.351	7.289	11.070	15.086	20.517
6	2.204	5.348	8.558	12.592	16.812	22.457
7	2.833	6.346	9.803	14.067	18.475	24.322
8	3.490	7.344	11.303	15.507	20.090	26.125
9	4.168	8.343	12.242	16.919	21.666	24.877
10	4.865	9.342	13.442	18.307	23.209	29.588

Note: The shading in this table emphasizes the area of increasing probability that the null hypothesis should be rejected; that is, the area of increased confidence that the two samples represent two different populations. In evaluating data from the Investigations in this course, p values of less than 0.05 will be considered as reason for rejection.

   Degrees of freedom. This expression refers to the value n − 1. It may be defined as the number of individuals or events, or sets of individuals or events, in a given sample which are free to vary.

   In chi-square tests, the degrees of freedom (d.f.) are one less than the number of attributes being observed, or n − 1, where n equals the number of attributes. If there are two attributes, the d. f. is 1.

TABLE 8. **Distribution of *t* Probability**

Degrees of Freedom	Probability 0.1	0.05	0.01	0.001
1	6.314	12.706	63.657	636.619
2	2.920	4.303	9.925	31.598
3	2.353	3.182	5.841	12.941
4	2.132	2.776	4.604	8.610
5	2.015	2.571	4.032	6.859
6	1.943	2.447	3.707	5.959
7	1.895	2.365	3.499	5.405
8	1.860	2.306	3.355	5.041
9	1.833	2.262	3.250	4.781
10	1.812	2.228	3.169	4.587
11	1.796	2.201	3.106	4.437
12	1.782	2.179	3.055	4.318
13	1.771	2.160	3.012	4.221
14	1.761	2.145	2.977	4.140
15	1.753	2.131	2.947	4.073
16	1.746	2.120	2.921	4.015
17	1.740	2.110	2.898	3.965
18	1.734	2.101	2.878	3.922
19	1.729	2.093	2.861	3.883
20	1.725	2.086	2.845	3.850
21	1.721	2.080	2.831	3.819
22	1.717	2.074	2.819	3.792
23	1.714	2.069	2.807	3.767
24	1.711	2.064	2.797	3.745
25	1.708	2.060	2.787	3.725
26	1.706	2.056	2.779	3.707
27	1.703	2.052	2.771	3.690
28	1.701	2.048	2.763	3.674
29	1.699	2.045	2.756	3.659
30	1.697	2.042	2.750	3.646
40	1.684	2.025	2.704	3.551
60	1.671	2.000	2.660	3.460
120	1.658	1.980	2.617	3.373
∞	1.645	1.960	2.576	3.291

Note: *The shading in this table emphasizes the areas of increasing probability that the null hypothesis should be rejected—that is, the areas of increased confidence that the two samples represent two different populations. In evaluating data from the Investigations in this course,* p *values of less than 0.05 will generally be considered as adequate for rejection.*

Source: Abridged from Table III of R. A. Fisher and F. Yates: *Statistical Tables for Biological, Agricultural, and Medical Research,* published by Oliver and Boyd Ltd., Edinburgh, by permission of the authors and publisher.

APPENDIX G

BIBLIOGRAPHY

ALPHABETICAL BIBLIOGRAPHY

Allee, Warder C. 1951. Cooperation among animals. Abelard-Schuman Ltd., New York. 233p.

————. Social life of animals. Beacon Press, Boston.

Allen, R. D. 1953. The moment of fertilization. Scientific American. June.

Arey, L. V. 1954. Developmental anatomy. W. B. Saunders Co., Philadelphia. 680p.

Armstrong, E. A. 1963. A study of bird song. Oxford University Press, New York. 335p.

Bailey, N. T. J. 1959. Statistical methods in biology. John Wiley and Sons, Inc., New York. 200p.

Balinsky, B. I. 1960. An introduction to embryology. W. B. Saunders Co., Philadelphia. 562p.

Barth, L. G. 1953. Embryology. Holt-Dryden, New York. 516p.

Beveridge, W. I. B. 1957. The art of scientific investigation. Vintage Books, New York. 178p.

Birney, Robert C., and **Richard C. Teeven.** 1961. Instinct. D. Van Nostrand Co., Inc., Princeton, N. J. 181p.

Bliss, E. L. (Editor). 1962. Roots of behavior. Harper and Row, New York. 339p.

Bonner, D., and **S. Mills.** 1964. Heredity. Prentice-Hall, Inc., Englewood Cliffs, N. J. 115p.

Braun, W. 1953. Bacterial genetics. W. B. Saunders Co., Philadelphia. 238p.

Brock, Thomas H. 1961. Milestones in microbiology. Prentice-Hall, Inc., Englewood Cliffs, N. J. 275p.

Bronowski, J. 1958. The creative process. Scientific American. September pp.58–65.

Brower, L. P., and **J. V. Z. Brower.** 1962. Investigations into mimicry. Natural History. 71:8–19 (April).

Brown, F. 1962. Biological clocks. BSCS Pamphlet No. 2. D. C. Heath and Co., Boston.

Brown, M. E. (Editor). 1957. The physiology of fishes. Academic Press, New York. 2 vols.

BSCS. 1963. Biological science: molecules to man. Blue version. Houghton Mifflin Co., Boston. 716p.

BSCS. 1963. High school biology. Green version. Rand McNally and Co., Chicago. 729p.

BSCS. 1963. Biological science: an inquiry into life. Yellow version. Harcourt, Brace and World, Inc., New York. 748p.

BSCS. 1964. Innovations in equipment and techniques for the biology teaching laboratory. D. C. Heath and Co., New York.

Buddenbrock, Wolfgang von. 1958. The senses. University of Michigan Press (Ann Arbor Science), Ann Arbor, Mich. 167p.

Bullough, W. S. 1961. Vertebrate reproductive cycles. Second Edition. John Wiley and Sons, Inc., New York. 123p.

Bunting, M. I. 1940. A description of some color variants produced by *Serratia marcescens*, strain 274. Journal of Bacteriology. 59:241.

Butler, W. L., and **R. J. Downs.** 1960. Light and plant development. Scientific American. December. pp.56–63.

Carr, A. 1962. Guideposts of animal navigation. BSCS Pamphlet No. 1. D. C. Heath and Co., Boston.

Carson, Rachel. 1962. Silent spring. Houghton Mifflin Co., Boston. 368p.

Carthy, J. D. 1956. Animal navigation. Charles Scribner's Sons, New York.

————. 1959. An introduction to the behavior of invertebrates. The Macmillan Co., New York. 380p.

Clifton, C. I. 1957. Introduction to bacterial physiology. McGraw-Hill Book Co., Inc., New York. 414p.

Cloudsley-Thompson, J. L. 1961. Rhythmic activity in animal physiology and behavior. Academic Press, New York. 263p.

Conant, James B. 1951. Science and common sense. Yale University Press, New Haven, Conn. 344p.

Corner, G. W. 1948. Ourselves unborn. Yale University Press, New Haven, Conn. 188p.

Darling, F. F. 1937. A herd of red deer. Oxford University Press, New York.

Deason, H. J., and **W. Blacklow** (Editors). 1957. A guide to science reading. The New American Library of World Literature, Inc., New York.

Dethier, V. G. 1963. To know a fly. Holden-Day, Inc., San Francisco. 119p.

Dethier, V. G., and **E. Stellar.** 1964. Animal behavior. Second Edition. Prentice-Hall, Inc., Englewood Cliffs, N. J. 118p.

Dixon W. J., and **F. J. Massey.** 1957. Introduction to statistical analysis. McGraw-Hill Book Co., Inc., New York. 488p.

Dorst, J. 1962. The migration of birds. Houghton Mifflin Co., Boston. 476p.

Downie, N. M., and **R. W. Heath.** 1959. Basic statistical methods. Harper and Brothers, New York. 289p.

Dubos, R. 1962. The torch of life. Pocket Books, Inc., New York.

Ebert, J. 1959. The first heartbeats. Scientific American. March. pp.87–92.

Edwards, A. L. 1961. Statistical methods for the behavioral sciences. Holt, Rinehart and Winston, Inc., New York.

Etkin, William (Editor). 1964. Social behavior and organization among vertebrates. University of Chicago Press, Chicago. 307p.

Evans, Howard E. 1963. Predatory wasps. Scientific American. April. pp.145–150.

————. 1963. Wasp farm. Natural History Press, Garden City, N. Y. 178p.

Fabre, J. Henri. 1961. Insect world. Apollo Editions, Inc., New York. 333p.

Farner, D. 1964. Photoperiodism in animals. BSCS Pamphlet No. 15. D. C. Heath and Co., Boston.

Fischberg, M., and **A. W. Blackler.** 1961. How cells specialize. Scientific American. September. pp.124–128.

Fisher, R. A., and **F. Yates.** 1953. Statistical tables for biological, agricultural, and medical research. Oliver and Boyd, Ltd., Edinburgh. 126p.

Ford, Clellan S., and **Frank A. Beach.** Patterns of sexual behavior (K128S). Ace Books, New York.

Fraenkel, Gottfield S., and **Donald L. Gunn.** 1961. The orientation of animals. Dover Publications, Inc., New York. 376p.

Freund, E. 1960. Modern elementary statistics. Prentice-Hall, Inc., Englewood Cliffs, N. J. 413p.

Frisch, Karl von. 1955. The dancing bees. Harcourt, Brace and World, Inc., New York. 183p.

————. 1961. The dancing bees: an account of the life and senses of the honey bee. Harcourt, Brace and World, Inc., New York.

Frobisher, M. 1962. Fundamentals of microbiology. W. B. Saunders Co., Philadelphia. 610p.

Fuller, John L., and **W. R. Thompson.** 1960. Behavior genetics. John Wiley and Sons, Inc., New York. 396p.

Gabriel, M. L., and **S. Fogel** (Editors). 1955. Great experiments in biology. Prentice-Hall, Inc., Englewood Cliffs, N. J. 317p.

Galston, A. W. 1964. The life of the green plant. Second Edition. Prentice-Hall, Inc., Englewood Cliffs, N. J. 118p.

Gans, C. 1961. A bullfrog and its prey. Natural History. 70:26–37 (February).

Garner, H. R. 1962. Bacteria: reproduction and heredity. Holt, Rinehart and Winston, Inc., New York.

Gerard, R. W. 1949. Unresting cells. Harper and Brothers, New York. 439p.

Glass, Bentley. 1961. Revolution in biology. BSCS Newsletter No. 9, September. pp.2–5.

Goetsch, Wilhelm. 1957. Ants. University of Michigan (Ann Arbor Science), Ann Arbor, Mich. 169p.

Gray, G. W. 1957. The organizer. Scientific American. November. pp.79–88.

Gray, Sir James. 1953. How animals move. Cambridge University Press, New York. 114p.

Green, J. A., and **R. P. Williams.** 1957. Studies on pigmentation of *Serratia marcescens*. IV. Analysis of syntrophic pigment. Journal of Bacteriology. 74:633.

Griffin, Donald R. 1948. The navigation of birds. Scientific American. December. pp.18–25.

————. 1950. The navigation of bats. Scientific American. August. pp.52–55.

————. 1958. Listening in the dark. Yale University Press, New Haven, Conn. 413p.

————. 1958. More about bat radar. Scientific American. July. p.40

————. 1959. Echoes of bats and men. Doubleday and Co., Inc. (Anchor Books), Garden City, N. Y. 156p.

Grobman, A. B. 1961. The threshold of a revolution in biological education. The Journal of Medical Education. October.

Hafez, E. (Editor). 1962. The behavior of domestic animals. The Williams and Wilkins Co., Baltimore. 619p.

Hamburger, V. 1960. A manual for experimental embryology. Revised Edition. University of Chicago Press, Chicago. 320p.

Harlow, H. F., and **M. K. Harlow.** 1961. A study of animal affection. Natural History. 70:48–55 (December).

Hasler, Arthur D., and **James A. Larsen.** 1955. The homing salmon. Scientific American. August. p.72.

Hediger, H. 1955. Studies of the psychology and behavior of captive animals in zoos and circuses. Butterworth's Scientific Publications, London.

Heinroth, Oskar and **Katharina.** 1958. Birds. University of Michigan Press (Ann Arbor Science), Ann Arbor, Mich. 181p.

Hess, Eckhard. 1958. Imprinting in animals. Scientific American. March. p.81.

Holton, Gerald, and **Duane H. D. Roller.** 1958. Foundations of modern physical science. Addison-Wesley Publishing Co., Inc., Reading, Mass. 782p.

Hurd, P. D. 1961. Biological education in American secondary schools 1890–1960. A BSCS publication. Waverly Press, Inc., Baltimore.

Huxley, Julian. 1963. The human crisis. University of Washington Press, Seattle. 88p.

Jacobs, W. P. 1959. What substance normally controls a given biological process? 1. Formulation of some rules. Developmental Biology. 1:527–533.

Jacobs, W. P., and **F. N. Rossetter.** 1953. Studies on abscission: the stimulating role of nearby leaves. American Journal of Botany. 40:276–280.

Jacobs, W. P., and **R. H. Wetmore.** 1953. Studies on abscission: the inhibiting effect of auxin. American Journal of Botany. 40:272–275.

Jameson, William. 1959. Wandering albatross. William Morrow and Co., Inc., New York. 128p.

Jensen, C. O., W. Sacks, and **F. A. Baldavski.** 1951. The reduction of triphenyltetra-zolium chloride by dehydrogenases of corn embryos. Science. 113 (2925):65–66.

Kellog, W. N. 1962. Dolphins and hearing. Natural History. 71:30–39 (February).

————. 1963. Porpoises and sonar. University of Chicago Press, Chicago. 177p.

Klopfer, P. 1962. Behavioral aspects of ecology. Prentice-Hall, Inc., Englewood Cliffs, N. J. 166p.

Klüver, Heinrich. 1957. Behavior mechanisms in monkeys. University of Chicago Press (Phoenix Books), Chicago. 387p.

Köhler, Wolfgang. 1959. Mentality of apes. Vintage Books, New York. 301p.

Koller, D. 1959. Germination. Scientific American. April. pp.75–78.

Krogh, August. 1948. The language of the bees. Scientific American. August. p.18.

LaRue, C. D. 1936. The effect of auxin on the abscission of petioles. Proceedings of the National Academy of Science (Washington). 22:254–259.

Leopold, A. C. 1955. Auxins and plant growth. University of California Press. Berkeley. 354p.

Lindauer, M. 1961. Communication among social bees. Harvard University Press, Cambridge, Mass. 143p.

Lissman, H. W. 1963. Electricity location by fish. Scientific American. March. pp.50–59.

Little, J. M. 1961. An introduction to the experimental method. Burgess Publishing Co., Minneapolis.

Lockley, Ronald M. 1954. Shearwaters. The Devin-Adair Co., New York.

Lorenz, Konrad Z. 1958. The evolution of behavior. Scientific American. December. p.67.

———. 1961. King Solomon's ring. Apollo Editions, Inc., New York. 202p.

McElroy, William D. 1964. Cell physiology and biochemistry. Prentice-Hall, Inc., Englewood Cliffs, N. J. 120p.

Matthews, L. H., and **M. Knight.** 1963. The senses of animals. Philosophical Library, New York. 240p.

Mattson, A. M., C. O. Jensen, and **R. A. Dutcher.** 1947. Triphenyltetrazolium chloride as a dye for vital tissues. Science. 106 (2752):294–295.

Maxwell, Gavin. 1962. Ring of bright water. Fawcett. New York.

Meyerriecks, A. J. 1962. Courtship in animals. BSCS Pamphlet No. 3. D. C. Heath and Co., Boston.

Miller, E. C. 1938. Plant physiology. McGraw-Hill Book Co., Inc., New York. 1201p.

Monsoy, A. 1950. Fertilization of the egg. Scientific American. December.

Moog, F. 1950. Up from the embryo. Scientific American. February. pp.52–55.

Newport, George. 1853. On the impregnation of the ovum in the amphibia and on the direct agency of the spermatozoan. Trans. Royal Society, London, 1853:233–290.

Northrop, F. S. C. 1962. Man, nature and god. Pocket Books, Inc. New York.

Otto, M. 1949. Science and the moral life. The New American Library of World Literature, Inc., New York.

Patten, B. M. 1958. Foundations of embryology. McGraw-Hill Book Co., Inc., New York. 578p.

Pavlov, Ivan P. 1960. Conditioned reflexes. Dover Publications, Inc., New York.

Pfeiffer, J. 1962. Vision in frogs. Natural History. 71:41–47 (November).

Pontecorvo, G. 1958. Trends in genetic analysis. Columbia University Press, New York.

Pontecorvo, G., and **E. Kafer.** 1958. Genetic analysis by means of mitotic recombination. Advances in Genetics. 9:71–104.

Portmann, Adolf. 1959. Animal camouflage. University of Michigan Press (Ann Arbor Science), Ann Arbor, Mich. 111p.

——. 1961. Animals as social beings. Viking Press, New York. 256p.

Pringle, J. 1961. The flight of the bumblebee. Natural History. 70:20–29 (August).

Rheingold, H. (Editor). 1963. Maternal behavior in mammals. John Wiley and Sons, Inc., New York. 349p.

Richards, O. W. 1961. The social insects. Harper and Row (Torch Books). New York. 219p.

Roe, A., and **G. G. Simpson.** 1958. Behavior and evolution. Yale University Press, New Haven, Conn. 557p.

Roeder, K. 1963. Nerve cells and insect behavior. Harvard University Press, Cambridge, Mass. 188p.

Roper, J. A., and **R. H. Pritchard.** 1955. The recovery of the reciprocial products of mitotic crossing-over. Nature. (London). 175:639.

Rugh, R. 1951. The frog: its reproduction and development. McGraw-Hill Book Co., Inc., New York. 336p.

Sackheim, George. 1964. A programmed text—logarithms. Harper and Row, Evanston, Ill. and New York.

Santer, U. V., and **H. J. Vogel.** 1956. Prodigiosin synthesis in *Serratia marcescens:* isolation of a pyrrole containing precursor. Biochimica et Biophysica Acta. 19:578.

Schaller, G. 1963. The mountain gorilla. University of Chicago Press, Chicago. 431p.

Schneirla, T. C., and **Gerard Piel.** 1948. The army ant. Scientific American. June. pp.16–23.

Schwab, Joseph J. (Supervisor). 1963. The BSCS biology teacher's handbook. John Wiley and Sons, Inc., New York. 585p.

Scott, J. P. 1963. Animal behavior. Doubleday and Co., Inc., (Anchor Books), Garden City, N. Y. 331p.

Sherrington, Charles S. 1947. Integrative action of the nervous system. Yale University Press, New Haven, Conn.

Shumway, Waldo. 1940. The anatomical record. Vol. 78, No. 2, October.

Singer, M. 1958. The regeneration of body parts. Scientific American. October. pp.79–80.

Sinnott, Edmund W. 1955. Biology of the spirit. Viking Press, New York. 180p.

Skaife, S. H. Dwellers in darkness (termites). Doubleday and Co., Inc., Garden City, N. Y.

Smith, F. E. 1951. Tetrazolium salt. Science. 113 (2948):751–754.

————. 1954. Quantitative aspects of population growth. Princeton University Press, Princeton, N. J.

Snedecor, G. W. 1956. Statistical methods. Fifth Edition. Iowa State College Press, Ames, Iowa. 534p.

Snow, C. P. 1962. The two cultures and the scientific revolution. Cambridge University Press, New York. 51p.

Southwick, Charles H. 1963. Primate social behavior. D. Van Nostrand Co., Inc., Princeton, N. J. 191p.

Stainer, R. Y., M. Duodoroff, and **E. A. Adelberg.** 1963. The microbial world. Second Edition. Prentice-Hall, Inc., Englewood Cliffs, N. J. 753p.

Stearman, R. L. 1955. Statistical concepts in microbiology. Bacteriological Reviews, 19:160–215.

Sussman, M. 1964. Growth and development. Second Edition. Prentice-Hall, Inc., Englewood Cliffs, N. J. 116p.

Thompson, Robert. 1959. The psychology of thinking. Pelican Books, Baltimore.

Thorpe, W. H. 1956. Learning and instinct in animals. Harvard University Press, Cambridge, Mass. 493p.

Thorpe, W. H., and **O. W. Zangwill.** 1961. Current problems in animal behavior. Cambridge University Press, New York. 493p.

Tinbergen, N. 1951. The study of instinct. Oxford University Press, New York. 228p.

————. 1952. The curious behavior of the stickleback. Scientific American. December. p.22

————. 1953. Social behavior in animals. John Wiley and Sons, Inc. New York. 150p.

————. 1959. Curious naturalists. Basic Books, Inc., New York. 280p.

————. 1961. The herring gull's world. Revised Edition. Basic Books, Inc., New York. 255p.

Trembley, Abraham. 1744. *Histoire des polypes.* Verbeek, Leiden, Holland.

Underkofler, L. A., and **R. J. Hickey.** 1954. Industrial fermentations. 2 vols. Chemical Publishing Co., New York.

van Bergeijk, Willem A. M., J. R. Pierce, and **E. E. David, Jr.** 1960. Waves and the ear. Doubleday and Co., Inc., (Anchor Books), Garden City, N. Y. 235p.

Van Norman, R. W. 1963. Experimental biology. Prentice-Hall, Inc., Englewood Cliffs, N. J. 243p.

Waddington, C. H. 1953. How do cells differentiate? Scientific American. September. pp.108–114.

Wasserman, H. H., J. E. McKeon, L. Smith, and **P. Forgione.** 1960. Prodigiosin, structure and partial synthesis. Journal of the American Chemical Society. 82:506.

Watermann, T. 1961. The physiology of crustacea: sense organs, integration, and behavior (vol. 2). Academic Press, Inc., New York. 2 vols.

Weissman, August. 1893. The germ-plasm: a theory of heredity. (Translated from the German). Walter Scott, Ltd., London.

Wells, M. J. 1962. Brain and behavior in *Cephalopoda.* Stanford University Press, Palo Alto, Calif. 171p.

Wenner, A. M. 1962. Buzzing the queen. Scientific American. December pp.70–73.

Went, F. W. 1957. The experimental control of plant growth. Chronica Botanica Co., Waltham, Mass. 343p.

Wigglesworth, V. B. 1959. Metamorphosis, polymorphism and differentiation. Scientific American. February. pp.100–102.

Williams, C. B. 1958. Insect migration. The Macmillan Co., New York. 235p.

Williams, C. M. 1950. The metamorphosis of insects. Scientific American. April.

Wilson, Edward O. 1963. Pheromones. Scientific American. May. p.100.

Woodward, D. O. 1959. Enzyme complementation *in vitro* between adenylosuceinase-less mutants of *Neurospora crassa.* Proceedings of the National Academy of Science (Washington). 45:846.

————. 1960. A gene concept based on genetic and chemical studies in *Neurospora.* Quarterly Review of Biology. 35:313–323.

Wynne-Edwards, V. C. 1962. Animal dispersion in relation to social behavior. Hafner Publishing Co., Inc., New York. 653p.

Young, John. 1960. Doubt and certainty in science: a biologist's reflections on the brain. Oxford University Press, New York. 168p.

BIBLIOGRAPHY BY PHASE

PHASE ONE

Sections 1, 2, and 3

Bronowski, J. 1958. The creative process. Scientific American. September. pp. 58–65.

BSCS. 1963. Biological science: molecules to man. Blue version. Houghton Mifflin Co., Boston. 716p.

BSCS. 1963. High school biology. Green version. Rand McNally and Co., Chicago. 729p.

BSCS. 1963. Biological science: an inquiry into life. Yellow version. Harcourt, Brace and World, Inc., New York. 748p.

Conant, James B. 1951. Science and common sense. Yale University Press, New Haven, Conn. 344p.

Corner, G. W. 1948. Ourselves unborn. Yale University Press, New Haven, Conn. 188p.

Glass, Bentley. 1961. Revolution in biology. BSCS Newsletter No. 9, September. pp.2–5.

Grobman, A. B. 1961. The threshold of a revolution in biological education. The Journal of Medical Education. October.

Holton, Gerald, and **Duane H. D. Roller.** 1958. Foundations of modern physical science. Addison-Wesley Publishing Co., Inc., Reading, Mass. 782p.

Hurd, P. D. 1961. Biological education in American secondary schools, 1890–1960. A BSCS Publication. Waverly Press, Inc., Baltimore.

Schwab, Joseph J. (Supervisor). The BSCS biology teacher's handbook. John Wiley and Sons, Inc., New York. 585p.

PHASE TWO

Sections 4, 5, 6, 7, and 8

Bailey, N. T. J. 1959. Statistical methods in biology. John Wiley and Sons, Inc., New York. 200p.

Beveridge, W. I. B. 1957. The art of scientific investigation. Vintage Books, New York. 178p.

Dixon, W. J., and **F. J. Massey.** 1957. Introduction to statistical analysis. McGraw-Hill Book Co., Inc., New York. 488p.

Downie, N. M., and **R. W. Heath.** 1959. Basic statistical methods. Harper and Brothers, New York. 289p.

Edwards, A. L. 1961. Statistical methods for the behavioral sciences. Holt, Rinehart and Winston, Inc., New York.

Fisher, R. A., and **F. Yates.** 1953. Statistical tables for biological, agricultural, and medical research. Oliver and Boyd, Ltd., Edinburgh. 126p.

Freund, E. 1960. Modern elementary statistics. Prentice-Hall, Inc., Englewood Cliffs, N. J. 413p.

Gabriel, M. L., and **S. Fogel** (Editors). 1955. Great experiments in biology. Prentice-Hall, Inc., Englewood Cliffs, N. J. 317p.

Little, J. M. 1961. An introduction to the experimental method. Burgess Publishing Co., Minneapolis.

Snedecor, G. W. 1956. Statistical methods. Fifth Edition. Iowa State College Press, Ames, Iowa. 534p.

Van Norman, R. W. 1963. Experimental biology. Prentice-Hall, Inc., Englewood Cliffs, N. J. 243p.

PHASE THREE

Sections 9, 10, and 11

Braun, W. 1953. Bacterial genetics. W. B. Saunders Co., Philadelphia. 238p.

Brock, Thomas H. 1961. Milestone in microbiology. Prentice-Hall, Inc., Englewood Cliffs, N. J. 275p.

Buntning, M. I. 1940. A description of some color variants produced by *Serratia marcescens*, strain 274. Journal of Bacteriology. 59:241.

Clifton, C. I. 1957. Introduction to bacterial physiology. McGraw-Hill Book Co., Inc., New York. 414p.

Frobisher, M. 1962. Fundamentals of microbiology. W. B. Saunders Co., Philadelphia. 610p.

Gabriel, M. L., and **S. Fogel** (Editors). 1955. Great experiments in biology. Prentice-Hall Inc., Englewood Cliffs, N. J. 317p.

Garner, H. R. 1962. Bacteria: reproduction and heredity. Holt, Rinehart and Winston, Inc., New York.

Pontecorvo, G. 1958. Trends in a genetic analysis. Columbia University Press, New York.

Pontecorvo, G., and **E. Kafer.** 1958. Genetic analysis by means of mitotic recombination. Advances in Genetics. 9:71–104.

Roper, J. A., and **R. H. Pritchard.** 1955. The recovery of the reciprocial products of mitotic crossing-over. Nature (London). 175:639.

Santer, U. V., and **H. J. Vogel.** 1956. Prodigiosin synthesis in *Serratia marcescens:* isolation of a pyrrole containing precursor. Biochimica et Biophysica Acta. 19:578.

Smith, F. E. 1954. Quantitative aspects of population growth. Princeton University Press, Princeton, N. J.

Stanier, R. Y., M. Duodoroff, and **E. A. Adelberg.** 1963. The microbial world. Second Edition. Prentice-Hall, Inc., Englewood Cliffs, N. J. 753p.

Stearman, R. L. 1955. Statistical concepts in microbiology. Bacteriological Reviews. 19:160–215.

Underkofler, L. A., and **R. J. Hickey.** 1954. Industrial fermentations. 2 vols. Chemical Publishing Co., New York.

Wasserman, H. H., J. E. McKeon, L. Smith, and **P. Forgione.** 1960. Prodigiosin structure and partial synthesis. Journal American Chemical Society. 82:506.

Woodward, D. O. 1959. Enzyme complementation *in vitro* between adenylosuceinase-less mutants of *Neurospora crassa.* Proceedings of the National Academy of Science (Washington). 45:846.

———— 1960. A gene concept based on genetic and chemical studies in *Neurospora.* Quarterly Review of Biology. 35:313–323.

PHASE FOUR

Sections 12, 13 14, and 15

Allee, Warder C. 1951. Cooperation among animals. Abelard-Schuman. Ltd., New York. 233p.

Armstrong, E. A. 1963. A study of bird song. Oxford University Press, New York. 335p.

Bliss, E. L. (Editor). 1962. Roots of behavior. Harper and Row, New York. 339p.

Brower, L. P., and **J. V. Z. Brower.** 1962. Investigations into mimicry. Natural History. 71:8–19 (April).

Brown, F. 1962. Biological clocks. BSCS Pamphlet No. 2. D. C. Heath and Co., Boston.

Brown, M. E. (Editor). 1957. The physiology of fishes. 2 vols. Academic Press, New York.

Bullough, W. S. 1961. Vertebrate reproductive cycles. Second Edition. John Wiley and Sons, Inc., New York. 123p.

Carr, A. 1962. Guideposts of animal navigation. BSCS Pamphlet No. 1. D. C. Heath and Co., Boston.

Carthy, J. D. 1956. Animal navigation. Charles Scribner's Sons, New York.

————. 1959. An introduction to the behavior of invertebrates. The Macmillan Co., New York. 380p.

Cloudsley-Thompson, J. L. 1961. Rhythmic activity in animal physiology and behavior. Academic Press, New York. 263p.

Darling, F. F. 1937. A herd of red deer. Oxford University Press, New York.

Dethier, V. G. 1963. To know a fly. Holden-Day, Inc., San Francisco. 119p.

Dethier V. G., and **E. Stellar.** 1964. Animal behavior. Second Edition. Prentice-Hall, Inc., Englewood Cliffs, N. J. 118p.

Dorst, J. 1962. The migration of birds. Houghton Mifflin Co., Boston. 476p.

Etkin, William (Editor). 1964. Social behavior and organization among vertebrates. University of Chicago Press, Chicago. 307p.

Evans, Howard E. 1963. Predatory wasps. Scientific American. April. pp.145–150.

————. 1963. Wasp farm. Natural History Press, Garden City, N. Y. 178p.

Farner, D. 1964. Photoperiodism in animals. BSCS Pamphlet No. 15. D. C. Heath and Co., Boston.

Frisch, Karl von. 1955. The dancing bees. Harcourt, Brace and World, Inc., New York. 183p.

Fuller, John L., and **W. R. Thompson.** 1960. Behavior genetics. John Wiley and Sons, Inc., New York. 396p.

Gans, C. 1961. A bullfrog and its prey. Natural History. 70:26–37 (February).

Gray, Sir James. 1953. How animals move. Cambridge University Press, New York. 114p.

Griffin, Donald R. 1948. The navigation of birds. Scientific American. December. pp.18–25.

————. 1950. The navigation of bats. Scientific American. August. pp.52–55.

————. 1958. Listening in the dark. Yale University Press, New Haven, Conn. 413p.

————. 1958. More about bat radar. Scientific American. July. p.40.

Hafez, E. (Editor). 1962. The behavior of domestic animals. The Williams and Wilkins Co., Baltimore. 619p.

Harlow, H. F., and **M. K. Harlow.** 1961. A study of animal affection. Natural History. 70:48–55 (December).

Hasler, Arthur D., and **James A. Larsen.** 1955. The homing salmon. Scientific American. August. p.72.

Hediger, H. 1955. Studies of the psychology and behavior of captive animals in zoos and circuses. Butterworth's Scientific Publications, London.

Hess, Eckhard. 1958. Imprinting in animals. Scientific American. March. p.81.

Kellog, W. N. 1962. Dolphins and hearing. Natural History. 71:30–39 (February).

Klopfer, P. 1962. Behavioral aspects of ecology. Prentice-Hall, Inc., Englewood Cliffs, N. J. 166p.

Krogh, August. 1948. The language of the bees. Scientific American. August. p.18.

Lindauer, M. 1961. Communication among social bees. Harvard University Press, Cambridge, Mass. 143p.

Lissman, H. W. 1963. Electricity location by fish. Scientific American. March. pp.50–59.

Lorenz, Konrad Z. 1958. The evolution of behavior. Scientific American. December. p.67.

Matthews, L. H., and M. Knight. 1963. The senses of animals. Philosophical Library, New York. 240p.

Meyerriecks, A. J. 1962. Courtship in animals. BSCS Pamphlet No. 3. D. C. Heath and Co., Boston.

Pfeiffer, J. 1962. Vision in frogs. Natural History. 71:41–47 (November).

Portmann, Adolf. 1961. Animals as social beings. Viking Press, New York. 256p.

Pringle, J. 1961. The flight of the bumblebee. Natural History. 70:20–29 (August).

Rheingold, H. (Editor). 1963. Maternal behavior in mammals. John Wiley and Sons, Inc., New York. 349p.

Roe, A., and G. G. Simpson. 1958. Behavior and evolution. Yale University Press, New Haven, Conn. 557p.

Roeder, K. 1963. Nerve cells and insect behavior. Harvard University Press, Cambridge, Mass. 188p.

Schaller, G. 1963. The mountain gorilla. University of Chicago Press, Chicago. 431p.

Schneirla, T. C., and Gerard Piel. 1948. The army ant. Scientific American. June. pp.16–23.

Thorpe, W. H. 1956. Learning and instinct in animals. Harvard University Press, Cambridge, Mass. 493p.

Thorpe, W. H., and O. W. Zangwill. 1961. Current problems in animal behavior. Cambridge University Press, New York. 493p.

Tinbergen, N. 1951. The study of instinct. Oxford University Press, New York. 228p.

———. 1952. The curious behavior of the stickleback. Scientific American. December. p.22.

———. 1959. Curious naturalists. Basic Books, Inc., New York. 280p.

———. 1961. The herring gull's world. Revised Edition. Basic Books, Inc., New York. 255p.

Watermann, T. 1961. The physiology of crustacea: sense organs, integration, and behavior (vol. 2). Academic Press, Inc., New York. 2 vols.

Wells, M. J. 1962. Brain and behavior in *Cephalopoda.* Stanford University Press, Palo Alto, Calif. 171p.

Wenner, A. M. 1962. Buzzing the queen. Scientific American. December. pp.70–73.

Williams, C. B. 1958. Insect migration. The Macmillan Co., New York. 235p.

Wilson, Edward O. 1963. Pheromones. Scientific American. May. p.100.

Wynne-Edwards, V. C. 1962. Animal dispersion in relation to social behavior. Hafner Publishing Co., Inc., New York. 653p.

Section 12

Allen, R. D. 1953. The moment of fertilization. Scientific American. June.

Bonner, D., and S. Mills. 1964. Heredity. Prentice-Hall, Inc., Englewood Cliffs, N. J. 115p.

Butler, W. L., and **R. J. Downs.** 1960. Light and plant development. Scientific American. December. pp.56–63.

Galston, A. W. 1964. The life of the green plant. Second Edition. Prentice-Hall, Inc., Englewood Cliffs, N. J. 118p.

Gerard, R. W. 1949. Unresting cells. Harper and Brothers, New York. 439p.

Jacobs, W. P. 1959. What substance normally controls a given biological process? 1. Formulation of some rules. Developmental Biology. 1:527–533.

Jacobs, W. P., and **F. N. Rossetter.** 1953. Studies on abscission: the stimulating role of nearby leaves. American Journal of Botany. 40:276–280.

Jacobs, W. P., and **R. H. Wetmore.** 1953. Studies on abscission: the inhibiting effect of auxin. American Journal of Botany. 40:272–275.

Jensen, C. O., W. Sacks, and **F. A. Baldavski.** 1951. The reduction of triphenyltetra-zolium chloride by dehydrogenases of corn embryos. Science. 113 (2925):65–66.

Koller, D. 1959. Germination. Scientific American. April. pp.75–78.

LaRue, C. D. 1936. The effect of auxin on the abscission of petioles. Proceedings of the National Academy of Science (Washington). 22:254–259.

Mattson, A. M., C. O. Jensen, and **R. A. Dutcher.** 1947. Triphenyltetrazolium chloride as a dye for vital tissues. Science. 106 (2752):294–295.

Miller, E. C. 1938. Plant physiology. McGraw-Hill Book Co., Inc., New York. 1201p.

Smith, F. E. 1951. Tetrazolium salt. Science. 113 (2948):751–754.

Went, F. W. 1957. The experimental control of plant growth. Chronica Botanica Co., Waltham, Mass. 343p.

Section 13

Patten, B. M. 1958. Foundations of embryology. McGraw-Hill Book Co., Inc., New York. 578p.

Rugh, R. 1951. The frog: its reproduction and development. McGraw-Hill Book Co., Inc., New York. 336p.

Shumway, Waldo. 1940. The Anatomical Record. Vol. 78, No. 2, October.

Singer, M. 1958. The regeneration of body parts. Scientific American. October. pp.79–80.

Trembley, Abraham. 1744. *Histoire des polypes.* Verbeek, Leiden, Holland.

Waddington, C. H. 1953. How do cells differentiate? Scientific American. September. pp.108–114.

Weissmann, August. 1893. The germ-plasm: a theory of heredity. (Translated from the German). Walter Scott, Ltd., London.

Wiggleworth, V. B. 1959. Metamorphosis, polymorphism, and differentiation. Scientific American. February. pp.100–102.

Williams, C. M. 1950. The metamorphosis of insects. Scientific American. April.

Section 15

Allee, Warder C., Social life of animals. Beacon Press, Boston.

Birney, Robert C., and **Richard C. Teeven.** 1961. Instinct. D. Van Nostrand Co., Inc., Princeton, N. J. 181p.

Buddenbrock, Wolfgang von. 1958. The senses. University of Michigan Press (Ann Arbor Science), Ann Arbor, Mich. 167p.

Fabre, J. Henri. 1961. Insect world. Apollo Editions, Inc., New York.

Ford, Clellan S., and **Frank A. Beach.** Patterns of sexual behavior (K128S). Ace Books, New York.

Fraenkel, Gottfield S., and **Donald L. Gunn.** 1961. The orientation of animals. Dover Publications, Inc., New York. 376p.

Frisch, Karl von, 1961. The dancing bees: an account of the life and senses of the honeybee. Harcourt, Brace and World, Inc., New York.

Goetsch, Wilhelm. 1857. Ants. University of Michigan Press (Ann Arbor Science), Ann Arbor, Mich. 169p.

Griffin, Donald R. 1959. Echoes of bats and men. Doubleday and Co., Inc., (Anchor Books), Garden City, N. Y. 156p.

Heinroth, Oskar and **Katharina.** 1958. Birds. University of Michigan Press (Ann Arbor Science), Ann Arbor, Mich. 181p.

Jameson, William. 1959. Wandering albatross. William Morrow and Co., Inc., New York. 128p.

Kellog, Winthrop N. 1963. Porpoises and sonar. University of Chicago Press, Chicago. 177p.

Klüver, Heinrich. 1957. Behavior mechanisms in monkeys. University of Chicago Press (Phoenix), Chicago. 387p.

Köhler, Wolfgang. 1959. Mentality of apes. Vintage, New York. 301p.

Lockley, Ronald M. 1954. Shearwaters. The Devin-Adair Co., New York.

Lorenz, Konrad. 1961. King Solomon's ring. Apollo Books, New York. 202p.

Maxwell, Gavin. 1962. Ring of bright water. Fawcett, New York.

Pavlov, Ivan P. Conditioned reflexes. Dover Publications, Inc., New York.

Portmann, Adolf. 1959. Animal camouflage. University of Michigan Press (Ann Arbor Science), Ann Arbor, Mich. 111p.

Richards, O. W. 1961. The social insects. Harper and Row (Torch Books), New York. 219p.

Scott, J. P. 1963. Animal behavior. Doubleday and Co., Inc., (Anchor Books), Garden City, N. Y. 331p.

Sherrington, Charles S. 1947. Integrative action of the nervous system. Yale University Press, New Haven, Conn.

Sinnott, Edmund W. 1955. The biology of the spirit. Viking Press, New York. 180p.

Skaife, S. H. Dwellers in darkness (termites). Doubleday and Co., Inc., Garden City, N. Y.

Southwick, Charles H. 1963. Primate social behavior. D. Van Nostrand Co., Inc., Princeton, N. J. 191p.

Thompson, Robert. 1959. The psychology of thinking. Pelican Books, Baltimore.

Tinbergen, N. 1953. Social behavior in animals. John Wiley and Sons, Inc., New York. 150p.

van Bergeijk, Willem A. M., J. R. Pierce, and **E. E. David, Jr.** 1960. Waves and the ear. Doubleday and Co., Inc., (Anchor Books), Garden City, N. Y. 235p.

Young, John. 1960. Doubt and certainty in science: a biologist's reflections on the brain. Oxford University Press, New York. 168p.

Phase Five

Carson, Rachel. 1962. Silent spring. Houghton Mifflin Co., Boston. 368p.

Deason, H. J., and **W. Blacklow** (Editors). 1957. A guide to science reading. The New American Library of World Literature, Inc., New York.

Dubos, R. 1962. The torch of life. Pocket Books, Inc., New York.

Huxley, Julian. 1963. The human crisis. University of Washington Press, Seattle. 88p.

Northrop, F. S. C. 1962. Man, nature and god. Pocket Books, Inc., New York.

Otto, M. 1949. Science and the moral life. The New American Library of World Literature, Inc., New York.

Snow, C. P. 1962. The two cultures and the scientific revolution. Cambridge University Press, New York. 51p.

INDEX

A

Abscission
  effect of ethylene, 262
  leaf
    control by other leaves, 256–263
    effect of removing leaf blades,
      252–253
    inhibition by auxin, 246,
      249–255, 262
    inhibition by NAA, 250–253
    studies by W. P. Jacobs, 242–264
    study by Küster, 240–241, **241**
    phenomenon of, 240
Abscission layer, development of,
  250, **251, 252**
Acetaldehyde, 22, **22**
Acetobacter and fermentation, 41
Activation, energy of, 33–35, **34**
Activators and enzyme activity, 33
Adenine, 204–205
ADP (adenosine diphosphate), 21
Aerobic respiration, 41
Agar
  as microbial culture medium, 117
  preparation of agar plates, **137**
  preparation of YAG plate, **158**
  transfer of slant cultures, 118–120,
    119
Agricultural revolution, 337
Alcohol, production in fermentation,
  21–22, **22**
Allelic genes, 156
Amino acids
  and composition of enzymes, 33
  determined by DNA, 205
Amplexus, 210
Anaerobic respiration, 41
Angstrom unit, 178
Animal communication, classification
  of, 282–283
Animals, laboratory requirements,
  359
Anther, 166–167
Antibiotics, effect on population
  development, 130, **130**

Antilogarithms, 108–109
Arabinose, 300
Army ant
  movement in columns, 273
  "suicide mill," **273**, 274
Ascarite, use in volumeter, 43, 45
Aspergillus nidulans
  biosynthesis of pigment, 147
  complementation in, 152–153
    Investigation 15, 152
  description and life history,
    144–147, **145, 146, 147**
  gene loci, 150
    Investigation 14, 148
  genetic recombination in
    Investigation 17, 160
    Investigation 18, 161
  linkage in, 156
    Investigation 16, 156
  minimal medium, preparation of,
    388–389
  strain 180
    genotype of, 150
    test for nutritional deficiency,
      151
  strain 183
    genotype of, 150
    test for nutritional deficiency,
      151
Assay, biological,
  Investigation 31, 227
ATP (adenosine triphosphate)
  and energy transfer, 21–22, **22**
  formation in fermentation, 41–42,
    21–22, **21, 22**
  utilization of, 21, **21**
Autoclaving, 379
Auxin, *See also* IAA
  effect on plant growth and
    regulation, **265**
  and IAA, 226
  influence on cell elongation, 227
  inhibition of abscission 249–255
  movement of, 227
  study by Darwin, 222–226, **223, 225**
Average, *See* Mean

B

Bacillus subtilis
  preparation and transfer of cultures,
    118–120, **119**
  transfer of broth culture, 120–121,
    121
Back mutations, 131, 148
Bacteria
  formation of colonies, 115–116
  gram-negative, 134
  gram-positive, 134
Bakanae, 231
Balbiani rings, 204
B. A. S. I. C., **90**, 95
Bats, 278–280, **280**
Bean plants, cuttings of, **237**
Bees, *See* Honeybee
Behavior
  analysis of, 289–306
  effects of individual genes, 304–305
  evidence for heritability of, 303
  function of, 278
  selection for in *Drosophila* 303, **303**
  understanding of, 266
  use in taxonomy, 274–276, **275**
Bibliography
  alphabetical, 398–405
  by phase, 406–413
Biological Abstracts, 90–95, **90, 91, 92,
    93, 94**
  author index, **94,** 95
  subject index, 90, **92, 93,** 95
Biological assay, Investigation 31, 227
Biological investigation, processes of,
    12–100
Biological knowledge, increase of,
    7–8
Biology
  emergence as science, 3
  literature of, 77–97
  role of inquiry in, 9–10
Bird census, 78
Blastema, 208
Blastomeres, 203
Blastopore, **198,** 200, **201**
Blastula, development in frog, **198,**
    200

Blowfly
  determining sensitivity level of, **298**
  handling of, **294**
  life cycle and culture of, 290–292
  maintaining, **300**
  selection of protein and sugar,
    Investigation 38, 302
Bottle holder, **236**
Brine shrimp, orientation by light,
    271, **272**
Broth cultures, volumetric transfer
    of, 120–121, **121**
Brown, Harrison, 310, 340, 348
Budding of yeast, 126, **126**

C

Carbohydrate solutions, preparation
    of, 383
Carbon dioxide
  and differentiation, 203
  production in fermentation, 13,
    21–22
    Investigation 1, 13, Investigation
    2, 18
  rate of production, Investigation 1,
    13, Investigation 2, 18
  used to anesthetize flies, 292–293
Carson, Rachel, 318
Catalysts, effect on chemical reactions,
    32
Cells, counting in yeast suspension,
    124–125
Characteristic of logarithms, 106–107
Chemicals, laboratory requirements,
    356–359
Chemical reactions, influence of
    kinetic energy on, 53
Chemical solutions
  preparation of, 378–385
    carbohydrate solutions, 383
    gibberellic acid, 383
    growth regulator solutions, 380
    Holtfreter's solution, 381
    IAA, 383
    iodine-potassium iodide, 380
    narcotic solution, 381
    phosphate buffer solution, 382

Chemical solutions (cont.)
   physiological saline, 382
   respiratory inhibitor, 381–382
   by serial dilution, 378–379
   sex hormones, 382
   staining, 382–383
   tetrazolium test solution, 380
   thyroid hormone, 380–381
   sterilizing
      by autoclaving, 379
      by pasteurizing, 379
Chicks
   behavior changes in, 218–219
   comb development in, 217
   control of development in,
      Investigation 28, 215
   gonads of, Investigation 29, 219
   maintaining in laboratory, 393
   method of injecting hormones,
      216–218
   method of killing, 220
   method of removing gonads, 220
Chi-square, 71–76
   comparison with t test, 76
   critical values, **73**
   degrees of freedom, 72–73
   and null hypothesis, 71–72
   requirements for use, 71
   with more than 2 attributes, 75
Chlorella, 339
Chlorophyll, structure of molecule,
   139
Chorionic gonadotrophin,
   Investigation 28, 215
Chromosome map
   estimation of units, 156
   preparation of, Investigation 16,
      156
Citric acid cycle, 41–42
Clam mite, detection of host, 271–272
Cleavage of frog egg, **198,** 200, **201**
Coenzymes, 33
Coleoptiles
   device for cutting, **230**
   of oat seedling, 227
   prevention of bending, 225
Comb factor
   calculation, 216

Comb factor (cont.)
   description, **217**
   effect of testosterone on,
      Investigation 28, 215
Communication, animal, 282–288
   classification, 283
   honeybee, 283–286
   pheromones, 287
   visual, 287
      wolf tail expression, 288
   interspecies, 282, **282**
Complementation, 152–153
   and heterokaryosis, Investigation
      15, 152
Computations, statistical, 52–61
Conant, James B., 4
Conclusions, technique of drawing,
   100
Continuous variables, 50
Controversy, contribution to science,
   317
Corn grains, use in seed viability
   study, 173
Culture media, nutrient broth, 117
Cytosine, 204–205

                        D

Darwin, Charles, 222–227
Darwin, Sir Charles, 333–345, **334**
Darwin, Francis, 222–227
Data
   evaluation of, Pattern of Inquiry 3,
      39
   as raw material of science, 29
   statistical evaluation of, 48–77
DDT, use of, 320, 325, 329, 330
Death phase, 112–113
Decker, George C., 319–328
Degrees of freedom, 68, 72
   for chi-square, 72–73
Design of experiments, use of, 12–13,
      See also Experimental design
Differentiation, genetic control of,
      203–205
Diphosphoglyceric acid, 22, **22**
Discrete variables, 50

Distribution, normal, 54–55, **54**
DNA (deoxyribonucleic acid)
    action as gene, 152, **204**, 306
    duplication of, 205
    structure of molecule, 204–205, **204**
Dormancy, 177, 183
Drosophila,
    effects of genes on behavior,
        304–305
    selection for behavior responses,
        303, **303**
DuBridge, L. A., 309–316
Ducklings,
    escape response of, 268, **269**
    imprinting in, 276–277, **276, 277**
Dufour's gland, 280, **281**
Dutch elm disease, **321**
    control of, 323, 329–330

                    E

Echolocation
    by bats, 278, 280, **278, 280**
    by other animals, 279–280, **280**
Egg, function of, 190
Elk, visual communication by, 287
Embden-Meyerhof-Parnas system,
    22
Embryo
    development in plants, 169, **170,
        171**
    frog
        development of, **198**, 200, **201**
        gastrulation of, **198**, 200–202,
            201
        Investigation 25, 197
Embryo cultures, frog, establishing
        and maintaining, 195–197, **196**
Embryo sac, 169
Endergonic reactions, 20–21
Endocrine glands, 209–210
Endosperm, 169, **170, 171**
Energy,
    light, concepts of, 178–180
    release in catabolism of glucose, 33
    supply and use of, 343–344
Energy of activation, 33–35, **34**
    required for sucrose hydrolysis, 35

Enzymes,
    activators of, 33
    composition of, 33
    definition of, 33
    and fermentation, 32–35
    formation of substrate complex,
        34, **35**
    isolation of, Investigation 20, 174
    naming of, 35
    specificity of, 33
Enzyme activity
    and complementation, Investigation
        15, 152
    in germinating seeds, Investigation
        19, 172
Equipment, laboratory requirements,
    353–355
Ergosterol, conversion to vitamin D,
    180
Error
    random, 49
        Pattern of Inquiry 3, 39
    systematic, 49
        Pattern of Inquiry 3, 39
Ethylene, effect on abscission, 262
Euglena, formation of chloroplasts,
    203
Evolution, 273, 275, 290, 301
Exergonic reactions, 20–21, **21**
Experiment
    controlled, 29
    definition of, 29
Experimental design
    principles of biological, 23
    problems of, 23
    simplicity in, 98–99
    use of, 12–13
Experimental organisms
    care of, 24
    choice of, 23
Experimental variables, 23
Exponential growth, 104–106, **105**

                    F

Fairy shrimp, orientation by light,
    271, **272**

Fermentation
  acetic acid, 41
  alcoholic, 21–22
    studies on by T. Schwann, 27–28
    summary of steps in, **22**
  and energy, 20–22
  and respiration, 40–42
  carbon dioxide production by yeast,
    13, 15, 21–22, Investigation 1,
    13; Investigation 2, 18
  factors affecting
    enzyme concentration,
      Investigation 6, 35
    substrate concentration,
      Investigation 1, 13;
      Investigation 2, 18;
      Investigation 3, 24;
      Investigation 4, 26
    temperature, Investigation 5, 30
  role of ATP, 21
  value to cell, 20
  by yeast protoplast, 81–88
Fermentation tubes, preparation of,
    17, **17**
Fertilization, 191–194
File cards, use of, 96, **96**
Flowering plant, life history of,
    166–172, **166, 167, 168, 170,
    171**
Fluorescent lamps, light emitted from
    180, **180**
Fly culture medium, preparation of,
    387
Food selection, relation to nutrition,
    Investigation 37, 300
Frisch, Karl von, 283–286
Frog,
  detection of prey, **269**
  development of embryo, **198,**
    200–202, **201**
    Investigation 25, 197
    influence of hormones,
      Investigation 27, 212
  egg
    cleavage of, **198,** 200, **201**
  embryos, maintaining in laboratory,
    393
  induced hibernation in, 393

Frog, induced hibernation in, (cont.)
  metamorphosis in, 202, 214
  regeneration in, 206
    Investigation 27, 212
  reproduction, influence of
    hormones, 210
  vision of, **269**
Fructose diphosphate, **22**
Fusion of gametes, 190–191

G

Gametes
  chromosome number in, 166
  fusion of, 190–191
  production of, in flowering plants,
    166–169
  production of, in moss plants, 166
Gametogenesis in animals, 189–190,
    189
Gastrula, development in frog, **198,**
    200–202
Gastrulation, **198,** 200–202, **201**
Gelatinase, 117
Generation time, 104, 110
Genes,
  allelic, 156
  DNA component, 204–205
  effect on behavior, 303–306
Genotypes
  confirmation of, Investigation 14,
    148
  of *A. nidulans,* strains 180 and 183,
    150
Geotactic orientation
  in dung beetle, 286
  of honeybee, 284
Germinating seeds, enzyme activity
    in, Investigation 19, 172
Germination
  effect of light on, 178
    Investigation 22, 181;
    Investigation 23, 182
  enzyme activity in, Investigation 19,
    172
  of meiospores, 147
  of oat grain, 227
  of pollen grain, 169

Germination (cont.)
  of seeds, 10, 177
    Pattern of Inquiry 7, 177
Germination box, 228
Germination tests, 175
  Investigation 21, 175
Gibberellic acid
  discovery, 231
  effect of, Investigation 32, 232
  preparation of, 383
Gibberllin, *See* Gibberellic acid
Glass, Bentley, 7–8
Glassware, laboratory requirements,
    355–356
Glucose
  comparison with molasses in
    carbon dioxide production,
    Investigation 3, 24
  fermentation of, 21–22, **22**, 41, 85
  respiration of, 41, 85
Glyceraldehyde phosphate, **22**
Glycolysis, 22
Goiters, cause of, 212
Gonadotrophins, 210
Gonads
  of hormone-treated chicks,
    Investigation 29, 219
  method of removal, 220
Goose, imprinting in, 276–277
Gosset, W. S., developer of *t* test,
    63–64
Graham, Samuel A., 328–332
Gram-negative bacteria, determination
    of, 134–135
Gram-positive bacteria, determination
    of, 134–135
Gram's stain, 134–135
Grass seedlings, bending in unilateral
    light, 223
Griffin, Donald, 278–279
Growth, *See also* Animal growth and
    Plant growth
  animal
    development of frog embryo,
      198, 200–202, **201**
    effect of temperature on frog
      embryo development, 202
    exponential or logarithmic, 104–106,
      105

Growth (cont.)
  of microbes
    expressed as logarithms, 104–106
    geometric progression in, 104
    generation time, 104
  plant, 166–188
Growth curves, 111–114
Growth phase, **112,** 113
Growth rate, determination of, 110
Growth regulator paste, preparation
    of, 383
Growth regulator solution,
    preparation of, 380
Growth regulating substances, effect
    on plants, Investigation 33,
    236
Guanine, 204–205
Gudernatsch, Frederick, 211
Gyplune, 287
Gypsy moth
  eradication of, 331
  production and detection of
    gyplune, 287

H

Haploidization, 162
Harrington, Sir Charles, 211
Hemocytometer
  description, 121–123, **122**
  use in counting yeast cells, 124–125
Hemoglobin, structure of molecule,
    139
Heterokaryon, formation by cell
    fusion, **145**
Heterokaryosis, 144–145, **145**
  and complementation, Investigation
    15, 152
Hibernation, induced in frogs, 393
Holtfreter's solution, preparation of,
    381
Holton, Gerald, 4–6
Homokaryon, 144
Honeybee
  ability to locate food source,
    283–284
    by use of sound, 285, **285**
  ability to orient by polarized light,
    286

Honeybee (cont.)
  communication, 283–286
  genetic control of behavior, 305
  geotactic orientation, 284
  phototactic orientation, 284, **284, 285, 286**
Hormonal regulation in animals, 209–210
Hormones
  control of sex differentiation, Investigation 28, 215
  differences in response to, 212
  effect of sex hormones on chick, Investigation 28, 215
  function in animals, 209–210
  influence on frog reproduction, 210
  influence on gonads of chicks, Investigation 29, 219
  plant hormones, *See* Auxin, IAA, Gibberellic acid
  production in animals, 209
Hoyle, Fred, 345–348
Human population, increase of, 336, 341, 346
Hydrolysis of sucrose, 35
Hypothesis
  description, 12
  formulation of, 12–13
    Investigation 1, 13;
    Investigation 2, 18
  null, 63
  refining, 27
  use in experimental design, 13

I

IAA, 226–227
  effect of light on, 234
  effect on growth, 227, 243–248
  effect on leaf abscission, 249–255, 256–264
  measurement, Investigation 31, 227
  response of roots and stems to, **235**
  solution, preparation of, 383
Imprinting, 227
Incandescent lamp, light emitted from, 180, **180**
Indoleacetic acid, *See* IAA

Inheritance
  of behavior, 303
  polygenic, 305
Inquiry
  meaning of, 9
  Patterns of
    description, 9–10
    model, 10
Insecticides
  advent of, 319–320
  consumption of, 320
  effect on wildlife, 322, 329
  use of, 318–332
Instincts, 273–276
Insulin, function of, 209
Interactions
  between organisms, 136–144
  between unknown mutants, Investigation 12, 141
  intracellular
    steps in, 162
  of two bacterial mutants, Investigation 10, 137
Invertase, 86
Iodine in hormones, 211–212
Iodine-potassium iodide solution, preparation of, 380

J

Jacobs, W. P., 242–264
Journals, scientific, listing, 78

K

Kinesis, 270–271
Kinetic energy and rate of chemical reaction, 33
Koch, Robert, 115–118, **116**
Krebs cycle, 41–42
Küster, 240–241

L

Laboratory requirements
  biological materials
    animals, 359
    microorganisms, 359

Laboratory requirements (cont.)
plant items, 359–360
chemicals, 356–359
for each investigation, 362–377
general equipment, 353–355
glassware, 355–356
Laboratory rules, 14, 118
Lag period, 112–113, **112**
Learning, 276
Leech, response to heat, 271
Lettuce seeds, effect of light on
germination of, Investigation
22, 181
Light
corpuscular theory, 178
photon, 178, 180
quantum, 178
effect on germination, 178,
Investigation 22, 181
Investigation 23, 182
effect on plant growth, 221
orientation in animals by light,
271, **272**
spectrum, 178–179, **179**
wavelength emitted by fluorescent
and incandescent lights, **180,**
182
waves, 178–180
Linkage in *A. nidulans,* 156
Literature, searching the, 89–90
Living cultures
maintaining
of chicks, 393
of frog embryos, 393
of tadpoles, 393
Logarithmic growth, *see* Exponential
growth
Logarithms, 104, 106–109, 394–396
Lorenz, Konrad, 276–277, **276**

M

Maltase, production by yeast, 35
Malthus, Thomas, 310, 338, 342
Mantissa of logarithms, 106–107
Math tables
common logarithms, 394–396
critical values of chi-square, 396

Math tables (cont.)
distribution of *t* probability, 397
Maze learning in rats, 304, **304**
Mean, 53–54
Measurement
problems in, 38–39
rules for making accurate, 38–39
Media, preparation of, 386–390
Aspergillus nidulans minimal,
388–389
fly culture, 387
nutrient agar, 387
nutrient broth, 387
Serratia marcescens agar, 387–388
starch agar, 388
supplement for M medium, 389–390
tryptone glucose agar, 388
YAG, 388
Megagametophyte, 169
Megaspore, production in ovule, 169
Megaspore mother cell, 169
Meiosis, 166, **167**
genetic recombination at,
Investigation 16, 156
in microspore mother cell, 167
in animals, 189
Meiosporangia, 147, **147**
Meiospores, 147, **147**
Mendel, Gregor, application of
statistics to study of heredity,
38
Metamorphosis of frog, 202, 214
Mice
comparison of behavior, 303
"waltzing" in, 305–306
Microbes
counting of, 103–104
total count, 104
cultures required, 392
rate of growth in culture, 392
Microorganisms
culturing, 114–118
early methods of, 115–117
laboratory requirements of, 359
maintaining in culture
"Pliofilm-coating", 391
soil preservation, 391–392
storage at cold temperatures,
391

Microorganisms (cont.)
    storage under mineral oil, 392
    storage under reduced oxygen
        tension, 391
Microscope, invention of, 27
Microspores, 167, *See also* Pollen
Microspore mother cell, 167
Migratory locust, formation of
        swarms, 265
Millbank, T. W., 80–96
Millimicron, 178
Mineral nutrition, technique for
        studying, **187**
Mineral requirements of sorghum
        plants, Investigation 24, 184
Minnows, olfactory communication,
        287
Mitosis, genetic recombination at,
        Investigation 18, 161
Mitospores, 145–147
M medium supplement, preparation
        of, 389–390
Mormyrid fish, production and
        detection of electric charges,
        268, 287
Moths, response to sound, 281, **281**
Mutants, theoretical increase in a
        population, **132**
Mutation equilibrium, 131, 133
Mutation frequency, 131
    determination of in bacteria,
        Investigation 9, 133
    factors influencing, 131
Mutation rate, 131, **132**
Mutations, back, 131, 148
Mycelium, 144

N

NAA (naphthaleneacetic acid), effect
        on leaf abscission, 250–253
Narcotic solution, preparation of, 381
National Audubon Society, bird
        census, 78
Negative results, value of, 77
Nervous system, formation in frog
        embryo, 202
Newport, George, 190–191

Nonviable, meaning, 103
Normal distribution, 54–55
    percentage of classes within 1, 2, or
        3 standard deviations, **57, 58,
        59**
Normality, determination of, 40
Null hypothesis
    and chi-square, 71–72
    rejection of, 68
Nutrient agar, preparation of, 387
Nutrient broth, 117
    preparation of, 381
Nutrition, relation of food selection
        to, Investigation 37, 300

O

Odor, used by animals for orientation,
        280, **281**
Odor trail, produced by fire ants,
        280, **281**
Oögenesis in animals, **189**
Orientation, 273–281
    echolocation, 278–280
    odor, 280
    sun, 281
    in honeybees, 283–286
Ovulary, 166, 168–169
Ovule, 168–169
Ovum
    functions of, 190
    parts of, 190
    formation of, 189, **189**
Oxygen, amount used by germinating
        seeds, **49**

P

Palolo worm (*Palolo viridis*), breeding
        behavior, 264–265
Pancreas, production of insulin, 209
Parasexual cycle in *A. nidulans,*
        161–162
Pasteur, Louis, 115, **115**
Pasteurizing, 379
Pattern of Inquiry
    general description, 9–10
    model, 10

Pearson, Karl, devised chi-square test, 71
Personal records, 95–96
  use of file cards, 96, **96**
Phenylketonuria, 305
Phenylalanine, 305
Pheromones, used in animal communication, 286–287
Phosphate buffer solution, preparation of, 382
Photon, 178, 180
Photoperiodism, 184
Phototactic orientation
  in dung beetle, 286
  of honeybee, 284, **284, 285, 286**
Phylogeny of wasps, **275**
Physiological saline solution, preparation of, 382
Phytochrome, 184
Pigmentation in *S. marcescens,* 138, **139**
Pistil, 166–167
Pituitaries
  injecting, 193
  obtaining frog, 191–193, **192**
  release of gonadotrophins, 210
Planarian worm, response to light, 270, **271**
Plant growth, life history of flowering plant, 166–172, **169, 170, 171**
Plant items, laboratory requirements of, 359–360
Plants, regulation in, 184, 221, 226, 227, 234–235, 249–255, **235, 265**
Polarized light
  used by arthropods to orient, 286
  used by bees to orient, 286
Polar nuclei, 169
Pollen, 166–169
Pollen tube, 169
Polygenic inheritance, 305
Population
  and samples, 50–52
  constitution of, 50–51
  dependence on food, 309–310, 345
  determining growth rate of, 110
  estimate of change, 103

Population (cont.)
  factors affecting development, Pattern of Inquiry 5, 130
  human
    increase of, 336, 341, 346
    in United States from 1800–1960, **103**
    theoretical increase of mutants, **132**
Population dynamics, 103–133
Probability, 61–63
  and chi-square, 71–76
  and test of significant differences, 61–77
  and *t* test, 63–70
  meaning of, 61–62
  null hypothesis, 63
  principles of, 62
Process in science, meaning of, 12
Prodigiosin, 138–139
  Investigation 11, 140;
  Investigation 12, 141
Putnam, P. C., 340
Pyrroles, 138–139, **139**
Pyruvic acid, production in fermentation, 22, **22**

Q

Quantum, 178

R

Random error, Pattern of Inquiry 3, 49
Random samples, 51–52
  bias in, 52
Rats, ability to learn maze, 304, **304**
Rattlesnake
  detection of temperature changes, 268
Recombination, in *A. nidulans,* Investigation 16, 156; Investigation 18, 161
Reducing sugars, detection by tetrazolium test, 175
Reflexes, 272

Regeneration
 definition, 208
 importance of, 208–209
 in man, 208
 in multicellular animals, 208–209
 in salamanders, 208
 in tadpoles, 206, Investigation 27, 212
Regenerating tissues, observations of, Investigation 27, 212
Respiration
 aerobic, 41
 anaerobic, 41
 and fermentation, 40–42
 carbon dioxide production as a measure of, Investigation 7, 42
 meaning of, 41
 measuring rates of, Investigation 7, 42
Respiratory inhibitor, preparation of, 381–382
Respiratory quotient, 47
Respiratory ratio
 meaning of, 47
 Pattern of Inquiry 4, 47
Review articles, 89
RNA (ribonucleic acid)
 as gene messenger, 152, 205, 306
 production by chromosomes, 204
Roller, Duane H. D., 4–6
Rossetter, F. N., 256–264

S

Salk, Jonas, 75
Sampling, 50–52
 bias, 52
 random, 51–52
 and populations, 50–52
 comparison of by statistics, **64**
 used to estimate populations, 51
Scent, use in animal communication, 286
Schneirla, T. C., 273
Schroeter, Karl, 115
Schwann, Theodore, 27–28
Science
 and controversy, 317, *See also* Decker, George C., and

Science (cont.)
  Graham, Samuel A.; Darwin, Sir Charles, and Hoyle, Fred
 as process of inquiry, 9
 definition, 6
 dynamic view of, 4
 importance of literature, 77, 89
 influence on society, 309, *See also* DuBridge, L. A.
 meaning of, 3–7
 measurement in, 38
 private, 5–6
 public, 5–6
 role of data, 29
 static view of, 4
 uncertainty in, 28–29
Scientific journals, 78–79
 foreign, 97
Scientific knowledge, growth of, 3
Scientific literature, importance of, 98
Scientific papers, 80, 81–88, 89
 preparation of, Investigation 13, 142
Scientific revolution, 337, 339
Scientists
 goals of, 311–312
 relation to government, 315–316
 responsibility of, 309
Seedlings
 bending in unilateral light, 223
 developing, Pattern of Inquiry 6, 172
 effect of light on growth of, Investigation 30, 221
Seeds
 development of, **170**
 germination of, *See* Germination
Seed viability, two tests for, Investigation 21, 171
Serial dilution, 15–17, **16**
Serratia marcescens
 agar, preparation of, 387–388
 determining mutation frequency, Investigation 9, 133
 interactions between unknown mutants, Investigation 12, 141
 mutants of, 137
  Investigation 10, 137;

Serratia marcescens (cont.)
  Investigation 12, 141
  mutation in, Investigation 11, 140
  pigmentation in, 138, **139**
  production of prodigiosin, 138
    Investigation 11, 140
  strain D1, 137
  strain 933, 137
  strain WCF, 137
Sex hormones, preparation of solution
    of, 382
Shumway, Waldo, chart of frog
    development, **198**
Significant results, by use of t-test, 68
Sorbitol, 300
Spallanzani, Lazzaro, 278
Spemann, Hans, 203
Spermatogenesis, **189**
Spermatozoan, 189–191, **189**
Sperm suspension, preparation of, 194
Sporophore, 145, **146**
Staining material, preparation of,
    382–383
Stamen, 166–167
Standard deviation, 57–60
Starch agar, preparation of, 388
Standard error of mean, 60–61
Starvation, as population control, 347
Statistics
  application to data, 50
  mean, 53–54
  normal distribution, 54–55, **55**
  and probability, 50, 61–62, 76–77
  standard deviation, 57–60
  standard error of mean, 60–61
  variance, 55–56
Steward, F. C., 203
Sugar, selection by blowfly,
    Investigation 38, 302
Sun, used by animals for orientation,
    281
Synapse of chromosomes, 166
Synchrony, 211
Systematic error, 49
  Pattern of Inquiry 3, 39

T

Tadpoles, maintaining in laboratory,
    393

Taxis, 271–272, **272**
  geotaxis, 303–304, **304**
Temperature
  effect on development of frog
    embryo, 202
  as a variable affecting fermentation,
    29
    Investigation 5, 30
Temperature gradient box, **196**
Temperature gradient tubes,
    preparation of, 30
Testes
  production of testosterone, 209
  removal of frog's, 194
Testosterone
  effect on chick gonads,
    Investigation 29, 219
  effect on comb development of
    chicks, Investigation 28, 215
  function of, 209
Testosterone propionate, Investigation
    28, 215
Test tube warming apparatus, **31**
Tetrazolium (2,3,5-triphenyltetrazolium
    chloride)
  test for reducing sugars, 175
  test solution, preparation of, 380
  use in germination tests, 177
Thermobarometer, 42, **42**
Thyroid gland
  effect of removal, 211
  function, 212
  production of thyroxin, 209,
    211–212
Thyroid hormone solutions,
    preparation of, 380–381
Thyroxin
  compared to triiodothyronine, 212
    Investigation 27, 212
  description, 211
  function of, 209
Thymine, 204–205
Total count of microbes, 104
Toxicity, 321
Trembley, Abraham, 205–206
Triiodothyronine
  description, 211
  effects compared with thyroxin,
    212
    Investigation 27, 212

Tryptone glucose agar, preparation of, 388
t-test, 63–70
  comparison with chi-square, 76
  distribution of *t* probability, **67**
  requirements for use of, 70
Two-way frequency table, example of, **63**

U

Ultraviolet radiation, 179

V

van Leeuwenhoek, Antony, 27, 190
Variables
  continuous, 50
  discrete, 50
  interaction of, Pattern of Inquiry 1, 26
  problems in control of, 28–29
Variance, 55–56
Viability, two tests for seed, Investigation 21, 175
Vision, frog, **269**
Volume, comparison of 1 mm and 1 cm cubes, **123**
Volumeter
  preparation of, 42–43, **43**
  thermobarometer, 42, **42**
  used in measuring respiration, Investigation 7, 42
Volumeter tubes, preparation of, 44–45, **45**

W

"Waltzing" in mice, 305–306
Wasps
  digger
    phylogeny, **275**
    prey-carrying behavior, 274–276

Wasps (cont.)
    egg-laying behavior, 274
  spider
    prey-carrying behavior, 274–275
Weissmann, August, 203
Western newt, **266**
  migration of, 265–266
  recognition of breeding site by odor, 280
Wetmore, R. H., 249–255
Wolf, visual communication by, 287, **288**
Woodlice, response to moisture, 270–271

X

X-radiation, 179

Y

YAG medium, preparation of, 388
Yeast (*Saccharomyces cerevisiae*)
  derivation of name, 13
  invertase content of, 86
  method of counting cells, 124–125
  oxidation and fermentation of sugars by, 81–88
  population growth, 126
  production of carbon dioxide in fermentation, 13, **15**
  production of maltase, 35
  protein content of, 83
  reproduction, **126**
  use of ATP in fermentation, 21
Yellow-shafted flicker
  behavior during breeding season, 268
  distinction of sexes, 268, **268**

Z

Zygote, 166
  production of, 169, 191